6502

ASSEMBLY LANGUAGE
PROGRAMMING

Coláiste Oideachais Mhuire Gan Smal
Luimneach

6502
ASSEMBLY LANGUAGE PROGRAMMING

Lance A. Leventhal

OSBORNE/McGraw-Hill
Berkeley, California

Published by

Osborne/McGraw-Hill

2600 Tenth Street

Berkeley, California 94710

For information on translations and book distributors outside of the U.S.A., please write OSBORNE/McGraw-Hill at the above address.

6502 ASSEMBLY LANGUAGE PROGRAMMING

9 0 DODO 8 7 6 5 4

ISBN 0-931988-27-6

Cover design by Timothy Sullivan.

ACKNOWLEDGMENTS

The author would like to acknowledge the following people: Mr. Curt Ingraham and Ms. Janice Enger of OSBORNE/McGraw-Hill, who made many corrections, improvements, and suggestions; Mr. Gary Hankins, Mr. Michael Lehman, Mr. Winthrop Saville, and Mr. Stanley St. John of Sorrento Valley Associates, who provided assistance and examples; Mr. Leo Scanlon of Rockwell International, who provided constant encouragement and reference materials; Mr. Charles Peddle of Commodore International, who provided some reference material; Ms. Marielle Carter of Sorrento Valley Associates, who typed some of the material; Mr. Stanley Rogers of the Society for Computer Simulation, who has continually encouraged clear and concise technical writing; and his wife Donna, for her patience and understanding throughout the writing of this book.

Others who provided assistance and suggestions were Mr. Colin Walsh, Mr. Romeo Favreau, Mr. Richard Deisher, Mr. Karl Amatneek, Mr. Robert Stow, and Mr. Irv Stafford. Other students and colleagues also helped to keep the author on the right track.

The author, of course, bears responsibility for any remaining errors, misconceptions, and misinterpretations.

A special note of acknowledgment should go to the magazine MICRO, which is entirely dedicated to 6502-based personal computers. Besides numerous articles, MICRO also contains resource and reference lists related to the 6502. MICRO is published monthly by Dr. Robert Tripp, The Computerist Inc., P.O. Box 3, South Chelmsford, MA 01824.

This book is dedicated on behalf of Amanda Catherine (Elizabeth Bramble) to some very special people — Catherine Greenlee, Max and Peggy Leventhal, Al and Rose Rosen, and Julius and Jeanette Ross.

The author would like to thank Karl Amatneek, Mel Evans, and particularly Philip Hooper for their lists of corrections to earlier printings of this book.

Contents

Contents (Continued)

Contents (Continued)

Contents (Continued)

Contents (Continued)

Contents (Continued)

Contents (Continued)

Contents (Continued)

Contents (Continued)

Contents (Continued)

Figures

Figures (Continued)

Tables

Chapter 1
INTRODUCTION TO ASSEMBLY
LANGUAGE PROGRAMMING

This book describes assembly language programming. It assumes that you are familiar with An Introduction To Microcomputers: Volume 1 — Basic Concepts[1] (particularly Chapters 6 and 7). This book does not discuss the general features of computers, microcomputers, addressing methods, or instruction sets; you should refer to An Introduction To Microcomputers: Volume 1 for that information.

HOW THIS BOOK HAS BEEN PRINTED

Notice that text in this book has been printed in boldface type and lightface type. **This has been done to help you skip those parts of the book that cover subject matter with which you are familiar. You can be sure that lightface type only expands on information presented in the previous boldface type.** Therefore, only read boldface type until you reach a subject about which you want to know more, at which point start reading the lightface type.

THE MEANING OF INSTRUCTIONS

The instruction set of a microprocessor is the set of binary inputs that produce defined actions during an instruction cycle. An instruction set is to a microprocessor what a function table is to a logic device, such as a gate, adder, or shift register. Of course, the actions that the microprocessor performs in response to its instruction inputs are far more complex than the actions that logic devices perform in response to their inputs.

An instruction is a binary bit pattern — it must be available at the data inputs to the microprocessor at the proper time in order to be interpreted as an instruction. For example, when the 6502 microprocessor receives the 8-bit binary pattern 11101000 as the input during an instruction fetch operation, the pattern means:

> "Increment (add 1 to) the contents of Register X".

Similarly, the pattern 10101001 means:

> "Load the Accumulator with the contents of the next word of program memory".

The microprocessor (like any other computer) recognizes only binary patterns as instructions or data; it does not recognize words or octal, decimal, or hexadecimal numbers.

A COMPUTER PROGRAM

A program is a series of instructions that causes a computer to perform a particular task.

Actually, a computer program includes more than instructions; it also contains the data and memory addresses that the microprocessor needs to accomplish the tasks defined by the instructions. Clearly, if the microprocessor is to perform an addition, it must have two numbers to add and a place to put the result. The computer program must determine the sources of the data and the destination of the result as well as the operation to be performed.

> COMPUTER PROGRAM

All microprocessors execute instructions sequentially unless one of the instructions changes the execution sequence or halts the computer, i.e., the processor gets the next instruction from the next consecutive memory address unless the current instruction specifically directs it to do otherwise.

Ultimately every program is translated into a set of binary numbers. For example, this is a 6502 program that adds the contents of memory locations 0060_{16} and 0061_{16} and places the result in memory location 0062_{16}:

```
10100101
01100000
01100101
01100001
10000101
01100010
```

This is a machine language, or object, program. If this program were entered into the memory of a 6502-based microcomputer, the microcomputer would be able to execute it directly.

> OBJECT PROGRAM
>
> MACHINE LANGUAGE PROGRAM

THE PROGRAMMING PROBLEM

There are many difficulties associated with creating programs as object, or binary machine language, programs. These are some of the problems:

1) The programs are difficult to understand or debug (binary numbers all look the same, particularly after you have looked at them for a few hours).
2) The programs are slow to enter since you must determine each bit individually.
3) The programs do not describe the task which you want the computer to perform in anything resembling a human readable format.
4) The programs are long and tiresome to write.
5) The programmer often makes careless errors that are very difficult to locate and correct.

For example, **the following version of the addition object program contains a single bit error. Try to find it:**

```
10100101
01100000
01110101
01100001
10000101
01100010
```

Although the computer handles binary numbers with ease, people do not. People find binary programs long, tiresome, confusing, and meaningless. Eventually, a programmer may start remembering some of the binary codes, but such effort should be spent more productively.

USING OCTAL OR HEXADECIMAL

We can improve the situation somewhat by writing instructions using octal or hexadecimal, rather than binary numbers. We will use hexadecimal numbers in this book because they are shorter, and because they are the standard for the microprocessor industry. Table 1-1 defines the hexadecimal digits and their binary equivalents. **The 6502 program to add two numbers now becomes:**

A5
60
65
61
85
62

At the very least, the hexadecimal version is shorter to write and not quite so tiring to examine.

Errors are somewhat easier to find in a sequence of hexadecimal digits. The erroneous version of the addition program, in hexadecimal form, becomes:

A5
60
75
61
85
62

The mistake is far more obvious.

What do we do with this hexadecimal program? The microprocessor understands only binary instruction codes. The answer is that we must convert the hexadecimal numbers to binary numbers. This conversion is a repetitive, tiresome task. People who attempt it make all sorts of petty mistakes, such as looking at the wrong line, dropping a bit, or transposing a bit or a digit.

This repetitive, grueling task is, however, a perfect job for a computer. The computer never gets tired or bored and never makes silly mistakes. **The idea then is to write a program that accepts hexadecimal numbers and converts them into binary numbers. This is a standard program provided with many microcomputers; it is called a hexadecimal loader.**

Is a hexadecimal loader worth having? If you are willing to write a program using binary numbers, and you are prepared to enter the program in its binary form into the computer, then you will not need the hexadecimal loader.

If you choose the hexadecimal loader, you will have to pay a price for it. The hexadecimal loader is itself a program that you must load into memory. Furthermore, the hexadecimal loader will occupy memory — memory that you may want to use in some other way.

The basic tradeoff, therefore, is the cost and memory requirements of the hexadecimal loader versus the savings in programmer time.

A hexadecimal loader is well worth its small cost.

A hexadecimal loader certainly does not solve every programming problem. The hexadecimal version of the program is still difficult to read or understand; for example, it does not distinguish instructions from data or addresses, nor does the program listing provide any suggestion as to what the program does. What does 85 or D0 mean? Memorizing a card full of codes is hardly an appetizing proposition. Furthermore, the codes will be entirely different for a different microprocessor, and the program will require a large amount of documentation.

Table 1-1. Hexadecimal Conversion Table

Hexadecimal Digit	Binary Equivalent	Decimal Equivalent
0	0000	0
1	0001	1
2	0010	2
3	0011	3
4	0100	4
5	0101	5
6	0110	6
7	0111	7
8	1000	8
9	1001	9
A	1010	10
B	1011	11
C	1100	12
D	1101	13
E	1110	14
F	1111	15

INSTRUCTION CODE MNEMONICS

An obvious programming improvement is to assign a name to each instruction code. The instruction code name is called a "mnemonic" or memory jogger. The instruction mnemonic should describe in some way what the instruction does.

In fact, every microprocessor manufacturer (they can't remember hexadecimal codes either) provides a set of mnemonics for the microprocessor instruction set. **You do not have to abide by the manufacturer's mnemonics;** there is nothing sacred about them.

PROBLEM WITH MNEMONICS

However, they are standard for a given microprocessor and therefore understood by all users. These are the instruction codes that you will find in manuals, cards, books, articles, and programs. The problem with selecting instruction mnemonics is that not all instructions have "obvious" names. Some instructions do (e.g., ADD, AND, OR), others have obvious contractions (e.g., SUB for subtraction, XOR for exclusive-OR), while still others have neither. The result is such mnemonics as WMP, PCHL, and even SOB (guess what that means!). Most manufacturers come up with some reasonable names and some hopeless ones. However, users who devise their own mnemonics rarely do much better than the manufacturer.

Along with the instruction mnemonics, the manufacturer will usually assign names to the CPU registers. As with the instruction names, some register names are obvious (e.g., A for Accumulator) while others may have only historical significance. Again, we will use the manufacturer's suggestions simply to promote standardization.

If we use standard 6502 instruction and register mnemonics, as defined by MOS Technology, Inc., our 6502 addition program becomes:

ASSEMBLY LANGUAGE PROGRAM

```
LDA     $60
ADC     $61
STA     $62
```

The program is still far from obvious, but at least some parts are comprehensible. ADC is a considerable improvement over 65; LDA and STA suggest loading and storing the contents of the Accumulator. We now know which lines are instructions and which are data or addresses. **Such a program is an assembly language program.**

THE ASSEMBLER PROGRAM

How do we get the assembly language program into the computer? We have to translate it, either into hexadecimal or into binary numbers. **You can translate an assembly language program by hand,** instruction by instruction. This is called hand assembly.

HAND
ASSEMBLY

Hand assembly of the addition program may be illustrated as follows:

Instruction Mnemonic	Addressing Method	Hexadecimal Equivalent
LDA	Zero Page (direct)	A5
ADC	Zero Page (direct)	65
STA	Zero Page (direct)	85

As with hexadecimal to binary conversion, hand assembly is a rote task which is uninteresting, repetitive, and subject to numerous minor errors. Picking the wrong line, transposing digits, omitting instructions, and misreading the codes are only a few of the mistakes that you may make. Most microprocessors complicate the task even further by having instructions with different word lengths. Some instructions are one word long while others are two or three words long. Some instructions require data in the second and third words, others require memory addresses, register numbers, or who knows what?

Assembly is another rote task that we can assign to the microcomputer. The microcomputer never makes any mistakes when translating codes; it always knows how many words and what format each instruction requires. The program that does this job is an "assembler." The assembler program translates a user program, or "<u>source</u>" program written with mnemonics, into a machine language program, or "<u>object</u>" program, which the microcomputer can execute. The assembler's input is a source program and its output is an object program.

ASSEMBLER

SOURCE
PROGRAM

OBJECT
PROGRAM

The tradeoffs that we discussed in connection with the hexadecimal loader are magnified in the case of the assembler. Assemblers are more expensive, occupy more memory, and require more peripherals and execution time than do hexadecimal loaders. While users may (and often do) write their own loaders, few care to write their own assemblers.

Assemblers have their own rules that you must learn. These include the use of certain markers (such as spaces, commas, semicolons, or colons) in appropriate places, correct spelling, the proper control information, and perhaps even the correct placement of names and numbers. These rules are usually simple and can be learned quickly.

ADDITIONAL FEATURES OF ASSEMBLERS

Early assemblers did little more than translate the mnemonic names of instructions and registers into their binary equivalents. However, most assemblers now provide such additional features as:

1) Allowing the user to assign names to memory locations, input and output devices, and even sequences of instructions.

2) Converting data or addresses from various number systems (e.g., decimal or hexadecimal) to binary and converting characters into their ASCII or EBCDIC binary codes.

3) Performing some arithmetic as part of the assembly process.

4) Telling the loader program where in memory parts of the program or data should be placed.

5) Allowing the user to assign areas of memory as temporary data storage and to place fixed data in areas of program memory.

6) Providing the information required to include standard programs from program libraries, or programs written at some other time, in the current program.

7) Allowing the user to control the format of the program listing and the input and output devices employed.

All of these features, of course, involve additional cost and memory. Microcomputers generally have much simpler assemblers than do larger computers, but the tendency always is for the size of assemblers to increase. You will often have a choice of assemblers. The important criterion is not how many offbeat features the assembler has, but rather how convenient it is to work with in normal practice.

CHOOSING AN ASSEMBLER

DISADVANTAGES OF ASSEMBLY LANGUAGE

The assembler, like the hexadecimal loader, does not solve all the problems of programming. One problem is the tremendous gap between the microcomputer instruction set and the tasks which the microcomputer is to perform. Computer instructions tend to do things like add the contents of two registers, shift the contents of the Accumulator one bit, or place a new value in the Program Counter. On the other hand, a user generally wants a microcomputer to do something like check if an analog reading has exceeded a threshold, look for and react to a particular command from a teletypewriter, or activate a relay at the proper time. An assembly language programmer must translate such tasks into a sequence of simple computer instructions. The translation can be a difficult, time-consuming job.

Furthermore, **if you are programming in assembly language, you must have detailed knowledge of the particular microcomputer that you are using.** You must know what registers and instructions the microcomputer has, precisely how the instructions affect the various registers, what addressing methods the computer uses, and a myriad of other information. None of this information is relevant to the task which the microcomputer must ultimately perform.

In addition, assembly language programs are not portable.
Each microcomputer has its own assembly language, which reflects its own architecture. An assembly language program written for the 6502 will not run on a 6800, Z80, 8080, or 3870 microprocessor. For example, the addition program written for the 8080 would be:

PORTABILITY

```
LDA    60H
MOV    B.A
LDA    61H
ADD    B
STA    62H
```

The lack of portability not only means that you won't be able to use your assembly language program on another microcomputer, but it also means that you won't be able to use any programs that weren't specifically written for the microcomputer you are using. This is a particular drawback for microcomputers, since these devices are new and few assembly language programs exist for them. The result, too frequently, is that you are on your own. If you need a program to perform a particular task, you are not likely to find it in the small program libraries that most manufacturers provide. Nor are you likely to find it in an archive, journal article, or someone's old program file. You will probably have to write it yourself.

HIGH-LEVEL LANGUAGES

The solution to many of the difficulties associated with as- COMPILER
sembly language programs is to use, instead, "high-level" or
"procedure-oriented" languages. Such languages allow you to describe tasks in forms that are problem oriented rather than computer oriented. Each statement in a high-level language performs a recognizable function; it will generally corres-pond to many assembly language instructions. A program called a compiler trans-lates the high-level language source program into object code or machine language instructions.

Many different high-level languages exist for different types of FORTRAN
tasks. If, for example, you can express what you want the com-
puter to do in algebraic notation, you can write your program in FORTRAN (Formula Translation Language), the oldest and most widely used of the high-level languages. Now, if you want to add two numbers, you just tell the computer:

$$SUM = NUMB1 + NUMB2$$

That is a lot simpler (and a lot shorter) than either the equivalent machine language pro-gram or the equivalent assembly language program. Other high-level languages in-clude COBOL (for business applications), PASCAL (another algebraic language), PL/1 (a combination of FORTRAN, ALGOL, and COBOL), and APL and BASIC (languages that are popular for time-sharing systems).

ADVANTAGES OF HIGH-LEVEL LANGUAGES

Clearly, high-level languages make programs easier and faster to write. A common estimate is that a programmer can write a program about ten times as fast in a high-level language as compared to assembly language.[1-3] That is just writing the program; it does not include problem definition, program design, debugging, testing, or documentation, all of which become simpler and faster. The high-level language pro-gram is, for instance, partly self-documenting. Even if you do not know FORTRAN, you probably could tell what the statement illustrated above does.

High-level languages solve many other problems associ-ated with assembly language programming. The high-level language has its own syntax (usually defined by a national or international standard). The language does not mention the in-struction set, registers, or other features of a particular com-

MACHINE INDEPENDENCE OF HIGH-LEVEL LANGUAGES

puter. The compiler takes care of all such details. Programmers can concentrate on their own tasks; they do not need a detailed understanding of the underlying CPU architec-ture — for that matter, they do not need to know anything about the computer they are programming.

Programs written in a high-level language are portable — at least, in theory. They will run on any computer that has a standard compiler for that language.

PORTABILITY OF HIGH-LEVEL LANGUAGES

At the same time, all previous programs written in a high-level language for prior computers are available to you when programming a new computer. This can mean thousands of programs in the case of a common language like FORTRAN or BASIC.

DISADVANTAGES OF HIGH-LEVEL LANGUAGES

Well, if all the good things we have said about high-level languages are true, if you can write programs faster and make them portable besides, why bother with assembly languages? Who wants to worry about registers, instruction codes, mnemonics, and all that garbage! As usual, there are disadvantages that balance the advantages.

One obvious problem is that **you have to learn the "rules" or "syntax" of any high-level language** you want to use. A high-level language has a fairly complicated set of rules. You will find that it takes a lot of time just to get a program that is syntactically

> **SYNTAX OF HIGH-LEVEL LANGUAGES**

correct (and even then it probably will not do what you want). A high-level computer language is like a foreign language. If you have a little talent, you will get used to the rules and be able to turn out programs that the compiler will accept. Still, learning the rules and trying to get the program accepted by the compiler does not contribute directly to doing your job.

Here, for example, are some FORTRAN rules:

- Labels must be numbers placed in the first five card columns
- Statements must start in column seven
- Integer variables must start with the letters I, J, K, L, M, or N

Another obvious problem is that you need a compiler to translate programs written in a high-level language. Compilers are expensive and use a large amount of memory. While most assemblers

> **COST OF COMPILERS**

occupy 2K to 16K bytes of memory (1K = 1024), compilers occupy 4K to 64K bytes. So the amount of overhead involved in using the compiler is rather large.

Furthermore, **only some compilers will make the implementation of your task simpler.** FORTRAN, for example, is well-suited to problems that can be expressed as algebraic formulas. If,

> **ALGEBRAIC NOTATION**

however, your problem is controlling a printer, editing a string of characters, or monitoring an alarm system, your problem cannot be easily expressed in algebraic notation. In fact, formulating the solution in algebraic notation may be more awkward and more difficult than formulating it in assembly language. One answer is to use a more suitable high-level language. Some such languages exist, but they are far less widely used and standardized than FORTRAN. You will not get many of the advantages of high-level languages if you use these so-called system implementation languages.

High-level languages do not produce very efficient machine language programs. The basic reason for this is that compilation is an automatic process which is riddled with compromises to allow for many ranges of possibilities. The compiler works much like a computerized language translator —

> **INEFFICIENCY OF HIGH-LEVEL LANGUAGES**
>
> **OPTIMIZING COMPILER**

sometimes the words are right but the sounds and sentence structures are awkward. A simple compiler cannot know when a variable is no longer being used and can be discarded, when a register should be used rather than a memory location, or when variables have simple relationships. The experienced programmer can take advantage of shortcuts to shorten execution time or reduce memory usage. A few compilers (known as optimizing compilers) can also do this, but such compilers are much larger and slower than regular compilers.

The general advantages and disadvantages of high-level languages are:

Advantages:

- More convenient descriptions of tasks
- Less time spent writing programs
- Easier documentation
- Standard syntax
- Independence of the structure of a particular computer
- Portability
- Availability of library and other programs

Disadvantages:

- Special rules
- Extensive hardware and software support required
- Orientation of common languages to algebraic or business problems
- Inefficient programs
- Difficulty of optimizing code to meet time and memory requirements
- Inability to use special features of a computer conveniently

HIGH-LEVEL LANGUAGES FOR MICROPROCESSORS

Microprocessor users will encounter several special difficulties when using high-level languages. Among these are:

- **Few high-level languages exist for microprocessors**
- **Few standard languages are widely available**
- **Compilers usually require a large amount of memory or even a completely different computer**
- **Most microprocessor applications are not well-suited to high-level languages**
- **Memory costs are often critical in microprocessor applications**

The lack of high-level languages is partly a result of the fact that microprocessors are quite new and are the products of semiconductor manufacturers rather than computer manufacturers. Very few high-level languages exist for microprocessors. The most common are BASIC,[5] PASCAL,[6] FORTRAN, and the PL/I-type languages such as PL/M,[7] MPL, and PLμS.

Many of the high-level languages that exist do not conform to recognized standards, so that the microprocessor user cannot expect to gain much program portability, access to program libraries, or use of previous experience or programs. The main advantages remaining are the reduction in programming effort and the smaller amount of detailed understanding of the computer architecture that is necessary.

The overhead involved in using a high-level language with microprocessors is considerable. Microprocessors themselves are better suited to control and slow interactive applications than they are to the character manipulation and language analysis involved in compilation. Therefore, some compilers for microprocessors will

not run on a microprocessor-based system. Instead, they require a much larger computer; i.e., they are cross-compilers rather than self-compilers. A user must not only bear the expense of the larger computer but must also physically transfer the program from the larger computer to the micro.

Some self-compilers are available. These compilers run on the microcomputer for which they produce object code. Unfortunately, they require large amounts of memory (16K or more), plus special supporting hardware and software.

High-level languages also are not generally well-suited to microprocessor applications. Most of the common languages were devised either to help solve scientific problems or to handle large-scale business data processing. Few microprocessor applications fall in either of these areas. Most microprocessor applications involve sending data and control information to output devices and receiving data and status information from input devices. Often the control and status information consists of a few binary digits with very precise hardware-related meanings. If you try to write a typical control program in a high-level language, you often feel like someone who is trying to eat soup with chopsticks. For tasks in such areas as test equipment, terminals, navigation systems, signal processing, and business equipment, the high-level languages work much better than they do in instrumentation, communications, peripherals, and automotive applications.

UNSUITABILITY OF HIGH-LEVEL LANGUAGES

Applications better suited to high-level languages are those which require large memories. If, as in a valve controller, electronic game, appliance controller, or small instrument, the cost of a single memory chip is important, then the inefficiency of high-level languages is intolerable. If, on the other hand, as in a terminal or test equipment, the system has many thousands of bytes of memory anyway, the inefficiency of high-level languages is not as important. Clearly the size of the program and the volume of the product are important factors as well. A large program will greatly increase the advantages of high-level languages. On the other hand, a high-volume application will mean that fixed software development costs are not as important as memory costs that are part of each system.

APPLICATION AREAS FOR LANGUAGE LEVELS

WHICH LEVEL SHOULD YOU USE?

That depends on your particular application. Let us briefly note some of the factors which may favor particular levels:

Machine Language:

APPLICATIONS FOR MACHINE LANGUAGE

- Virtually no one programs in machine language because it is inefficient and difficult to document. An assembler costs very little and greatly reduces programming time.

Assembly Language:

APPLICATIONS FOR ASSEMBLY LANGUAGE

- Short to moderate-sized programs
- Applications where memory cost is a factor
- Real-time control applications
- Limited data processing
- High-volume applications
- Applications involving more input/output or control than computation

High Level Languages:

- **Long programs**
- **Low-volume applications requiring long programs**
- **Applications where the amount of memory required is already very large**
- **Applications involving more computation than input/output or control**
- **Compatibility with similar applications using larger computers**
- **Availability of specific programs in a high-level language which can be used in the application**

APPLICATIONS FOR HIGH-LEVEL LANGUAGE

Many other factors are also important, such as the availability of a larger computer for use in development, experience with particular languages, and compatibility with other applications.

If hardware will ultimately be the largest cost in your application, or if speed is critical, you should favor assembly language. But be prepared to spend extra time in software development in exchange for lower memory costs and higher execution speeds. If software will be the largest cost in your application, you should favor a high-level language. But be prepared to spend the extra money required for the supporting hardware and software.

Of course, no one except some theorists will object if you use both assembly and high-level languages. You can write the program originally in a high-level language and then patch some sections in assembly language.[7] However, most users prefer not to do this because of the havoc it creates in debugging, testing, and documentation.

HOW ABOUT THE FUTURE?

We expect that the future will favor high-level languages for the following reasons:

- Programs always seem to add extra features and grow larger
- Hardware and memory are becoming less expensive
- Software and programmers are becoming more expensive
- Memory chips are becoming available in larger sizes, at lower "per bit" cost, so actual savings in chips are less likely
- More suitable and more efficient high-level languages are being developed
- More standardization of high-level languages will occur

FUTURE TRENDS IN LANGUAGE LEVELS

Assembly language programming of microprocessors will not be a dying art any more than it is now for large computers. But longer programs, cheaper memory, and more expensive programmers will make software costs a larger part of most applications. The edge in many applications will therefore go to high-level languages.

WHY THIS BOOK?

If the future would seem to favor high-level languages, why have a book on assembly language programming? The reasons are:

1) Most current microcomputer users program in assembly language (almost two thirds, according to one recent survey).

2) Many microcomputer users will continue to program in assembly language since they need the detailed control that it provides.

3) No suitable high-level language has yet become widely available or standardized.

4) Many applications require the efficiency of assembly language.

5) An understanding of assembly language can help in evaluating high-level languages.

The rest of this book will deal exclusively with assemblers and assembly language programming. However, we do want readers to know that assembly language is not the only alternative. You should watch for new developments that may significantly reduce programming costs if such costs are a major factor in your application.

REFERENCES

1. A. Osborne, An Introduction to Microcomputers: Volume 1 — Basic Concepts, Osborne/McGraw-Hill, Berkeley, CA., 1976.

2. M. H. Halstead, Elements of Software Science, American Elsevier, New York, 1977.

3. V. Schneider, "Prediction of Software Effort and Project Duration," SIGPLAN Notices, June 1978, pp. 49-55.

4. M. Phister Jr., Data Processing Technology and Economics, Santa Monica Publishing Co., Santa Monica, CA, 1976.

5. Albrecht, Finkel, and Brown, BASIC for Home Computers, Wiley, New York, 1978.

6. K. L. Bowles, Microcomputer Problem Solving Using PASCAL, Springer-Verlag, New York, 1977.

7. D. D. McCracken, A Guide to PL'M Programming for Microcomputer Applications, Addison-Wesley, Reading, Mass., 1978.

8. P. Caudill, "Using Assembly Coding to Optimize High-Level Language Programs," Electronics, February 1, 1979, pp. 121-124.

Chapter 2
ASSEMBLERS

This chapter discusses the functions performed by assemblers, beginning with features common to most assemblers and proceeding through more elaborate capabilities such as macros and conditional assembly. You may wish to skim this chapter for the present and return to it when you feel more comfortable with the material.

FEATURES OF ASSEMBLERS

As we mentioned previously, today's assemblers do much more than translate assembly language mnemonics into binary codes. But we will describe how an assembler handles the translation of mnemonics before describing additional assembler features. Finally, we will explain how assemblers are used.

ASSEMBLER INSTRUCTIONS

Assembly language instructions (or "statements") are divided into a number of fields, as shown in Table 2-1.

The operation code field is the only field that can never be empty; it always contains either an instruction mnemonic or a directive to the assembler, called a pseudo-instruction, pseudo-operation, or pseudo-op.

> ASSEMBLY
> LANGUAGE
> FIELDS

The operand or address field may contain an address or data, or it may be blank.

The comment and label fields are optional. A programmer will assign a label to a statement or add a comment as a personal convenience: namely, to make the program easier to read and use.

Table 2-1. The Fields of an Assembly Language Instruction

Label Field	Operation Code or Mnemonic Field	Operand or Address Field	Comment Field
START	LDA	VAL1	;LOAD FIRST NUMBER INTO A
	ADC	VAL2	;ADD SECOND NUMBER TO A
	STA	SUM	;STORE SUM
NEXT	?	?	;NEXT INSTRUCTION
•			
•			
•			
VAL1	*=*+1		
VAL2	*=*+1		
SUM	*=*+1		

2-1

Table 2-2. Standard 6502 Assembler Delimiters

'space'	between label and operation code and between operation code and address
,	between operands in the address field
; or !	before a comment

Note that 6502 assemblers vary greatly and some may not use these delimiters.

Of course, the assembler must have some way of telling where one field ends and another begins. Assemblers that use punched card input often require that each field start in a specific card column. This is a fixed format. However, fixed formats are inconvenient when the input medium is paper tape; fixed formats are also a nuisance to programmers. The alternative is a free format where the fields may appear anywhere on the line.

FORMAT

If the assembler cannot use the position on the line to tell the fields apart, it must use something else. **Most assemblers use a special symbol or delimiter at the beginning or end of each field.** The most common delimiter is the space character. Commas, periods, semicolons, colons, slashes, question marks, and other characters that would not otherwise be used in assembly language programs may also serve as delimiters. Table 2-2 lists standard 6502 assembler delimiters.

DELIMITERS

You will have to exercise a little care with delimiters. Some assemblers are fussy about extra spaces or the appearance of delimiters in comments or labels. A well-written assembler will handle these minor problems, but many assemblers are not well-written. Our recommendation is simple: avoid potential problems if you can. The following rules will help:

1) Do not use extra spaces, particularly after commas that separate operands.

2) Do not use delimiter characters in names or labels.

3) Include standard delimiters even if your assembler does not require them. Your programs will then run on any assembler.

LABELS

The label field is the first field in an assembly language instruction; it may be blank. If a label is present, the assembler defines the label as equivalent to the address into which the first byte of the object program resulting from that instruction is loaded. You may subsequently use the label as an address or as data in another instruction's address field. The assembler will replace the label with the assigned value when creating an object program.

LABEL
FIELD

Labels are most frequently used in Jump, Call, or Branch instructions. These instructions place a new value in the Program Counter and so alter the normal sequential execution of instructions. JUMP 150_{16} means "place the value 150_{16} in the Program Counter". The next instruction to be executed will be the one in memory location 150_{16}. The instruction JUMP START means "place the value assigned to the label START in the Program Counter". The next instruction to be executed will be the one at the address corresponding to the label START. Table 2-3 contains an example.

LABELS
IN JUMP
INSTRUCTIONS

Table 2-3. Assigning and Using a Label

```
                    ASSEMBLY LANGUAGE PROGRAM

START           LOAD ACCUMULATOR 100
                •
                •
                •
                • (MAIN PROGRAM)
                •
                •
                •
                JUMP START
```

When the machine language version of this program is executed, the instruction JUMP START causes the address of the instruction labeled START to be placed in the Program Counter. That instruction will then be executed.

Why use a label? Here are some reasons:

1) A label makes a program location easier to find and remember.

2) A label can easily be moved, if required, to change or correct a program. The assembler will automatically change all instructions that use that label when the program is reassembled.

3) The assembler or loader can relocate the whole program by adding a constant (a relocation constant) to each address for which a label was used. Thus we can move the program to allow for the insertion of other programs or simply to rearrange memory.

> RELOCATION CONSTANT

4) The program is easier to use as a library program; i.e., it is easier for someone else to take your program and add it to some totally different program.

5) You do not have to figure out memory addresses. Figuring out memory addresses is particularly difficult with microprocessors which have instructions that vary in length.

You should assign a label to any instruction that you might want to refer to later.

The next question is how to choose a label. The assembler often places some restrictions on the number of characters (usually 5 or 6), the leading character (often must be a letter), and the trailing characters (often must be letters, numbers, or one of a few special characters). Beyond these restrictions, the choice is up to you.

> CHOOSING LABELS

Our own preference is to **use labels that suggest their purpose,** i.e., mnemonic labels. Typical examples are ADDW in a routine that adds one word into a sum, SRETX in a routine that searches for the ASCII character ETX, or NKEYS for a location in data memory that contains the number of key entries. Meaningful labels are easier to remember and contribute to program documentation. Some programmers use a standard format for labels, such as starting with L0000. These labels are self-sequencing (you can skip a few numbers to permit insertions), but they do not help document the program.

Some label selection rules will keep you out of trouble. We recommend the following:

1) Do not use labels that are the same as operation codes or other mnemonics. Most assemblers will not allow this usage; others will, but it is very confusing.

2) Do not use labels that are longer than the assembler permits. Assemblers have various truncation rules.

3) Avoid special characters (non-alphabetic and non-numeric) and lower-case letters. Some assemblers will not permit them; others allow only certain ones. The simplest practice is to stick to capital letters and numbers.

4) Start each label with a letter. Such labels are always acceptable.

5) Do not use labels that could be confused with each other. Avoid the letters I, O and Z, and the numbers 0, 1, and 2. Also avoid things like XXXX and XXXXX. There's no sense tempting fate and Murphy's laws.

6) When you are not sure if a label is legal, do not use it. You will not get any real benefit from discovering exactly what the assembler will accept.

These are recommendations, not rules. You do not have to follow them, but don't blame us if you waste time on silly problems.

ASSEMBLER OPERATION CODES (MNEMONICS)

The main task of the assembler is the translation of mnemonic operation codes into their binary equivalents. The assembler performs this task using a fixed table much as you would if you were doing the assembly by hand.

The assembler must, however, do more than just translate the operation codes. It **must also somehow determine how many operands the instruction requires and what type they are.** This may be rather complex — some instructions (like a Halt) have no operands, others (like an Addition or a Jump instruction) have one, while still others (like a transfer between registers or a multiple-bit shift) require two. Some instructions may even allow alternatives; e.g., some computers have instructions (like Shift or Clear) that can apply either to the Accumulator or to a memory location. We will not discuss how the assembler makes these distinctions; we will just note that it must do so.

PSEUDO-OPERATIONS

Some assembly language instructions are not directly translated into machine language instructions. These instructions are directives to the assembler; they assign the program to certain areas in memory, define symbols, designate areas of RAM for temporary data storage, place tables or other fixed data in memory, allow references to other programs, and perform minor housekeeping functions.

To use these assembler directives or pseudo-operations a programmer places the pseudo-operation's mnemonic in the operation code field, and, if the specified pseudo-operation requires it, an address or data in the address field.

The most common pseudo-operations are:

> DATA
> EQUATE (=) or DEFINE
> ORIGIN
> RESERVE

Linking pseudo-operations (used to connect separate programs) are:
> ENTRY
> EXTERNAL

Different assemblers use different names for these operations, but their functions are the same. Housekeeping pseudo-operations include:

    END
    LIST
    NAME
    PAGE
    SPACE
    TITLE
    PUNCH

We will discuss these pseudo-operations briefly, although their functions are usually obvious.

THE DATA PSEUDO-OPERATION

The DATA pseudo-operation allows the programmer to enter fixed data into program memory. This data may include:

- Lookup tables
- Code conversion tables
- Messages
- Synchronization patterns
- Thresholds
- Names
- Coefficients for equations
- Commands
- Conversion factors
- Weighting factors
- Characteristic times or frequencies
- Subroutine addresses
- Key identifications
- Test patterns
- Character generation patterns
- Identification patterns
- Tax tables
- Standard forms
- Masking patterns
- State transition tables

The DATA pseudo-operation treats the data as a permanent part of the program.

The format of a DATA pseudo-operation is usually quite simple. An instruction like:

    DZCON   DATA   12

will place the number 12 in the next available memory location and assign that location the name DZCON. Usually every DATA pseudo-operation has a label, unless it is one of a series of DATA pseudo-operations. The data and label may take any form that the assembler permits.

Most assemblers allow more elaborate DATA instructions that handle a large amount of data at one time, e.g.:

    EMESS   DATA   'ERROR'
    SQRS   DATA   1,4,9,16,25

2-5

A single instruction may fill many words of program memory, limited only by the length of a line. Note that if you cannot get all the data on one line, you can always follow one DATA instruction with another, e.g.,

```
MESSG   DATA    'NOW IS THE '
        DATA    'TIME FOR ALL '
        DATA    'GOOD MEN '
        DATA    'TO COME TO THE '
        DATA    'AID OF THEIR '
        DATA    'COUNTRY'
```

Microprocessor assemblers typically have some variations of standard DATA pseudo-operations. DEFINE BYTE or FORM CONSTANT BYTE handles 8-bit numbers; DEFINE WORD or FORM CONSTANT WORD handles 16-bit numbers or addresses. Other special pseudo-operations may handle character-coded data.

THE EQUATE (or DEFINE) PSEUDO-OPERATION

The EQUATE pseudo-operation allows the programmer to equate names with addresses or data. This pseudo-operation is almost always given the mnemonic EQU or =. The names may refer to device addresses, numeric data, starting addresses, fixed addresses, etc.

> DEFINING NAMES

The EQUATE pseudo-operation assigns the numeric value in its operand field to the label in its label field. Here are two examples:

```
TTY     EQU     5
LAST    EQU     5000
```

Most assemblers will allow you to define one label in terms of another, e.g.,

```
LAST    EQU     FINAL
ST1     EQU     START+1
```

The label in the operand field must, of course, have been previously defined. Often, the operand field may contain more complex expressions, as we shall see later. Double name assignments (two names for the same data or address) may be useful in patching together programs that use different names for the same variable (or different spellings of what was supposed to be the same name).

Note that an EQU pseudo-operation does not cause the assembler to place anything in memory. The assembler simply enters an additional name into a table (called a symbol table)

> SYMBOL TABLE

which the assembler maintains. This table, unlike the mnemonic table, must be in RAM since it varies with each program. The assembler always needs some RAM to hold the symbol table; the more RAM it has, the more symbols it can accept. This RAM is in addition to any which the assembler needs as temporary storage.

When do you use a name? The answer is: whenever you have a parameter that has some meaning besides its ordinary numeric value or the numeric value of the parameter might be changed.

> USE OF NAMES

We typically assign names to time constants, device addresses, masking patterns, conversion factors, and the like. A name like DELAY, TTY, KBD, KROW, or OPEN not only makes the parameter easier to change, but it also adds to program documentation. We also assign names to memory locations that have special purposes; they may hold data, mark the start of the program, or be available for intermediate storage.

What name do you use? The best rules are much the same as in the case of labels, except that here meaningful names really count. Why not call the teletypewriter TTY instead of X15, a bit time delay BTIME or BTDLY rather than WW, the number of the

> CHOICE OF NAMES

"GO" key on a keyboard GOKEY rather than HORSE? This advice seems straightforward, but a surprising number of programmers do not follow it.

Where do you place the EQUATE pseudo-operations? The **best place is at the start of the program,** under appropriate comment headings such as I/O ADDRESSES, TEMPORARY STORAGE, TIME CONSTANTS, or PROGRAM LOCATIONS. This

PLACEMENT OF DEFINITIONS

makes the definitions easy to find if you want to change them. Furthermore, another user will be able to look up all the definitions in one centralized place. Clearly this practice improves documentation and makes the program easier to use.

Definitions used only in a specific subroutine should appear at the start of the subroutine.

THE ORIGIN PSEUDO-OPERATION

The ORIGIN pseudo-operation (almost always abbreviated ORG) allows the programmer to locate programs, subroutines, or data anywhere in memory. Programs and data may be located in different areas of memory depending on the memory configuration. Startup routines, interrupt service routines, and other required programs may be scattered around memory at fixed or convenient addresses.

The assembler maintains a Location Counter (comparable to the computer's Program Counter) which contains the location in memory of the next instruction or data item being pro-

LOCATION COUNTER

cessed. An ORG pseudo-operation causes the assembler to place a new value in the Location Counter, much as a Jump instruction causes the CPU to place a new value in the Program Counter. The output from the assembler must not only contain instructions and data, but must also indicate to the loader program where in memory it should place the instructions and data.

Microprocessor programs often contain several ORIGIN statements for the following purposes:

> Reset (startup) address
> Interrupt service addresses
> Trap addresses
> RAM storage
> Memory stack
> Subroutines
> Memory addresses for input/output devices or
>   special functions

Still other ORIGIN statements may allow room for later insertions, place tables or data in memory, or assign vacant RAM space for data buffers. Program and data memory in microcomputers may occupy widely scattered addresses to simplify the hardware.

Typical ORIGIN statements are:

> ORG   RESET
> ORG   1000
> ORG   INT3

Some assemblers assume an origin of zero if the programmer does not put an ORG statement at the start of the program. The convenience is slight; we recommend the inclusion of an ORG statement to avoid confusion.

THE RESERVE PSEUDO-OPERATION

The RESERVE pseudo-operation allows the programmer to allocate RAM for various purposes such as data tables, temporary storage, indirect addresses, a Stack, etc.

ALLOCATING RAM

Using the RESERVE pseudo-operation, you assign a name to the memory area and declare the number of locations to be assigned. Here are some examples:

```
NOKEY    RESERVE    1
TEMP     RESERVE    50
VOLTG    RESERVE    80
BUFR     RESERVE    100
```

You can use the RESERVE pseudo-operation to reserve memory locations in program memory or in data memory; however, the RESERVE pseudo-operation is more meaningful when applied to data memory.

In reality, all the RESERVE pseudo-operation does is increase the assembler's Location Counter by the amount declared in the operand field. The assembler does not actually produce any object code.

Note the following features of RESERVE:

1) The label of the RESERVE pseudo-operation is assigned the value of the first address reserved. For example, the pseudo-operation:

```
TEMP    RESERVE    20
```

reserves 20 bytes of RAM and assigns the name TEMP to the address of the first byte.

2) You must specify the number of locations to be reserved. There is no default case.

3) No data is placed in the reserved locations. Any data that, by chance, may be in these locations will be left there.

Some assemblers allow the programmer to place initial values in RAM. We strongly recommend that you do not use this feature — it assumes that the program (along with

| INITIALIZING RAM |

the initial values) will be loaded from an external device (e.g., paper tape or floppy disk) each time it is run. Most microprocessor programs, on the other hand, reside in non-volatile ROM and start when power comes on. The RAM in such situations does not retain its contents, nor is it reloaded. Always include instructions to initialize the RAM in your program.

LINKING PSEUDO-OPERATIONS

We often want statements in one program or subroutine to use names that are defined elsewhere. Such names are called external references; a special linking program is necessary to ac-

| EXTERNAL REFERENCES |

tually fill in the values and determine if any names are undefined or doubly defined.

The pseudo-operation EXTERNAL, usually abbreviated EXT, signifies that the name is defined elsewhere.

The pseudo-operation ENTRY, usually abbreviated ENT, signifies that the name is available for use elsewhere; i.e., it is defined in this program.

The precise way in which linking pseudo-operations are implemented varies greatly from assembler to assembler. We will not refer to such **pseudo-operations** again, but they **are very useful in actual applications.**

HOUSEKEEPING PSEUDO-OPERATIONS

There are various housekeeping pseudo-operations that affect the operation of the assembler and its program listing rather than the output program itself. Common housekeeping pseudo-operations include:

- END, which marks the end of the assembly language source program.
- LIST, which tells the assembler to print the source program. Some assemblers allow such variations as NO LIST or LIST SYMBOL TABLE to avoid long, repetitive listings.
- NAME or TITLE, which prints a name at the top of each page of the listing.
- PAGE or SPACE, which skips to the next page or next line, respectively, and improves the appearance of the listing, making it easier to read.
- PUNCH, which transfers subsequent object code to the paper tape punch. This pseudo-operation may in some cases be the default option and therefore unnecessary.

LABELS WITH PSEUDO-OPERATIONS

Users often wonder if or when they can assign a label to a pseudo-operation. These are our recommendations:

- All EQUATE pseudo-operations must have labels; they are useless otherwise, since the purpose of an EQUATE is to define its label.
- DATA and RESERVE pseudo-operations usually have labels. The label identifies the first memory location used or assigned.
- Other pseudo-operations should not have labels. Some assemblers allow such labels, but we recommend against their use because there is no standard way to interpret them.

ADDRESSES AND THE OPERAND FIELD

Most assemblers allow the programmer a lot of freedom in describing the contents of the Operand or Address field. But remember that the assembler has built-in names for registers and instructions and may have other built-in names.

Some common options for the operand field are:

1) Decimal numbers

Most assemblers assume all numbers to be decimal unless they are marked otherwise. So:

> ADD   100

means "add the contents of memory location 100_{10} to the contents of the Accumulator."

2) Other number systems

Most assemblers will also accept binary, octal, or hexadecimal entries. But you must identify these number systems in some way, e.g., by preceding or following the number with an identifying character or letter. Here are some common identifiers:

> B or % for binary
>
> O, @, Q, or C for octal (the letter O should be avoided because of the confusion with zero).
>
> H or $ for hexadecimal (or standard BCD).
>
> D for decimal. D may be omitted; it is the default case.

Assemblers generally require hexadecimal numbers to start with a digit (e.g., 0A36 instead of A36) in order to distinguish between numbers and names or labels. It is good practice to enter numbers in the base in which their meaning is the clearest: i.e., decimal constants in decimal; addresses and BCD numbers in hexadecimal; masking patterns or bit outputs in binary if they are short and in hexadecimal if they are long.

3) Names

Names can appear in the operand field; they will be treated as the data that they represent. But remember, **there is a difference between data and addresses.** The sequence:

> FIVE   EQU   5
>   ADD   FIVE

will add the contents of memory location 0005 (not necessarily the number 5) to the contents of the Accumulator.

4) The current value of the location counter (usually referred to as * or $).

This is useful mainly in Jump instructions; for example:

JUMP   *+6

causes a Jump to the memory location six words beyond the word that contains the first byte of the JUMP instruction:

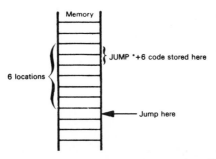

Most microprocessors have many two- and three-word instructions. Thus, you will have difficulty determining exactly how far apart two assembly language statements are. Therefore, using offsets from the Location Counter frequently results in errors that you can avoid if you use labels.

5) Character codes

Most assemblers allow text to be entered as ASCII strings. Such strings may be surrounded either with single or double quotation marks; strings may also use a beginning or ending symbol such as A or C. A few assemblers also permit EBCDIC strings.

> **ASCII CHARACTERS**

We recommend that you use character strings for all text. It improves the clarity and readability of the program.

6) Combinations of 1) through 5) with arithmetic, logical, or special operators.

Almost all assemblers allow simple arithmetic combinations such as START+1. Some assemblers also permit multiplication, division, logical functions, shifts, etc. These are referred to as expressions. Note that the assembler evaluates expressions at

> **ARITHMETIC AND LOGICAL EXPRESSIONS**

assembly time. Even though an expression in the operand field may involve multiplication, you may not be able to use multiplication in the logic of your own program — unless you write a subroutine for that specific purpose.

Assemblers vary in what expressions they accept and how they interpret them. Complex expressions make a program difficult to read and understand.

We have made some recommendations during this section but will repeat them and add others here. **In general, the user should strive for clarity and simplicity.** There is no payoff for being an expert in the intricacies of an assembler or in having the most complex expression on the block. **We suggest the following approach:**

1) Use the clearest number system or character code for data.

    Masks and BCD numbers in decimal, ASCII characters in octal, or ordinary numerical constants in hexadecimal serve no purpose and therefore should not be used.

2) Remember to distinguish data from addresses.

3) Don't use offsets from the Location Counter.

4) Keep expressions simple and obvious. Don't rely on obscure features of the assembler.

CONDITIONAL ASSEMBLY

Some assemblers allow you to include or exclude parts of the source program, depending on conditions existing at assembly time. This is called conditional assembly; it gives the assembler some of the flexibility of a compiler. **Most microcomputer assemblers have limited capabilities for conditional assembly. A typical form is:**

```
IF COND
    .
    .(CONDITIONAL PROGRAM)
    .
    .
ENDIF
```

If the expression COND is true at assembly time, the instructions between IF and ENDIF (two pseudo-operations) are included in the program.

Typical uses of conditional assembly are:

1) To include or exclude extra variables.
2) To place diagnostics or special conditions in test runs.
3) To allow data of various bit lengths.
4) To create specialized versions of a common program.

Unfortunately, conditional assembly tends to clutter programs and make them difficult to read. Use conditional assembly only if it is necessary.

MACROS

You will often find that particular sequences of instructions occur many times in a source program. Repeated instruction sequences may reflect the needs of your program logic, or they may be compensating for deficiencies in your microprocessor's

DEFINING A SEQUENCE OF INSTRUCTIONS

instruction set. You can avoid repeatedly writing out the same instruction sequence by using a macro.

Macros allow you to assign a name to an instruction sequence. You then use the macro name in your source program instead of the repeated instruction sequence. The assembler will replace the macro name with the appropriate sequence of instructions. This may be illustrated as follows:

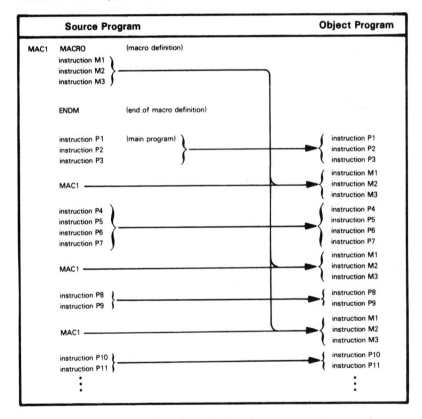

Macros are not the same as subroutines. A subroutine occurs once in a program, and program execution branches to the subroutine. A macro is expanded to an actual instruction sequence each time the macro occurs; thus a macro does not cause any branching.

Macros have the following advantages:

1) Shorter source programs.

2) Better program documentation.

3) Use of debugged instruction sequences — once the macro has been debugged, you are sure of an error-free instruction sequence every time you use the macro.

4) Easier changes. Change the macro definition and the assembler makes the change for you every time the macro is used.

5) Inclusion of commands, keywords, or other computer instructions in the basic instruction set. You can use macros to extend or clarify the instruction set.

The disadvantages of macros are:

1) Repetition of the same instruction sequences since the macro is expanded every time it is used.

2) A single macro may create a lot of instructions.

3) Lack of standardization makes programs difficult to read and understand.

4) Possible effects on registers and flags that may not be clearly described.

One problem is that variables used in a macro are only known within it (i.e., they are local rather than global). This can often create a great deal of confusion without any gain in return. You should be aware of this problem when using macros.[1]

COMMENTS

All assemblers allow you to place comments in a source program. Comments have no effect on the object code, but they help you to read, understand, and document the program. Good commenting is an essential part of writing assembly language programs; programs without comments are very difficult to understand.

We will discuss commenting along with documentation in a later chapter, but here are some guidelines.:

1) Use comments to tell what application task the program is performing, not how the microcomputer executes the instructions.

```
COMMENTING
TECHNIQUES
```

Comments should say things like "IS TEMPERATURE ABOVE LIMIT?", "LINE FEED TO TTY", or "EXAMINE LOAD SWITCH".

Comments should not say things like "ADD 1 TO ACCUMULATOR", "JUMP TO START", or "LOOK AT CARRY". You should describe how the program is affecting the system; internal effects on the CPU are seldom of any interest.

2) Keep comments brief and to the point. Details should be available elsewhere in the documentation.

3) Comment all key points.

4) Do not comment standard instructions or sequences that change counters or pointers; pay special attention to instructions that may not have an obvious meaning.

5) Do not use obscure abbreviations.

6) Make the comments neat and readable.

7) Comment all definitions, describing their purposes. Also mark all tables and data storage areas.

8) Comment sections of the program as well as individual instructions.

9) Be consistent in your terminology. You can and should be repetitive; you need not consult a thesaurus.

10) Leave yourself notes at points which you find confusing: e.g., "REMEMBER CARRY WAS SET BY LAST INSTRUCTION". You may drop these in the final documentation.

A well-commented program is easy to use. You will recover the time spent in commenting many times over. We will try to show good commenting style in the programming examples, although we often over-comment for instructional purposes.

TYPES OF ASSEMBLERS

Although all assemblers perform the same tasks, their implementations vary greatly. We will not try to describe all the existing types of assemblers; we will merely define the terms and indicate some of the choices.

A cross-assembler is an assembler that runs on a computer other than the one for which it assembles object programs.

| CROSS-ASSEMBLER |

The computer on which the cross-assembler runs is typically a large computer with extensive software support and fast peripherals — such as an IBM 360 or 370, a Univac 1108, or a Burroughs 6700. The computer for which the cross-assembler assembles programs is typically a micro like the 6502 or 8080. Most cross-assemblers are written in FORTRAN so that they are portable.

A self-assembler or resident assembler is an assembler that runs on the computer for which it assembles programs. The self-assembler will require some memory and peripherals, and it may run quite slowly.

| RESIDENT ASSEMBLER |

A macro assembler is an assembler that allows you to define sequences of instructions as macros.

| MACRO ASSEMBLER |

A microassembler is an assembler used to write the microprograms that define the instruction set of a computer. Microprogramming has nothing specifically to do with microcomputers.[2,3]

| MICRO-ASSEMBLER |

A meta-assembler is an assembler that can handle many different instruction sets. The user must define the particular instruction set being used.

| META-ASSEMBLER |

A one-pass assembler is an assembler that goes through the assembly language program only once. Such an assembler must have some way of resolving forward references, e.g., Jump instructions which use labels that have not yet been defined.

| ONE-PASS ASSEMBLER |

A two-pass assembler is an assembler that goes through the assembly language source program twice. The first time the assembler simply collects and defines all the symbols; the

| TWO-PASS ASSEMBLER |

second time it replaces the references with the actual definitions. A two-pass assembler has no problems with forward references but may be quite slow if no backup storage (like a floppy disk) is available; then the assembler must physically read the program twice from a slow input medium (like a teletypewriter paper tape reader). Most microprocessor-based assemblers require two passes.

ERRORS

Assemblers normally provide error messages, often consisting of a single coded letter. Some typical errors are:

- Undefined name (often a misspelling or an omitted definition)
- Illegal character (e.g., a 2 in a binary number)
- Illegal format (wrong delimiter or incorrect operands)
- Invalid expression (e.g., two operators in a row)
- Illegal value (usually too large)
- Missing operand
- Double definition (i.e., two different values assigned to one name)
- Illegal label (e.g., a label on a pseudo-operation that cannot have one)
- Missing label
- Undefined operation code

In interpreting assembler errors, you must remember that the assembler may get on the wrong track if it finds a stray letter, an extra space, or incorrect punctuation. Many assemblers will then proceed to misinterpret the succeeding instructions and produce meaningless error messages. Always look at the first error very carefully; subsequent ones may depend on it. Caution and consistent adherence to standard formats will eliminate many annoying mistakes.

LOADERS

The loader is the program which actually takes the output (object code) from the assembler and places it in memory. Loaders range from the very simple to the very complex. We will describe a few different types.

A bootstrap loader is a program that uses its own first few instructions to load the rest of itself or another loader program into memory. The bootstrap loader may be in ROM, or you may have to enter it into the computer memory using front panel switches. The assembler may place a bootstrap loader at the start of the object program that it produces.

`BOOTSTRAP LOADER`

A relocating loader can load programs anywhere in memory. It typically loads each program into the memory space immediately following that used by the previous program. The programs, however, must themselves be capable of being moved around in this way; i.e., they must be relocatable. **An absolute loader, in contrast, will always place the programs in the same area of memory.**

`RELOCATING LOADER`

A linking loader loads programs and subroutines that have been assembled separately; it resolves cross references — that is, instructions in one program that refer to a label in another program. Object programs loaded by a linking loader must be created by an assembler that allows external references.

`LINKING LOADERS`

An alternative approach is to separate the linking and loading functions and have the linking performed by a program called a link editor.

`LINK EDITOR`

REFERENCES

1. A complete monograph on macros is M. Campbell-Kelly, "An Introduction to Macros," American Elsevier, New York, 1973.

2. A. Osborne, An Introduction to Microcomputers: Volume 1 - Basic Concepts, OSBORNE/McGraw-Hill, Berkeley, CA, 1977.

3. A. K. Agrawala and T. G. Rauscher, Foundations of Microprogramming, Academic Press, New York, 1976.

4. D. W. Barron, "Assemblers and Loaders," American Elsevier, New York, 1972

5. C.W. Gear, Computer Organization and Programming, McGraw-Hill, New York, 1974.

Chapter 3
THE 6502 ASSEMBLY LANGUAGE
INSTRUCTION SET

We are now ready to start writing assembly language programs. We begin in this chapter by defining the individual instructions of the 6502 assembly language instruction set, plus the syntax rules of the MOS Technology assembler.

We do not discuss any aspects of microcomputer hardware, signals, interfaces, or CPU architecture in this book. This information is described in detail in An Introduction to Microcomputers: Volume 2 — Some Real Microprocessors and Volume 3 — Some Real Support Devices.

In this book, we look at programming techniques from the assembly language programmer's viewpoint, where pins and signals are irrelevant and there are no important differences between a minicomputer and a microcomputer.

Interrupts, direct memory access, and the Stack architecture for the 6502 will be described in later chapters of this book, in conjunction with assembly language programming discussions of the same subjects.

This chapter contains a detailed definition of each assembly language instruction.

The detailed description of individual instructions is preceded by a general discussion of the 6502 instruction set that divides instructions into those which are frequently used (Table 3-1), occasionally used (Table 3-2), and seldom used (Table 3-3). If you are an experienced assembly language programmer, this categorization is not particularly important — and, depending on your own programming prejudices, it may not even be accurate. If you are a novice assembly language programmer, we recommend that you begin by writing programs using only instructions in the "frequently used" category. Once you have mastered the concepts of assembly language programming, you may examine other instructions and use them where appropriate.

Table 3-1. Frequently Used Instructions of the 6502

Instruction Code	Meaning
ADC	Add with Carry
AND	Logical AND
ASL	Arithmetic Shift Left
BCC	Branch if Carry Clear
BCS	Branch if Carry Set
BEQ	Branch if Equal to Zero (Z = 1)
BMI	Branch if Minus (S = 1)
BNE	Branch if Not Equal to Zero (Z = 0)
BPL	Branch if Plus (S = 0)
CMP	Compare Accumulator to Memory
DEC	Decrement (by 1)
DEX (DEY)	Decrement Index Register X (Y) by 1
INC	Increment (by 1)
INX (INY)	Increment Index Register X (Y) by 1
JMP	Jump to New Location
JSR	Jump to Subroutine
LDA	Load Accumulator
LDX (LDY)	Load Index Register X (Y)
LSR	Logical Shift Right
PHA	Push Accumulator onto Stack
PLA	Pull Accumulator from Stack
ROL	Rotate Left through Carry
ROR	Rotate Right through Carry
RTS	Return from Subroutine
SBC	Subtract with Borrow
STA	Store Accumulator
STX (STY)	Store Index Register X (Y)

Table 3-2. Occasionally Used Instructions of the 6502

Instruction Code	Meaning
BIT	Bit Test
BRK	Break
CLC	Clear Carry
CLD	Clear Decimal Mode
CLI	Clear Interrupt Mask (Enable Interrupts)
CPX (CPY)	Compare with Index Register X (Y)
EOR	Logical Exclusive-OR
NOP	No Operation
ORA	Logical (Inclusive) OR
RTI	Return from Interrupt
SEC	Set Carry
SED	Set Decimal Mode
SEI	Set Interrupt Mask (Disable Interrupts)
TAX (TAY)	Transfer Accumulator to Index Register X (Y)
TXA (TYA)	Transfer Index Register X (Y) to Accumulator

Table 3-3. Seldom Used Instructions of the 6502

Instruction Code	Meaning
BVC	Branch if Overflow Clear
BVS	Branch if Overflow Set
CLV	Clear Overflow
PHP	Push Status Register onto Stack
PLP	Pull Status Register from Stack
TSX	Transfer Stack Pointer to Index Register X
TXS	Transfer Index Register X to Stack Pointer

CPU REGISTERS AND STATUS FLAGS

The 6502 microprocessor has an Accumulator, a Status (or P) register, two index registers, a Stack Pointer, and a Program Counter. These registers may be illustrated as follows:

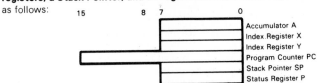

The 6502's Status register contains six status flags and an interrupt control bit. These are the six status flags:

Carry (C)
Zero (Z)
Overflow (V)
Sign (S)
Decimal Mode (D)
Break (B)

Flags are assigned bit positions within the Status register as follows:

The Accumulator (A) is a primary accumulator as described in <u>An Introduction to Microcomputers: Volume 1</u>.

The Index Registers (X and Y) are only eight bits long, unlike the typical microcomputer index registers described in An Introduction to Microcomputers: Volume 1. They are more like classical computer index registers that are used to hold indexes, short offsets, or counters.

The 6502 has a Stack implemented in memory and indexed by the Stack Pointer as described in Volume 1. The only difference from that description is that **the 6502 Stack Pointer is only eight bits wide,** which means that maximum Stack length is 256 bytes. The CPU always inserts 01_{16} as the high-order byte of any Stack address, which means that **memory locations 0100_{16} through $01FF_{16}$ are permanently assigned to the Stack:**

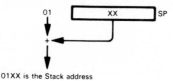

01XX is the Stack address

There is nothing very significant about the shorter 6502 Stack Pointer if you are using this CPU as a stand-alone product. A 256-byte Stack is usually sufficient for any typical microcomputer application; and its location in early memory simply means that low memory addresses must be implemented as read/write memory. 6502 literature represents the Stack Pointer by the letter S; we use the letters SP to prevent confusion with the Sign status.

The 6502 Program Counter is a typical program counter as described in Volume 1.

The Carry status flag holds carries out of the most significant bit in any arithmetic operation. The Carry flag is also included in Shift and Rotate instructions. The only unusual feature of **the 6502 Carry flag** is that it **has an inverted meaning in subtraction operations.** After an SBC instruction, the Carry is cleared if a borrow was required and set if no borrow was required. Note also that the SBC (Subtract with Carry) instruction results in $(A) = (A) - (M) - (1 - C)$ where M is the other operand. This usage is different from most microprocessors or other computers of recent vintage and the user should take heed of it.

The Zero status flag is standard. It is set to 1 when any arithmetic or logical operation produces a zero result. It is set to 0 when any arithmetic or logical operation produces a non-zero result.

The Sign status flag is standard. It will acquire the value of the high-order (Sign) bit of any arithmetic or logical result. Thus, a Sign status value of 1 identifies a negative result and a Sign value of 0 identifies a positive result. The Sign status will be set or reset on the assumption that you are using signed binary arithmetic. If you are not using signed binary arithmetic, you can ignore the Sign status, or you can use it to identify the value of the high-order bit of the result.

The Decimal Mode status, when set, causes the Add-with-Carry and Subtract-with-Carry instructions to perform BCD operations. Thus, when the Decimal Mode status is set and an Add-with-Carry or Subtract-with-Carry instruction is executed, CPU logic assumes that both source 8-bit values are valid BCD numbers — and the result generated will also be a valid BCD number. Because the 6502 CPU performs decimal addition and subtraction, there is no need for an intermediate or Half-Carry status. This status is described in Volume 1. One problem with the 6502 approach is that the same instruction sequence will produce different results, depending on whether the Decimal Mode status has been set or cleared. Thus, confusion and errors can occur if the Decimal Mode status has accidentally been given the wrong value.

The Break status pertains to software interrupts. **When a software interrupt (BRK instruction) is executed, 6502 CPU logic will set the Break status flag.**

I is a standard master interrupt enable/disable or interrupt mask flag. When I equals 1, interrupts are disabled; when I equals 0, interrupts are enabled.

The Overflow status is a typical overflow, except that it can be used as a control input on the 6502 microprocessor. Recall that, during signed binary arithmetic, Overflow status flags a result of magnitude too great to be represented in the given word size. The Overflow status has been discussed in detail in Volume 1 of An Introduction to Microcomputers; it equals the exclusive-OR of carries out of bits 6 and 7 during arithmetic operations. The 6502 microprocessor allows external logic to set the Overflow status, in which case it can be used subsequently as a general logic indicator; you must be very careful when using the Overflow status in this way, since the same status flag will be modified by arithmetic instructions. It is up to you, as a programmer, to make sure that an instruction which modifies the Overflow status is not executed in between the time external logic sets this status and subsequent program logic tests it.

6502 literature refers to the Sign bit as a negative bit, given the symbol N. Statuses (except for Carry) are nevertheless set and reset as described for our hypothetical microcomputer in An Introduction to Microcomputers: Volume 1. Henceforth, we will use the standard symbols S for Sign bit, as well as SP for the Stack Pointer; you should remember these minor differences when using the 6502 literature and instruction set summary cards.

| DIFFERENCES |
| IN NOTATION |

6502 MEMORY ADDRESSING MODES

The 6502 offers eleven basic addressing methods:

1) Memory — immediate
2) Memory — absolute or direct, non-zero-page
3) Memory — zero page (direct)
4) Implied or inherent
5) Accumulator
6) Pre-indexed indirect
7) Post-indexed indirect
8) Zero page, indexed (also called base page, indexed)
9) Absolute indexed
10) Relative
11) Indirect

There are tremendous variations in terms of which methods are allowed with which instructions. See Table 3-4 for the addressing options available with each instruction.

Memory — Immediate

In this form of addressing, one of the operands is present in the byte immediately following the first byte of object code. An immediate operand is specified by prefacing the operand with the # symbol. For example,

AND #$08

requests the Assembler to generate the instruction that will logically AND the value 08_{16} with the contents of the Accumulator.

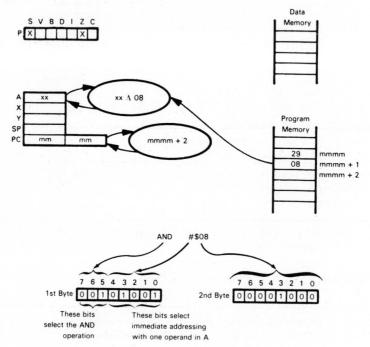

These bits select the AND operation

These bits select immediate addressing with one operand in A

Memory — Direct

This form of addressing uses the second — or second and third (if not on zero, or base, page) — bytes of the instruction to identify the address of an operand in memory. The zero page version is specified when the expression used as the operand in the instruction reduces to a value between 00_{16} and FF_{16}. For example,

AND $30

requests the Assembler to generate an AND instruction which will logically AND the value in memory location 0030_{16} with the contents of the Accumulator.

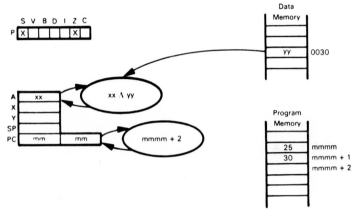

The non-zero-page (absolute) version is similar except that the address of the operand occupies two bytes. For example,

AND $31F6

requests the Assembler to generate an AND instruction that will logically AND the value in memory location $31F6_{16}$ with the contents of the Accumulator.

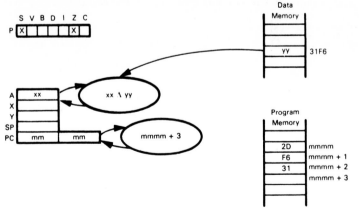

You should note that 16-bit addresses are stored with the eight least significant bits first (at the lower address) followed by the eight most significant bits (at the higher address). This is the same technique that is used in the 8080, 8085, and Z80 microprocessors, but the opposite of that used in the 6800 microprocessor.

STORING ADDRESSES

3-7

Implied or Inherent Addressing

This mode means that no addresses are required to execute the instruction. Typical examples of inherent addressing are CLC (Clear Carry) and TAX (Transfer Register A to Register X).

Accumulator Addressing

This mode means that the instruction operates on the data in the Accumulator. On the 6502 microprocessor, the only Accumulator instructions are the shifts ASL (Arithmetic Shift Left), LSR (Logical Shift Right), ROL (Rotate Left through Carry), and ROR (Rotate Right through Carry).

Pre-Indexed Indirect Addressing

This mode means that the second byte of the instruction is added to the contents of the X Index register to access a memory location in the first 256 bytes of memory, where the indirect address will be found. Wraparound addition is used, which means that any carry formed in address addition will be discarded. For example,

$$\text{AND} \quad (\$20,X)$$

requests the Assembler to generate the instruction which will logically AND the contents of the Accumulator with the contents of the byte addressed by the zero-page memory location given by the sum of 20_{16} and the contents of the X Index register. Note the use of parentheses in the address field to indicate indirection or "contents of"

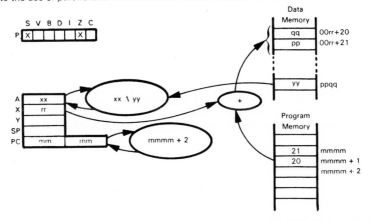

Remember that the carry from the address addition is ignored, i.e., the address of the first address byte is a number in mod 256. Note that the indirect address is stored with its least significant bits first (at the lower address); note also that an address occupies two bytes of memory.

Only the X Index register can be used for pre-indexed indirect addressing.

Post-Indexed Indirect Addressing

This mode means that the second byte of the instruction contains an address in the first 256 bytes of memory. That address and the next location contain an address which is added to the contents of the Y Index register to obtain the effective address.

Note the differences between this method and pre-indexed indirect addressing:

1) In pre-indexed indirect addressing the indexing is performed before the indirection, while in post-indexed indirect addressing the indirection is performed before the indexing.
2) Pre-indexed indirect addressing uses the X Index register, while post-indexed indirect addressing uses the Y Index register.
3) Pre-indexed indirect addressing is useful for choosing one of a set of indirect addresses to use, while post-indexed indirect addressing is useful for accessing elements in an array or table for which the base address has been obtained indirectly.

An example of post-indexed indirect addressing is

AND   ($20),Y

which requests the Assembler to generate the instruction which will logically AND the contents of the Accumulator with the contents of the byte addressed by adding the Y Index register to the address at memory location 0020_{16}. Note that here only the $20 is inside the parentheses, since only that part of the address is used indirectly.

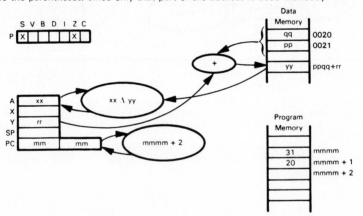

Here again the indirect address is stored with its least significant byte first (at the lower address). Unlike that in pre-indexed indirection, this address addition is a full 16-bit addition; however, it is wraparound so any carry from bit 15 is ignored. Only the Y Index register can be used with post-indexed indirect addressing.

Indexed Addressing

This form of addressing uses the second — or second and third (if not on zero page) — bytes of the instruction to specify the base address. That base address is then added to the contents of Index Register X or Y to get the effective address. X and Y are not interchangeable since no instructions have both forms of simple indexing with both X and Y. In fact, the only instructions which allow zero-page indexing with Y are LDX (Load Index Register X) and STX (Store Index Register X). You should consult Table 3-4 to determine which addressing options are available with each instruction.

A typical example of zero-page indexed addressing is

AND $20,X

which requests the Assembler to generate the instruction that will logically AND the contents of the Accumulator with the contents of the byte at the address given by the sum of 20_{16} and the contents of the X Index register. This is a two-byte instruction because the address is within the first 256 bytes of memory. Note that there is no two-byte form of AND $20,Y although there is a more general three-byte form of this instruction.

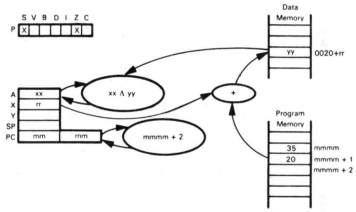

A typical example of absolute indexed addressing is

AND $31FE,Y

which requests the Assembler to generate the instruction that will logically AND the contents of the Accumulator with the contents of the byte at the address given by the sum of $31FE_{16}$ and the contents of the Y Index register. This is a 3-byte instruction since the base address is not within the first 256 bytes of memory.

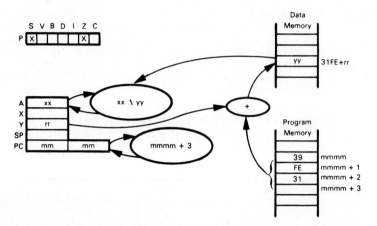

Either Index Register X or Index Register Y could be used here. However, some instructions (such as ASL, DEC, INC, LSR, ROL, and ROR) only allow Index Register X in this mode. This is also the case (more logically) with the instructions LDY (Load Index Register Y) and STY (Store Index Register Y).

Indirect Addressing

Indirect addressing only applies to the JMP (Jump to New Location) instruction. In this mode, the second and third bytes of the instruction contain the address at which the effective address is located. Note that the indirect address can have any value and can be located anywhere in memory. Obviously, this mode can be regarded as a special case of either post-indexed indirect addressing or pre-indexed indirect addressing in which the Index register contains zero. A typical example is:

JMP   ($31FE)

which requests the Assembler to generate a JMP instruction that will load the Program Counter from the memory locations addressed by the contents of memory locations $31FE_{16}$ and $31FF_{16}$. Remember that absolute addresses are 16 bits long and occupy two memory bytes; however, the data located at an address is eight bits long. This confusion applies to all 8-bit processors, but is a particular problem with the 6502 because of its numerous indirect and indexed addressing modes. Indirect addressing is described more fully in Volume 1 of An Introduction to Microcomputers, Chapter 6. Remember that all addresses are stored with their least significant byte first (at the lower address).

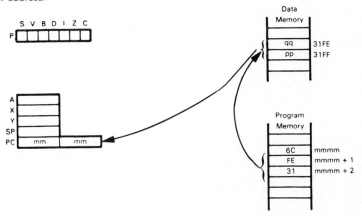

The final value of the Program Counter is ppqq.

Never let an indirect address cross a page boundary, as in JMP ($31FF). Although the high-order byte of the indirect address is in the first location of the next page (in this example, memory location 3200_{16}), the CPU will fetch the high-order byte from the first location of the same page (location 3100_{16} in our example).

Relative Addressing

Branch-on-Condition instructions use program relative addressing; a single byte displacement is treated as a signed binary number which is added to the Program Counter, after the Program Counter contents have been incremented to address the next sequential instruction. This allows displacements in the range $+129_{10}$ to -126_{10} bytes.

A typical example is

BCC *+5

which requests the Assembler to generate a BCC (Branch on Carry Clear; i.e., branch if Carry = 0) instruction that will load the Program Counter with its current value plus five if the Carry is, in fact, zero. If the Carry is one, the instruction does nothing. Note that the instruction itself occupies two bytes of memory and the offset is measured from the end of the instruction. Thus the offset should be 3 to generate a branch to the location five beyond the one in which the first byte of the instruction is located. Note that the symbol * is used for the current value of the Program Counter (actually, the Assembler's Location Counter as described in Chapter 2).

The execution of the BCC *+5 instruction may be described as shown below. Note that the entire instruction is fetched from memory before the destination address is calculated. Note also that there are no other addressing modes available with Branch-on-Condition instructions.

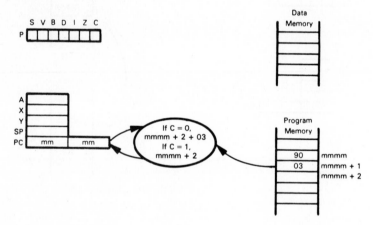

3-14

6502 INSTRUCTION SET

Instructions often frighten microcomputer users who are new to programming. Taken in isolation, the operations involved in the execution of a single instruction are usually easy to follow. The purpose of this chapter is to isolate and explain those operations.

Why are the instructions of a microcomputer referred to as an instruction "set"? Because the microcomputer designer selects (or at least should select) the instructions with great care; it must be easy to execute complex operations as a sequence of simple events, each of which is represented by one instruction from a well-designed instruction "set".

Remaining consistent with An Introduction to Microcomputers: Volume 2, Table 3-4 summarizes the 6502 microcomputer instruction set, with similar instructions grouped together. Individual instructions are listed numerically by object code in Table 3-5 and in alphabetical order by instruction mnemonic in Table 3-6. Table 3-6 also compares the 6800 instruction set with that of the 6502. We will discuss the 6800 and 6502 much later in this chapter, after detailing the 6502 instruction set.

In addition to simply stating what each instruction does, the individual instruction descriptions discuss the purpose of the instruction within normal programming logic.

ABBREVIATIONS

These are the abbreviations used in this chapter:

The registers:

A	Accumulator
X	Index Register X
Y	Index Register Y
PC	Program Counter
SP	Stack Pointer
P	Status register, with bits assigned as follows:

Statuses:

S	Sign or Negative status
V	Overflow status
B	Break status
D	Decimal Mode status
I	Interrupt Disable status
Z	Zero status
C	Carry status

Symbols in the column labeled STATUS:

(blank)	Operation does not affect status
X	Operation affects status
0	Operation clears status
1	Operation sets status
6	Operation reflects bit 6 of memory location
7	Operation reflects bit 7 of memory location
addr	8 bits of absolute or base address
[addr+1,addr]	The address constructed from the contents of memory locations addr and addr+1. This address is used in post-indexed indirect addressing.
addr16	16 bits of absolute or base address
data	8 bits of immediate data
disp	An 8-bit, signed address displacement
label	16-bit absolute address, destination of Jump or Jump-to-Subroutine
PC(HI)	The high-order 8 bits of the Program Counter
PC(LO)	The low-order 8 bits of the Program Counter
pp	The second byte of a two- or three-byte instruction object code
qq	The third byte of a three-byte object code
[ ]	Contents of the memory location designated inside the brackets. For example, [FFFE] represents the contents of memory location $FFFE_{16}$; [addr16+X] represents the contents of the location addressed by adding the contents of register X to addr16; [SP] represents the value at the top of the Stack (contents of the memory location addressed by the Stack Pointer).
[[ ]]	Indirect addressing: the contents of the memory byte addressed by the contents of the memory location designated within the inner brackets. For example, [[addr+X]] represents the contents of a memory location addressed via pre-indexed indirect addressing.
+	Addition — either unsigned binary addition or BCD addition, depending on the condition of the Decimal Mode status.
−	Binary or BCD subtraction, performed by adding the twos complement of the subtrahend to the minuend.
‾	The ones complement of the quantity denoted beneath the bar; for example, $\overline{A}$ represents the complement of the contents of the Accumulator; $\overline{C}$ represents the complement of the value of the Carry status.
Λ	Logical AND
V	Logical OR
⊻	Logical Exclusive-OR
←	Data is transferred in the direction of the arrow.

INSTRUCTION MNEMONICS

Table 3-4 summarizes the 6502 instruction set. The INSTRUCTION column shows the instruction mnemonic (LDA, STA, CLC) and the operands, if any, used with the instruction mnemonic.

The fixed part of an assembly language instruction is shown in UPPER CASE. The variable part (immediate data, address, or label) is shown in lower case.

If a mnemonic has more than one type of operand, each type is listed separately without repeating the mnemonic. For instance, some examples of the format entry

```
              STX
                    addr
                    addr,Y
                    addr16
```

```
        are:    STX $75
                STX $60,Y
                STX $4276
```

INSTRUCTiON OBJECT CODES

For instruction bytes without variations, object codes are represented as two hexadecimal digits (e.g., 8A). For instruction bytes with variations, the object code is shown as eight binary digits (e.g., 101aaa01).

The object code and instruction length in bytes is shown in Table 3-4 for each instruction variation. Table 3-5 lists the object codes in numerical order, and Table 3-6 shows the corresponding object codes for the mnemonics, listed in alphabetical order.

INSTRUCTION EXECUTION TIMES

Table 3-4 lists the instruction execution times in numbers of clock periods. Actual execution time can be derived by dividing the given number of clock periods by the clock speed. For example, for an instruction that requires 5 clock periods, a 2 MHz clock will result in a 2.5 microsecond execution time.

STATUS

The status flags are stored in the Status register (P) as follows:

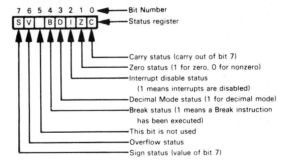

In the individual instruction descriptions, the effect of instruction execution on status is illustrated as follows:

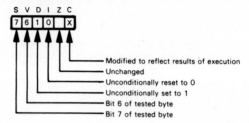

An X identifies a status that is set or reset. A 0 identifies a status that is always cleared. A 1 identifies a status that is always set. A blank means the status does not change. The numbers 7 and 6 show that the flag contains the value of bit 7 or bit 6 of the byte tested by the instruction.

STATUS CHANGES WITH INSTRUCTION EXECUTION

Table 3-4. A Summary of the 6502 Instruction Set

Type	Instruction	Object Code	Bytes	Clock Periods	S	V	D	I	Z	C	Operation Performed
I/O and Primary Memory Reference	**LDA**										Load Accumulator from memory.
	addr	A5 pp	2	3	X				X		A—[addr]	Zero page direct
	addr,X	B5 pp	2	4	X				X		A—[addr+X]	Zero page indexed
	(addr,X)	A1 pp	2	6	X				X		A—[[addr+X]]	Pre-indexed indirect
	(addr),Y	B1 pp	2	5*	X				X		A—[[addr+1,addr]+Y]	Post-indexed indirect
	addr16	AD ppqq	3	4	X				X		A—[addr16]	Extended direct
	addr16,X or Y	11011x01 ppqq	3	4*	X				X		A—[addr16+X] or A—[addr16+Y]	Absolute indexed
	STA										Store Accumulator to memory.
	addr	85 pp	2	3							[addr]—A	Zero page direct
	addr,X	95 pp	2	4							[addr+X]—A	Zero page indexed
	(addr,X)	81 pp	2	6							[[addr+X]]—A	Pre-indexed indirect
	(addr),Y	91 pp	2	6							[[addr+1,addr]+Y]—A	Post-indexed direct
	addr16	8D ppqq	3	4							[addr16]—A	Extended direct
	addr16,X or Y	10011x01 ppqq	3	5							[addr16+X]—A or [addr16+Y]—A	Absolute indexed
	LDX										Load Index Register X from memory. Index through Register Y only.
	addr	A6 pp	2	3	X				X		X—[addr]	Zero page direct
	addr,Y	B6 pp	2	4	X				X		X—[addr+Y]	Zero page indexed
	addr16	AE ppqq	3	4	X				X		X—[addr16]	Extended direct
	addr16,Y	BE ppqq	3	4*	X				X		X—[addr16+Y]	Absolute indexed
	STX										Store Index Register X to memory. Index through Register Y only.
	addr	86 pp	2	3							[addr]—X	Zero page direct
	addr,Y	96 pp	2	4							[addr+Y]—X	Zero page indexed
	addr16	8E ppqq	3	4							[addr16]—X	Extended direct
	LDY										Load Index Register Y from memory. Index through Register X only.
	addr	A4 pp	2	3	X				X		Y—[addr]	Zero page direct
	addr,X	B4 pp	2	4	X				X		Y—[addr+X]	Zero page indexed
	addr16	AC ppqq	3	4	X				X		Y—[addr16]	Extended direct
	addr16,X	BC ppqq	3	4	X				X		Y—[addr16+X]	Absolute indexed

* Add one clock period if page boundary is crossed. In the object code, "x" designates the Index register: x = 0 for Register Y, x = 1 for Register X.

Table 3-4. A Summary of the 6502 Instruction Set (Continued)

Type	Instruction	Object Code	Bytes	Clock Periods	S	V	D	I	Z	C	Operation Performed
I/O and Primary Memory Reference (Continued)	STY										Store Index Register Y to memory. Index through Register X only.
	addr	84 pp	2	3							[addr]—Y Zero page direct
	addr,X	94 pp	2	4							[addr+X]—Y Zero page indexed
	addr16	8C ppqq	3	4							[addr16]—Y Extended direct
Secondary Memory Reference (Memory Operate)	ADC										Add contents of memory location, with carry, to those of Accumulator.
	addr	65 pp	2	3	x	x			x	x	A—A+[addr]+C Zero page direct
	addr,X	75 pp	2	4	x	x			x	x	A—A+[addr+X]+C Zero page indexed
	(addr,X)	61 pp	2	6	x	x			x	x	A—A+[[addr+X]]+C Pre-indexed indirect
	(addr),Y	71 pp	2	5*	x	x			x	x	A—A+[[addr+1, addr]+Y]+C Post-indexed indirect
	addr16	6D ppqq	3	4	x	x			x	x	A—A+[addr16]+C Extended direct
	addr16,X or Y	01111x01 ppqq	3	4*	x	x			x	x	A—A+[addr16+X]+C or A—A+[addr16+Y]+C Absolute indexed (Zero flag is not valid in Decimal Mode).
	AND										AND contents of Accumulator with those of memory location.
	addr	25 pp	2	3	x				x		A—AΛ[addr] Zero page direct
	addr,X	35 pp	2	4	x				x		A—AΛ[addr+X] Zero page indexed
	(addr,X)	21 pp	2	6	x				x		A—AΛ[[addr+X]] Pre-indexed indirect
	(addr),Y	31 pp	2	5*	x				x		A—AΛ[[addr+1, addr]+Y] Post-indexed indirect
	addr16	2D ppqq	3	4	x				x		A—AΛ[addr16] Extended direct
	addr16,X or Y	00111x01 ppqq	3	4*	x				x		A—AΛ[addr16+X] or A—AΛ[addr16+Y] Absolute indexed
	BIT										AND contents of Accumulator with those of memory location. Only the status bits are affected.
	addr	24 pp	2	3	7	6			x		AΛ[addr] Zero page direct
	addr16	2C ppqq	3	4	7	6			x		AΛ[addr16] Extended direct

* Add one clock period if page boundary is crossed. In the object code, "x" designates the Index register: x = 0 for Register Y, x = 1 for Register X.

Table 3-4. A Summary of the 6502 Instruction Set (Continued)

Type	Instruction	Object Code	Bytes	Clock Periods	S	V	D	I	Z	C	Operation Performed	
	CMP										Compare contents of Accumulator with those of memory location. Only the status bits are affected.	
	addr	C5 pp	2	3	x				x	x	A−[addr]	Zero page direct
	addr,X	D5 pp	2	4	x				x	x	A−[addr+X]	Zero page indexed
	(addr,X)	C1 pp	2	6	x				x	x	A−[[addr+X]]	Pre-indexed indirect
	(addr),Y	D1 pp	2	5*	x				x	x	A−[[addr+1, addr]+Y]	Post-indexed indirect
	addr16	CD ppqq	3	4	x				x	x	A−[addr16]	Extended direct
	addr16,X or Y	11011x01 ppqq	3	4*	x				x	x	A−[addr16+X] or A−[addr16+Y]	Absolute indexed
	EOR										Exclusive-OR contents of Accumulator with those of memory location.	
	addr	45 pp	2	3	x				x		A−A⊻[addr]	Zero page direct
	addr,X	55 pp	2	4	x				x		A−A⊻[addr+X]	Zero page indexed
	(addr,X)	41 pp	2	6	x				x		A−A⊻[[addr+X]]	Pre-indexed indirect
	(addr),Y	51 pp	2	5*	x				x		A−A⊻[[addr+1, addr]+Y]	Post-indexed indirect
	addr16	4D ppqq	3	4	x				x		A−A⊻[addr16]	Extended direct
	addr16,X or Y	01011x01 ppqq	3	4*	x				x		A−A⊻[addr16+X] or A−A⊻[addr16+Y]	Absolute indexed
	ORA										OR contents of Accumulator with those of memory location.	
	addr	05 pp	2	3	x				x		A−AV[addr]	Zero page direct
	addr,X	15 pp	2	4	x				x		A−AV[addr+X]	Zero page indexed
	(addr,X)	01 pp	2	6	x				x		A−AV[[addr+X]]	Pre-indexed indirect
	(addr),Y	11 pp	2	5*	x				x		A−AV[[addr+1, addr]+Y]	Post-indexed indirect
	addr16	0D ppqq	3	4	x				x		A−AV[addr16]	Extended direct
	addr16,X or Y	00011x01 ppqq	3	4*	x				x		A−AV[addr16+X] or A−AV[addr16+Y]	Absolute indexed

Type: Secondary Memory Reference (Memory Operate) (Continued)

* Add one clock period if page boundary is crossed. In the object code, "x" designates the Index register: x = 0 for Register Y, x = 1 for Register X.

Table 3-4. A Summary of the 6502 Instruction Set (Continued)

Type	Instruction	Object Code	Bytes	Clock Periods	S	V	D	I	Z	C	Operation Performed
Secondary Memory Reference (Memory Operate) (Continued)	**SBC**										Subtract contents of memory location, with borrow, from contents of Accumultor.
	addr	E5 pp	2	3	x	x			x	x	$A \leftarrow A-[addr]-\bar{C}$ — Zero page direct
	addr,X	F5 pp	2	4	x	x			x	x	$A \leftarrow A-[addr+X]-\bar{C}$ — Zero page indexed
	(addr,X)	E1 pp	2	6	x	x			x	x	$A \leftarrow A-[[addr+X]]-\bar{C}$ — Pre-indexed indirect
	(addr),Y	F1 pp	2	5*	x	x			x	x	$A \leftarrow A-[[addr+1,addr]+Y]-\bar{C}$ — Post-indexed indirect
	addr16	ED ppqq	3	4	x	x			x	x	$A \leftarrow A-[addr16]-\bar{C}$ — Extended direct
	addr16,X or Y	11111x01 ppqq	3	4*	x	x			x	x	$A \leftarrow A-[addr16+X]-\bar{C}$ or $A \leftarrow A-[addr16+Y]-\bar{C}$ — Absolute indexed (Note that Carry value is the complement of the borrow.)
	INC										Increment contents of memory location. Index through Register X only.
	addr	E6 pp	2	5	x				x		$[addr] \leftarrow [addr]+1$ — Zero page direct
	addr,X	F6 pp	2	6	x				x		$[addr+X] \leftarrow [addr+X]+1$ — Zero page indexed
	addr16	EE ppqq	3	6	x				x		$[addr16] \leftarrow [addr16]+1$ — Extended direct
	addr16,X	FE ppqq	3	7	x				x		$[addr16+X] \leftarrow [addr16+X]+1$ — Absolute indexed
	DEC										Decrement contents of memory location. Index through Register X only.
	addr	C6 pp	2	5	x				x		$[addr] \leftarrow [addr]-1$ — Zero page direct
	addr,X	D6 pp	2	6	x				x		$[addr+X] \leftarrow [addr+X]-1$ — Zero page indexed
	addr16	CE ppqq	3	6	x				x		$[addr16] \leftarrow [addr16]-1$ — Extended direct
	addr16,X	DE ppqq	3	7	x				x		$[addr16+X] \leftarrow [addr16+X]-1$ — Absolute indexed
	CPX										Compare contents of X register with those of memory location. Only the status flags are affected.
	addr	E4 pp	2	3	x				x	x	$X-[addr]$ — Zero page direct
	addr16	EC ppqq	3	4	x				x	x	$X-[addr16]$ — Extended direct
	CPY										Compare contents of Y register with those of memory location. Only the status flags are affected.
	addr	C4 pp	2	3	x				x	x	$Y-[addr]$ — Zero page direct
	addr16	CC ppqq	3	4	x				x	x	$Y-[addr16]$ — Extended direct

*Add one clock period if page boundary is crossed. In the object code, "x" designates the Index register: x = 0 for Register Y, x = 1 for Register X.

Table 3-4. A Summary of the 6502 Instruction Set (Continued)

Type	Instruction	Object Code	Bytes	Clock Periods	S	V	D	I	Z	C	Operation Performed
Secondary Memory Reference (Memory Operate) (Continued)	**ROL**										Rotate contents of memory location one bit left through Carry. Index through Register X only. [addr] [addr+X] [addr16] [addr16+X]
	addr	26 pp	2	5	X				X	X	
	addr,X	36 pp	2	6	X				X	X	
	addr16	2E ppqq	3	6	X				X	X	
	addr16,X	3E ppqq	3	7	X				X	X	
	ROR										Rotate contents of memory location one bit right, through Carry. Index through Register X only. [addr] [addr+X] [addr16] [addr16+X]
	addr	66 pp	2	5	X				X	X	
	addr,X	76 pp	2	6	X				X	X	
	addr16	6E pp	3	6	X				X	X	
	addr16,X	7E ppqq	3	7	X				X	X	
	ASL										Arithmetic shift left contents of memory location. Index through Register X only. [addr] [addr+X] [addr16] [addr16+X]
	addr	06 pp	2	5	X				X	X	
	addr,X	16 pp	2	6	X				X	X	
	addr16	0E ppqq	3	6	X				X	X	
	addr16,X	1E ppqq	3	7	X				X	X	

3-23

Table 3-4. A Summary of the 6502 Instruction Set (Continued)

Type	Instruction	Object Code	Bytes	Clock Periods	S	V	D	I	Z	C	Operation Performed
Secondary Memory Ref. (Memory Operate) (Cont.)	**LSR** addr addr,X addr16 addr16,X	46 pp 56 pp 4E ppqq 5E ppqq	2 2 3 3	5 6 6 7	0 0 0 0				x x x x	x x x x	Logical shift right contents of memory location. Index through Register X only. [addr] [addr+X] [addr16] [addr16,X] 0 → 7 ... 0 → C
Immediate	LDA data	A9 pp	2	2	x				x		Load Accumulator with immediate data. A—data
Immediate	LDX data	A2 pp	2	2	x				x		Load Index Register X with immediate data. X—data
Immediate	LDY data	A0 pp	2	2	x				x		Load Index Register Y with immediate data. Y—data

3-24

Table 3-4. A Summary of the 6502 Instruction Set (Continued)

Type	Instruction	Object Code	Bytes	Clock Periods	S	V	D	I	Z	C	Operation Performed
Immediate Operate	ADC data	69 pp	2	2	X	X			X	X	Add immediate with Carry, to Accumulator. The Zero flag is not valid in Decimal Mode. A←A+data+C
	AND data	29 pp	2	2	X				X		AND immediate with Accumulator. A←A∧data
	CMP data	C9 pp	2	2	X				X	X	Compare immediate with Accumulator. Only the status flags are affected. A−data
	EOR data	49 pp	2	2	X				X		Exclusive-OR immediate with Accumulator. A←A⊻data
	ORA data	09 pp	2	2	X				X		OR immediate with Accumulator. A←A V data
	SBC data	E9 pp	2	2	X	X			X	X	Subtract immediate, with borrow, from Accumulator. A←A−data−C̄ (Note that Carry value is the complement of the borrow.)
	CPX data	E0 pp	2	2	X				X	X	Compare immediate with Index Register X. Only the status flags are affected. X−data
	CPY data	C0 pp	2	2	X				X	X	Compare immediate with Index Register Y. Only the status flags are affected. Y−data
Jump	JMP label	4C ppqq	3	3							Jump to new location, using extended or indirect addressing. PC←label or PC←[label]
	(label)	6C ppqq	3	5							

Table 3-4. A Summary of the 6502 Instruction Set (Continued)

Type	Instruction	Object Code	Bytes	Clock Periods	S	V	D	I	Z	C	Operation Performed
Branch on Condition											Note the following for all Branch-on-Condition instructions: If the condition is satisfied, the displacement is added to the Program Counter after the Program Counter has been incremented to point to the instruction following the Branch instruction.
	BCC disp	90 pp	2	2**							Branch relative if Carry flag is cleared. If C=0, then PC←PC+disp
	BCS disp	B0 pp	2	2**							Branch relative if Carry flag is set. If C=1, then PC←PC+disp
	BEQ disp	F0 pp	2	2**							Branch relative if result is equal to zero. If Z=1, then PC←PC+disp
	BMI disp	30 pp	2	2**							Branch relative if result is negative. If S=1, then PC←PC+disp
	BNE disp	D0 pp	2	2**							Branch relative if result is not zero. If Z=0, then PC←PC+disp
	BPL disp	10 pp	2	2**							Branch relative if result is positive. If S=0, then PC←PC+disp
	BVC disp	50 pp	2	2**							Branch relative if Overflow flag is cleared. If V = 0, then PC←PC+disp
	BVS disp	70 pp	2	2**							Branch relative if Overflow flag is set. If V=1, then PC←PC+disp

**Add one clock period if branch occurs to location in same page; add two clock periods if branch to another page occurs.

Table 3-4. A Summary of the 6502 Instruction Set (Continued)

Type	Instruction	Object Code	Bytes	Clock Periods	Status S	V	D	I	Z	C	Operation Performed
Subroutine Call and Return	JSR label	20 ppqq	3	6							Jump to subroutine beginning at address given in bytes 2 and 3 of the instruction. Note that the stored Program Counter points to the last byte of the JSR instruction. [SP]→PC(HI) [SP−1]→PC(LO) SP→SP−2 PC→label
	RTS	60	1	6							Return from subroutine, incrementing Program Counter to point to the instruction after the JSR which called the routine. PC(LO)←[SP+1] PC(HI)←[SP+2] SP→SP+2 PC→PC+1
Register-Register Move	TAX	AA	1	2	X				X		Move Accumulator contents to Index Register X. X→A
	TXA	8A	1	2	X				X		Move contents of Index Register X to Accumulator. A→X
	TAY	A8	1	2	X				X		Move Accumulator contents to Index Register Y. Y→A
	TYA	98	1	2	X				X		Move contents of Index Register Y to Accumulator. A→Y
	TSX	BA	1	2	X				X		Move contents of Stack Pointer to Index Register X. X→SP
	TXS	9A	1	2							Move contents of Index Register X to Stack Pointer. SP→X

3-27

Table 3-4. A Summary of the 6502 Instruction Set (Continued)

Type	Instruction	Object Code	Bytes	Clock Periods	Status S	V	D	I	Z	C	Operation Performed
Register Operate	DEX	CA	1	2	X				X		Decrement contents of Index Register X. X←X−1
	DEY	88	1	2	X				X		Decrement contents of Index Register Y. Y←Y−1
	INX	E8	1	2	X				X		Increment contents of Index Register X. X←X+1
	INY	C8	1	2	X				X		Increment contents of Index Register Y. Y←Y+1
	ROL A	2A	1	2	X				X	X	Rotate contents of Accumulator left through Carry.
	ROR A	6A	1	2	X				X	X	Rotate contents of Accumulator right, through Carry.
	ASL A	0A	1	2	X				X	X	Arithmetic shift left contents of Accumulator.
	LSR A	4A	1	2	0				X	X	Logical shift right contents of Accumulator.

Table 3-4. A Summary of the 6502 Instruction Set (Continued)

Type	Instruction	Object Code	Bytes	Clock Periods	S	V	D	I	Z	C	Operation Performed
Stack	PHA	48	1	3							Push Accumulator contents onto Stack. [SP]←A, SP←SP-1
	PLA	68	1	4	X				X		Load Accumulator from top of Stack ("Pull"). A←[SP+1], SP←SP+1
	PHP	08	1	3							Push Status register contents onto Stack. [SP]←P, SP←SP-1
	PLP	28	1	4	X	X	X	X	X	X	Load Status register from top of Stack ("Pull"). P←[SP+1], SP←SP+1
Interrupt	CLI	58	1	2				0			Enable interrupts by clearing interrupt disable bit of Status register. I←0
	SEI	78	1	2				1			Disable interrupts I←1
	RTI	40	1	6	X	X	X	X	X	X	Return from interrupt; restore Status P←[SP+1], PC(LO)←[SP+2], PC(HI)←[SP+3], SP←SP+3, PC←PC+1
	BRK	00	1	7				1			Programmed interrupt. BRK cannot be disabled. The Program Counter is incremented twice before it is saved on the Stack. [SP]←PC(HI), [SP-1]←PC(LO), [SP-2]←P, SP←SP-3, PC(HI)←[FFFF], PC(LO)←[FFFE], I←1, B←1

Status columns: S, V, D, I, Z, C

Table 3-4. A Summary of the 6502 Instruction Set (Continued)

Type	Instruction	Object Code	Bytes	Clock Periods	Status						Operation Performed
					S	V	D	I	Z	C	
Status	CLC	18	1	2						0	Clear Carry flag C→0
	SEC	38	1	2						1	Set Carry flag C→1
	CLD	D8	1	2			0				Clear Decimal Mode D→0
	SED	F8	1	2			1				Set Decimal Mode D→1
	CLV	B8	1	2		0					Clear Overflow flag V→0
	NOP	EA	1	2							No Operation

Table 3-5. 6502 Instruction Object Codes in Numerical Order

Object Code	Instruction		Object Code	Instruction	
00	BRK		68	PLA	
01 pp	ORA	(addr,X)	69 pp	ADC	data
05 pp	ORA	addr	6A	ROR	A
06 pp	ASL	addr	6C ppqq	JMP	(label)
08	PHP		6D ppqq	ADC	addr16
09 pp	ORA	data	6E ppqq	ROR	addr16
0A	ASL	A	70 pp	BVS	disp
0D ppqq	ORA	addr16	71 pp	ADC	(addr),Y
0E ppqq	ASL	addr16	75 pp	ADC	addr,X
10 pp	BPL	disp	76 pp	ROR	addr,X
11 pp	ORA	(addr),Y	78	SEI	
15 pp	ORA	addr,X	79 ppqq	ADC	addr16,Y
16 pp	ASL	addr,X	7D ppqq	ADC	addr16,X
18	CLC		7E ppqq	ROR	addr16,X
19 ppqq	ORA	addr16,Y	81 pp	STA	(addr,X)
1D ppqq	ORA	addr16,X	84 pp	STY	addr
1E ppqq	ASL	addr16,X	85 pp	STA	addr
20 ppqq	JSR	label	86 pp	STX	addr
21 pp	AND	(addr,X)	88	DEY	
24 pp	BIT	addr	8A	TXA	
25 pp	AND	addr	8C ppqq	STY	addr16
26 pp	ROL	addr	8D ppqq	STA	addr16
28	PLP		8E ppqq	STX	addr16
29 pp	AND	data	90 pp	BCC	disp
2A	ROL	A	91 pp	STA	(addr),Y
2C ppqq	BIT	addr16	94 pp	STY	addr,X
2D ppqq	AND	addr16	95 pp	STA	addr,X
2E ppqq	ROL	addr16	96 pp	STX	addr,Y
30 pp	BMI	disp	98	TYA	
31 pp	AND	(addr),Y	99 ppqq	STA	addr16,Y
35 pp	AND	addr,X	9A	TXS	
36 pp	ROL	addr,X	9D ppqq	STA	addr16,X
38	SEC		A0 pp	LDY	data
39 ppqq	AND	addr16,Y	A1 pp	LDA	(addr,X)
3D ppqq	AND	addr16,X	A2 pp	LDX	data
3E ppqq	ROL	addr16,X	A4 pp	LDY	addr
40	RTI		A5 pp	LDA	addr
41 pp	EOR	(addr,X)	A6 pp	LDX	addr
45 pp	EOR	addr	A8	TAY	
46 pp	LSR	addr	A9 pp	LDA	data
48	PHA		AA	TAX	
49 pp	EOR	data	AC ppqq	LDY	addr16
4A	LSR	A	AD ppqq	LDA	addr16
4C ppqq	JMP	label	AE ppqq	LDX	addr16
4D ppqq	EOR	addr16	B0 pp	BCS	disp
4E ppqq	LSR	addr16	B1 pp	LDA	(addr),Y
50 pp	BVC	disp	B4 pp	LDY	addr,X
51 pp	EOR	(addr),Y	B5 pp	LDA	addr,X
55 pp	EOR	addr,X	B6 pp	LDX	addr,Y
56 pp	LSR	addr,X	B8	CLV	
58	CLI		B9 ppqq	LDA	addr16,Y
59 ppqq	EOR	addr16,Y	BA	TSX	
5D ppqq	EOR	addr16,X	BC ppqq	LDY	addr16,X
5E ppqq	LSR	addr16,X	BD ppqq	LDA	addr16,X
60	RTS		BE ppqq	LDX	addr16,Y
61 pp	ADC	(addr,X)	C0 pp	CPY	data
65 pp	ADC	addr	C1 pp	CMP	(addr,X)
66 pp	ROR	addr	C4 pp	CPY	addr

Table 3-5. 6502 Instruction Object Codes in Numerical Order (Continued)

Object Code	Instruction	
C5 pp	CMP	addr
C6 pp	DEC	addr
C8	INY	
C9 pp	CMP	data
CA	DEX	
CC ppqq	CPY	addr16
CD ppqq	CMP	addr16
CE ppqq	DEC	addr16
DO pp	BNE	disp
D1 pp	CMP	(addr),Y
D5 pp	CMP	addr,X
D6 pp	DEC	addr,X
D8	CLD	
D9 ppqq	CMP	addr16,Y
DD ppqq	CMP	addr16,X
DE ppqq	DEC	addr16,X
EO pp	CPX	data
E1 pp	SBC	(addr,X)

Object Code	Instruction	
E4 pp	CPX	addr
E5 pp	SBC	addr
E6 pp	INC	addr
E8	INX	
E9 pp	SBC	data
EA	NOP	
EC ppqq	CPX	addr16
ED ppqq	SBC	addr16
EE ppqq	INC	addr16
FO pp	BEQ	disp
F1 pp	SBC	(addr),Y
F5 pp	SBC	addr,X
F6 pp	INC	addr,X
F8	SED	
F9 ppqq	SBC	addr16,Y
FD ppqq	SBC	addr16,X
FE ppqq	INC	addr16,X

The following symbols are used in the object codes in Table 3-6.

Address-mode Selection:

aaa

000	pre-indexed indirect - (addr,X)
001	direct - addr
010	immediate - data
011	extended direct - addr16
100	post-indexed indirect - (addr),Y
101	base page indexed - addr,X
110	absolute indexed - addr16,Y
111	absolute indexed - addr16,X

bb

00	direct - addr
01	extended direct - addr16
10	base page indexed - addr,X
11	absolute indexed - addr16,X

bbb

001	direct - addr
010	accumulator - A
011	extended direct - addr16
101	base page indexed - addr,X; addr,Y in STX
111	absolute indexed - addr16,X; addr16,Y in STX

cc

00	immediate - data
01	direct - addr
11	extended direct - addr16

ddd

000	immediate - data
001	direct - addr
011	extended direct - addr16
101	base page indexed - addr,Y in LDX; addr,X in LDY
111	absolute indexed - addr16,Y in LDX; addr16,X in LDY

pp   the second byte of a two- or three-byte instruction

qq   the third byte of a three-byte instruction

x   one bit choosing the address mode:
0	direct - addr
1	extended direct - addr16

y   one bit choosing the JMP address mode:
0	extended direct - label
1	indirect - (label)

Table 3-6. Summary of 6502 Object Codes with 6800 Mnemonics

Mnemonic	Operand	Object Code	Bytes	Clock Periods	MC6800 Instruction
ADC		011aaa01			ADCA
	data	pp	2	2	data8
	addr	pp	2	3	addr8
	addr,X	pp	2	4	index
	(addr,X)	pp	2	6	
	(addr),Y	pp	2	5*	
	addr16	ppqq	3	4	addr16
	addr16,X	ppqq	3	4*	
	addr16,Y	ppqq	3	4*	
AND		001aaa01			ANDA
	data	pp	2	2	data8
	addr	pp	2	3	addr8
	addr,X	pp	2	4	index
	(addr,X)	pp	2	6	
	(addr),Y	pp	2	5*	
	addr16	ppqq	3	4	addr16
	addr16,X	ppqq	3	4*	
	addr16,Y	ppqq	3	4*	
ASL	A	000bbb10	1	2	ASLA
	addr	pp	1	5	
	addr,X	pp	2	6	ASL index
	addr16	ppqq	3	6	ASL addr16
	addr16,X	ppqq	3	7	
BCC	disp	90 pp	2	2**	BCC disp
BCS	disp	B0 pp	2	2**	BCS disp
BEQ	disp	F0 pp	2	2**	BEQ disp
BIT		0010x100			BITA
	addr	pp	2	3	addr8
	addr16	ppqq	3	4	addr16
BMI	disp	30 pp	2	2**	BMI disp
BNE	disp	D0 pp	2	2**	BNE disp
BPL	disp	10 pp	2	2**	BPL disp
BRK		00	1	7	(SWI)
BVC	disp	50 pp	2	2**	BVC disp
BVS	disp	70 pp	2	2**	BVS disp
CLC		18	1	2	CLC
CLD		D8	1	2	
CLI		58	1	2	CLI
CLV		B8	1	2	CLV

*Add one clock period if page boundary is crossed.
**Add one clock period if branch occurs to location in same page; add two clock periods if branch to another page occurs.

Table 3-6. Summary of 6502 Object Codes with 6800 Mnemonics (Continued)

Mnemonic	Operand	Object Code	Bytes	Clock Periods	MC6800 Instruction
CMP		110aaa01			CMPA
	data	pp	2	2	data8
	addr	pp	2	3	addr8
	addr,X	pp	2	4	index
	(addr,X)	pp	2	6	
	(addr),Y	pp	2	5*	
	addr16	ppqq	3	4	addr16
	addr16,X	ppqq	3	4*	
	addr16,Y	ppqq	3	4*	
CPX		1110cc00			CPX
	data	pp	2	2	data8
	addr	pp	2	3	addr8
	addr16	ppqq	3	4	addr16
CPY		1100cc00			
	data	pp	2	2	
	addr	pp	2	3	
	addr16	ppqq	3	4	
DEC		110bb110			DEC
	addr	pp	2	5	
	addr,X	pp	2	6	index
	addr16	ppqq	3	6	addr16
	addr16,X	ppqq	3	7	
DEX		CA	1	2	DEX
DEY		88	1	2	
EOR		010aaa01			EORA
	data	pp	2	2	data8
	addr	pp	2	3	addr8
	addr,X	pp	2	4	index
	(addr,X)	pp	2	6	
	(addr),Y	pp	2	5*	
	addr16	ppqq	3	4	addr16
	addr16,X	ppqq	3	4*	
	addr16,Y	ppqq	3	4*	
INC		111bb110			INC
	addr	pp	2	5	
	addr,X	pp	2	6	index
	addr16	ppqq	3	6	addr16
	addr16,X	ppqq	3	7	
INX		E8	1	2	INX
INY		C8	1	2	
JMP		01y01100			JMP
	label	ppqq	3	3	addr16
	(label)	ppqq	3	5	
JSR	label	20 ppqq	3	6	JSR addr16

*Add one clock period if page boundary is crossed.
**Add one clock period if branch occurs to location in same page; add two clock periods if branch to another page occurs.

Table 3-6. Summary of 6502 Object Codes with 6800 Mnemonics (Continued)

Mnemonic	Operand	Object Code	Bytes	Clock Periods	MC6800 Instruction
LDA		101aaa01			LDAA
	data	pp	2	2	data8
	addr	pp	2	3	addr8
	addr,X	pp	2	4	index
	(addr,X)	pp	2	6	
	(addr),Y	pp	2	5*	
	addr16	ppqq	3	4	addr16
	addr16,X	ppqq	3	4*	
	addr16,Y	ppqq	3	4*	
LDX		101ddd10			LDX
	data	pp	2	2	(data8)
	addr	pp	2	3	addr8
	addr,Y	pp	2	4	(index)
	addr16	ppqq	3	4	addr16
	addr16,Y	ppqq	3	4*	
LDY		101ddd00			
	data	pp	2	2	
	addr	pp	2	3	
	addr,X	pp	2	4	
	addr16	ppqq	3	4	
	addr16,X	ppqq	3	4*	
LSR	A	010bbb10	1	2	LSRA
	addr	pp	2	5	
	addr,X	pp	2	6	LSR index
	addr16	ppqq	3	6	LSR addr16
	addr16,X	ppqq	3	7	
NOP		EA	1	2	NOP
ORA		000aaa01			ORAA
	data	pp	2	2	data8
	addr	pp	2	3	addr8
	addr,X	pp	2	4	index
	(addr,X)	pp	2	6	
	(addr),Y	pp	2	5*	
	addr16	ppqq	3	4	addr16
	addr16,X	ppqq	3	4*	
	addr16,Y	ppqq	3	4*	
PHA		48	1	3	PSHA
PHP		08	1	3	
PLA		68	1	4	PULA
PLP		28	1	4	
ROL	A	001bbb10	1	2	ROLA
	addr	pp	2	5	
	addr,X	pp	2	6	ROL index
	addr16	ppqq	3	6	ROL addr16
	addr16,X	ppqq	3	7	

*Add one clock period if page boundary is crossed.
**Add one clock period if branch occurs to location in same page; add two clock periods if branch to another page occurs.

Mnemonic	Operand	Object Code	Bytes	Clock Periods	MC6800 Instruction
ROR	A	011bbb10	1	2	RORA
	addr	pp	2	5	
	addr,X	pp	2	6	ROR index
	addr16	ppqq	3	6	ROR addr16
	addr16,X	ppqq	3	7	
RTI		40	1	6	RTI
RTS		60	1	6	RTS
SBC		111aaa01			SBCA
	data	pp	2	2	data8
	addr	pp	2	3	addr8
	addr,X	pp	2	4	index
	(addr,X)	pp	2	6	
	(addr),Y	pp	2	5*	
	addr16	ppqq	3	4	addr16
	addr16,X	ppqq	3	4*	
	addr16,Y	ppqq	3	4*	
SEC		38	1	2	SEC
SED		F8	1	2	
SEI		78	1	2	SEI
STA		100aaa01			STAA
	addr	pp	2	3	addr8
	addr,X	pp	2	4	index
	(addr,X)	pp	2	6	
	(addr),Y	pp	2	6	
	addr16	ppqq	3	4	addr16
	addr16,X	ppqq	3	5	
	addr16,Y	ppqq	3	5	
STX		100bb110			STX
	addr	pp	2	3	addr8
	addr,Y	pp	2	4	(index)
	addr16	ppqq	3	4	addr16
STY		100bb100			
	addr	pp	2	3	
	addr,X	pp	2	4	
	addr16	ppqq	3	4	
TAX		AA	1	2	
TAY		A8	1	2	
TSX		BA	1	2	TSX
TXA		8A	1	2	
TXS		9A	1	2	TXS
TYA		98	1	2	

*Add one clock period if page boundary is crossed.
**Add one clock period if branch occurs to location in same page; add two clock periods if branch to another page occurs.

ADC — ADD MEMORY, WITH CARRY, TO ACCUMULATOR

This instruction uses eight methods of addressing data memory and allows the contents of data memory and the carry status to be added to the Accumulator. The eight methods of addressing memory are:

1) Immediate - ADC data
2) Absolute (direct) - ADC addr16
3) Zero page (direct) - ADC addr
4) Pre-indexed with Index Register X - ADC (addr,X)
5) Post-indexed with Index Register Y - ADC (addr),Y
6) Zero-page indexed with Index Register X - ADC addr,X
7) Absolute indexed with Index Register X - ADC addr16,X
8) Absolute indexed with Index Register Y - ADC addr16,Y

The first byte of object code determines which addressing mode is selected as follows:

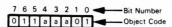

Bit Value for aaa	Hexadecimal Object Code	Addressing Mode	Number of bytes
000	61	Indirect, pre-indexed with X	2
001	65	Zero page (direct)	2
010	69	Immediate	2
011	6D	Absolute (direct)	3
100	71	Indirect, post-indexed with Y	2
101	75	Zero page indexed with X	2
110	79	Absolute indexed with Y	3
111	7D	Absolute indexed with X	3

We may illustrate the ADC instruction with immediate addressing as shown below. For other addressing modes, consult either the discussion of addressing modes or the description of other arithmetic or logical instructions since other illustrations show different addressing modes.

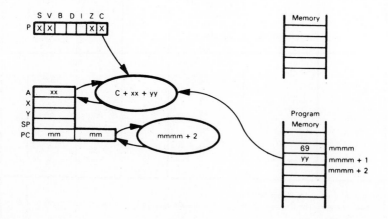

Add the contents of the next program memory byte (addressing mode selected by bits 2, 3, and 4 of the byte in the instruction register) and the Carry status to the Accumulator. Suppose $xx = 3A_{16}$, $yy = 7C_{16}$, $C = 1$. After the instruction

$$ADC \quad \#\$7C$$

has been executed, the Accumulator will contain $B7_{16}$.

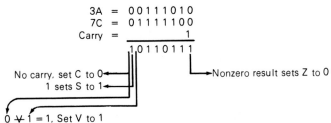

ADC is the only 6502 addition instruction. To use it in single-byte operations or to add the low-order bytes of two multibyte numbers, a previous instruction must explicitly set Carry to zero so that it does not affect the operation. Note that the 6502 microprocessor has no addition instruction that does not include the Carry. ADC will perform either binary or decimal (BCD) addition, depending on whether the Decimal Mode status is 0 or 1.

AND — AND MEMORY WITH ACCUMULATOR

This instruction logically ANDs the contents of a memory location with the contents of the Accumulator. This instruction offers the same memory addressing options as the ADC instruction. The first byte of object code selects the addressing mode as follows:

Bit Value for aaa	Hexadecimal Object Code	Addressing Mode	Number of Bytes
000	21	Indirect, pre-indexed with X	2
001	25	Zero page (direct)	2
010	29	Immediate	2
011	2D	Absolute (direct)	3
100	31	Indirect, post-indexed with Y	2
101	35	Zero page indexed with X	2
110	39	Absolute indexed with Y	3
111	3D	Absolute indexed with X	3

We will illustrate the AND instruction with zero page (direct) addressing. See the discussion of addressing methods and other arithmetic and logical instructions for examples of the other addressing modes.

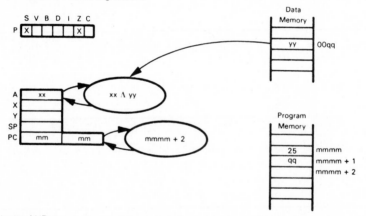

Logically AND the contents of the selected memory byte with the Accumulator and store the result in the Accumulator. Suppose $xx = FC_{16}$ and $yy = 13_{16}$. After the instruction

$$AND \quad \$40$$

(assuming that yy is in memory location 0040), the Accumulator will contain 10_{16}:

$$
\begin{array}{rl}
FC = & 1 1 1 1 1 1 0 0 \\
13 = & 0 0 0 1 0 0 1 1 \\
\hline
& 0 0 0 1 0 0 0 0
\end{array}
$$

0 in bit 7 sets S to 0 ⟵⎿   ⎿⟶ Nonzero result sets Z to 0

AND is a frequently used logical instruction.

ASL — SHIFT ACCUMULATOR OR MEMORY BYTE LEFT

Perform a one-bit arithmetic left shift of the contents of the Accumulator or the contents of the selected memory byte.

First, consider shifting the Accumulator:

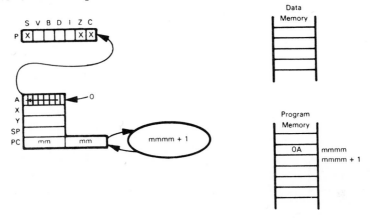

Suppose that the Accumulator contains $7A_{16}$. Performing an

$$\text{ASL} \quad \text{A}$$

instruction will set the Carry status to 0, the Sign status to 1, the Zero status to 0, and will store $F4_{16}$ in the Accumulator.

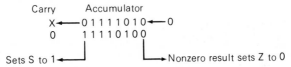

The ASL instruction uses four data memory addressing options:

1) Zero page (direct) - ASL addr
2) Absolute (direct) - ASL addr16
3) Zero page indexed with Index Register X - ASL addr,X
4) Absolute indexed with Index Register X - ASL addr16,X

The first byte of object code determines which addressing mode is selected as follows:

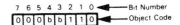

Bit Value for bb	Hexadecimal Object Code	Addressing Mode	Number of Bytes
00	06	Zero page (direct)	2
01	0E	Absolute (direct)	3
10	16	Zero page indexed with X	2
11	1E	Absolute indexed with X	3

We will show the ASL instruction with absolute (direct) addressing. The other addressing modes are shown in other instruction descriptions.

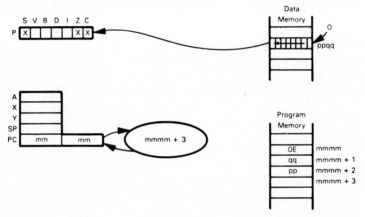

Suppose ppqq = $3F86_{16}$ and the contents of ppqq are CB_{16}. After executing an

ASL $3F86

instruction, the contents of location $3F86_{16}$ will be altered to 96_{16} and Carry will be set to 1:

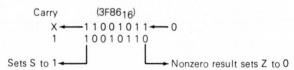

The ASL instruction is often used in multiplication routines and as a standard logical instruction. Note that a single ASL instruction multiplies its operand by 2.

BCC — BRANCH IF CARRY CLEAR (C = 0)

This instruction is a branch with relative addressing in which the branch is only executed if the Carry status equals 0; otherwise, the next instruction is executed.

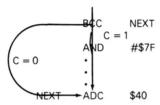

In the following instruction sequence:

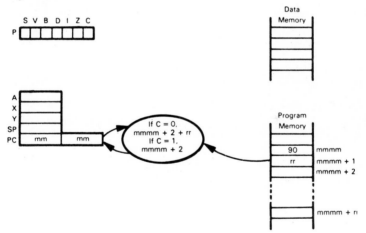

the ADC $40 instruction is executed right after the BCC instruction if the Carry status equals 0. The AND #$7F instruction is executed if the Carry status equals 1. The relative addressing operates as shown in the next illustration and as shown in the discussion of addressing methods presented earlier. No statuses and no registers — except the Program Counter — are affected.

If the Carry is zero, this instruction adds the contents of the second object code byte (taken as a signed 8-bit displacement) to the contents of the Program Counter plus 2; this becomes the memory address for the next instruction to be executed. The previous contents of the Program Counter are lost.

BCS — BRANCH IF CARRY SET (C = 1)

This instruction operates like the BCC instruction except that the branch is only executed if the Carry status equals 1; otherwise, the next instruction is executed.

$$\underbrace{BCS}_{B0}$$

In the following instruction sequence:

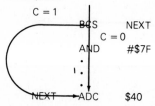

the ADC $40 instruction is executed right after the BCS instruction if the Carry status equals 1. The AND #$7F instruction is executed if the Carry status equals 0.

BEQ — BRANCH IF EQUAL TO ZERO (Z = 1)

This instruction is just like the BCC instruction except that the branch is executed if the Zero status equals 1; otherwise, the next instruction is executed.

$$\underbrace{BEQ}_{F0}$$

In the following sequence:

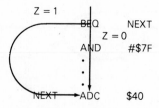

the ADC $40 instruction is executed right after the BEQ instruction if the Zero status equals 1. The AND #$7F instruction is executed if the Zero status equals 0.

BIT — BIT TEST

This instruction logically ANDs the contents of the Accumulator with the contents of a selected memory location, sets the condition flags accordingly, but does not alter the contents of the Accumulator or memory byte. The only addressing modes allowed are absolute (direct) and zero page (direct). The first byte of object code determines the addressing mode as follows:

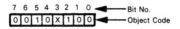

Bit Value for x	Hexadecimal Object Code	Addressing Mode	Number of Bytes
0	24	Zero page (direct)	2
1	2C	Absolute (direct)	3

We will illustrate the BIT instruction using absolute (direct) addressing. For the zero page mode, see the AND instruction and the discussion of addressing modes. We should note that BIT has a rather unusual effect on the status flags, since it sets the Z flag according to the result of the logical AND operation but sets the S and V flags according to bits 7 and 6 of the contents of the memory location being tested; that is,

$$Z = 1 \text{ if } A \wedge (M) = 0; Z = 0 \text{ if } A \wedge (M) \neq 0$$
$$S = \text{bit 7 of } (M)$$
$$V = \text{bit 6 of } (M)$$

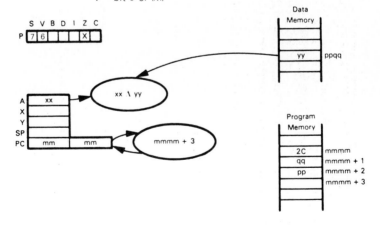

Logically AND the contents of the Accumulator with the contents of the specified memory location and set the Zero condition flag accordingly. Set the Sign and Overflow condition flags according to bits 7 and 6, respectively, of the selected memory location. Suppose $xx = A6_{16}$, $yy = E0_{16}$, and $ppqq = 1641_{16}$. After the instruction

$$\text{BIT} \quad \$1641$$

has executed, the Accumulator will still contain $A6_{16}$, and location 1641_{16} will still contain $E0_{16}$, but the statuses will be modified as follows:

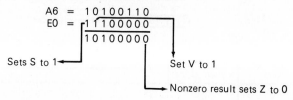

BIT instructions frequently precede conditional Branch instructions. BIT instructions are also used to perform masking functions on data.

BMI — BRANCH IF MINUS (S = 1)

This instruction works like the BCC instruction except that the branch is executed only if the Sign status is 1; otherwise, the next instruction is executed.

In the following instruction sequence:

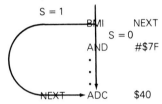

the ADC $40 instruction is executed right after the BMI instruction if the Sign status is 1. The AND #$7F instruction is executed if the Sign status is 0.

BNE — BRANCH IF NOT EQUAL TO ZERO (Z = 0)

This instruction is identical to the BCC instruction except that the branch is executed only if the Zero status is 0; otherwise, the next instruction in sequence is executed.

In the following instruction sequence:

Z = 0
BNE   NEXT
       Z = 1
AND   #$7F
.
.
.
NEXT   ADC $40

the ADC $40 instruction is executed right after the BNE instruction if the Zero status is 0. The AND #$7F instruction is executed if the Zero status is 1.

BPL — BRANCH IF PLUS (S = 0)

$$\underbrace{\text{BPL}}_{10}$$

This instruction operates like the BCC instruction except that the branch is executed only if the Sign status is 0; otherwise, the next instruction in sequence is executed.

In the following instruction sequence:

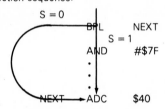

the ADC $40 instruction is executed right after the BPL instruction if the Sign status is 0. The AND #$7F instruction is executed if the Sign status is 1.

BRK — FORCE BREAK (TRAP OR SOFTWARE INTERRUPT)

BRK

00

The Program Counter is incremented by two and the Break status is set to 1, then the Program Counter and Status (P) register are pushed onto the Stack. The registers and the corresponding memory locations into which they are pushed are as follows:

Memory Location   Register
(Stack Pointer contains ss at start of instruction execution.)

Memory Location	Register
01ss	High byte of Program Counter
01ss − 1	Low byte of Program Counter
01ss − 2	Status (P) register with B = 1

(Stack Pointer contains ss − 3 at end of instruction execution.)

The Interrupt Mask bit is then set to 1. This disables the 6502's interrupt service ability, i.e., the processor will not respond to an interrupt from a peripheral device. The contents of the Interrupt Pointer (memory addresses $FFFE_{16}$ and $FFFF_{16}$) are then loaded into the Program Counter.

The BRK instruction can be used for a variety of functions. It can provide a breakpoint facility for debugging purposes or it can transfer control to a particularly important software system such as a disk operating system or a monitor. Note that the programmer must insert the code required to tell a BRK instruction from a regular interrupt response. The coding to do this checks the value of the B status flag in the Stack as follows:

```
PLA                 ;GET STATUS REGISTER
PHA                 ;BUT ALSO LEAVE IT ON STACK
AND      #$10       ;IS BREAK STATUS SET?
BNE      BRKP       ;YES, GO PROCESS BREAK
```

Note that the operation code for BRK is 00. This choice of operation code means that BRK can be used to patch programs in fusible-link PROMs since blowing all the fuses makes the contents of the word 00. Thus an erroneous instruction can be corrected by changing the first object code byte to 00 and inserting a patch via the interrupt vector routine. Remember that a bit in a fusible-link PROM can be set to zero (by blowing the fuse) but cannot be reset to one after the fuse has been blown. Such PROMs are not erasable.

The operation of the BRK instruction may be illustrated as follows:

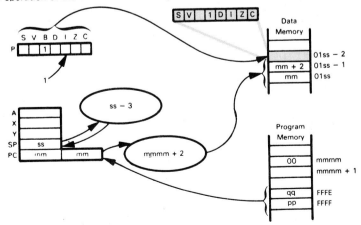

The final contents of the Program Counter are ppqq where pp represents the contents of the memory location $FFFF_{16}$ and qq the contents of memory location $FFFE_{16}$. Note that the Stack is always on page 1 of memory; i.e., the eight most significant bits of the Stack address are always 01_{16}.

BVC — BRANCH IF OVERFLOW CLEAR (V = 0)

BVC

50

This instruction operates like the BCC instruction except that the branch is executed only if the Overflow status is 0; otherwise, the next instruction in sequence is executed.

In the following instruction sequence:

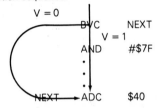

the ADC $40 instruction is executed right after the BVC instruction if the Overflow status is 0. The AND #$7F instruction is executed if the Overflow status is 1.

BVS — BRANCH IF OVERFLOW SET (V = 1)

BVS

70

This instruction is just like the BCC instruction except that the branch is executed only if the Overflow status is 1; otherwise, the next instruction in sequence is executed.

In the following instruction sequence:

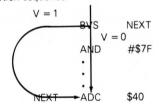

the ADC $40 instruction is executed right after the BVS instruction if the Overflow status equals 1. The AND #$7F instruction is executed if the Overflow status equals 0.

CLC — CLEAR CARRY

Clear the Carry status. No other status or register's contents are affected. Note that this instruction is required as part of a normal addition operation since the only addition instruction available on the 6502 microprocessor is ADC, which also adds in the Carry status. This instruction is also required at the start of a multi-byte addition since there is never a carry into the least significant byte.

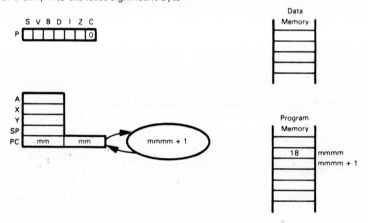

CLD — CLEAR DECIMAL MODE

CLD
⏜
D8

Clear the Decimal Mode status. No other status or register's contents are affected. This instruction is used to return the 6502 processor to the binary mode in which ADC and SBC instructions produce binary rather than BCD results. This instruction may be used to ensure that the mode is binary in situations where it may be uncertain whether the Decimal Mode status has been set or cleared most recently.

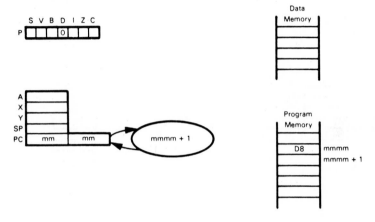

CLI — CLEAR INTERRUPT MASK (ENABLE INTERRUPTS)

Clear the interrupt mask bit in the Status (P) register. This instruction enables the 6502's interrupt service ability, i.e., the 6502 will respond to the Interrupt Request control line. No other registers or statuses are affected. Note that the I bit is a mask or disable bit. It must be cleared to enable interrupts and set to disable them.

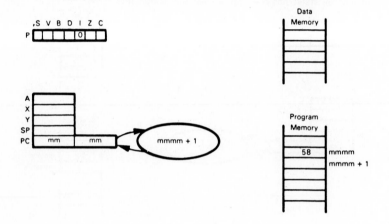

CLV — CLEAR OVERFLOW

CLV
⌣
B8

Clear the overflow bit in the Status register. No other registers or statuses are affected.
Note that the 6502 has no SET OVERFLOW instruction.

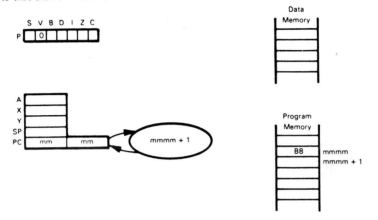

3-55

CMP — COMPARE MEMORY WITH ACCUMULATOR

This instruction subtracts the contents of a selected memory byte from the Accumulator, sets the condition flags accordingly, but does not alter the contents of the Accumulator or memory byte. This instruction offers the same memory addressing options as the ADC instruction. The first byte of object code selects the addressing mode as follows:

Bit Value for aaa	Hexadecimal Object Code	Addressing Mode	Number of Bytes
000	C1	Indirect, pre-indexed with X	2
001	C5	Zero page (direct)	2
010	C9	Immediate	2
011	CD	Absolute (direct)	3
100	D1	Indirect, post-indexed with Y	2
101	D5	Zero page indexed with X	2
110	D9	Absolute indexed with Y	3
111	DD	Absolute indexed with X	3

We will illustrate the CMP instruction with pre-indexed indirect addressing (using Index Register X). See the discussions of addressing methods and other instructions for examples of the other addressing modes.

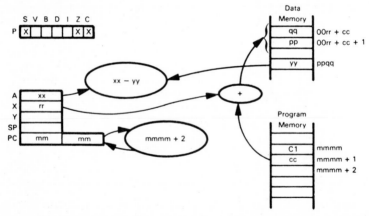

Subtract the contents of the selected memory byte from the contents of the Accumulator and set the Sign, Zero, and Carry statuses to reflect the result of the subtraction. Suppose $xx = FF_{16}$, $yy = 18_{16}$, $rr = 20_{16}$, $cc = 23_{16}$, $(0043_{16}) = 6D_{16}$, and $(0044_{16}) = 15_{16}$. Note that $0043 = rr + cc$ and we have assumed that $(156D_{16}) = yy = 18_{16}$.

After the instruction

$$CMP \quad (\$23,X)$$

has been executed, the Accumulator will still contain $F6_{16}$, and memory location $156D_{16}$ will still contain 18_{16}, but the statuses will be modified as follows:

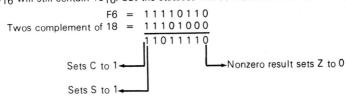

Note that C is equal to the resulting carry, not to its complement as is true on many other microprocessors. Thus $C = 0$ if a borrow is required and $C = 1$ if no borrow is necessary.

Compare instructions are most frequently used to set statuses before the execution of Branch-on-Condition instructions.

CPX — COMPARE INDEX REGISTER X WITH MEMORY

This instruction is the same as CMP except that the memory byte is subtracted from Index Register X instead of the Accumulator. The only addressing modes allowed are immediate, zero page (direct), and absolute (direct). The first byte of object code selects the addressing mode as follows:

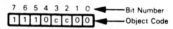

Bit Value for cc	Hexadecimal Object Code	Addressing Mode	Number of Bytes
00	E0	Immediate	2
01	E4	Zero page (direct)	2
10		Used for INX instruction	
11	EC	Absolute (direct)	3

We will illustrate the CPX instruction with immediate addressing. See the discussion of addressing methods and other arithmetic and logical instructions for examples of the other addressing modes.

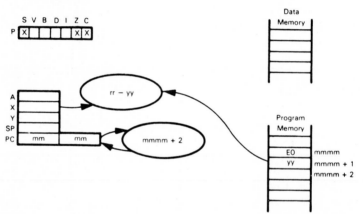

Subtract the contents of the selected memory byte from the contents of Index Register X. The Sign, Zero, and Carry statuses reflect the result of the subtraction in the same way as shown for the CMP instruction.

CPY — COMPARE INDEX REGISTER Y WITH MEMORY

This instruction is the same as CMP except that the memory byte is subtracted from Index Register Y instead of the Accumulator. The only addressing modes allowed are immediate, zero page (direct), and absolute (direct). The first byte of object code selects the addressing mode as follows:

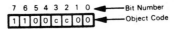

Bit Value for cc	Hexadecimal Object Code	Addressing Mode	Number of Bytes
00	C0	Immediate	2
01	C4	Zero page (direct)	2
10		Used for INY instruction	
11	CC	Absolute (direct)	3

We will illustrate the CPY instruction with zero page (direct) addressing. See the discussion of addressing methods and other arithmetic and logical instructions for examples of the other addressing modes.

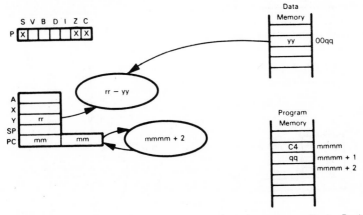

Subtract the contents of the selected memory byte from the contents of Index Register Y. The Sign, Zero, and Carry statuses reflect the result of the subtraction in the same way as shown for the CMP instruction.

DEC — DECREMENT MEMORY (BY 1)

This instruction decrements by 1 the contents of a selected memory location. The DEC instruction uses four data memory addressing options:

1) Zero page (direct) — DEC addr
2) Absolute (direct) — DEC addr16
3) Zero page indexed with Index Register X — DEC addr,X
4) Absolute indexed with Index Register X — DEC addr16,X

The first byte of object code determines which addressing mode is selected as follows:

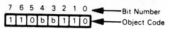

Bit Value for bb	Hexadecimal Object Code	Addressing Mode	Number of Bytes
00	C6	Zero page (direct)	2
01	CE	Absolute (direct)	3
10	D6	Zero page indexed with X	2
11	DE	Absolute indexed with X	3

We will illustrate the DEC instruction with absolute indexed addressing. The other addressing modes are shown elsewhere.

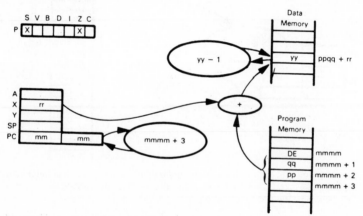

Decrement the contents of the specified memory byte.

If $yy = A5_{16}$, $ppqq = 0100_{16}$, and $rr = 0A_{16}$, then after execution of the instruction

　　　DEC $0100,X

the contents of memory location $010A_{16}$ will be altered to $A4_{16}$.

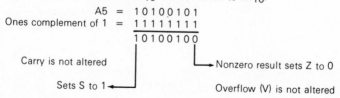

DEX — DECREMENT INDEX REGISTER X (BY 1)

This instruction decrements by 1 the contents of Index Register X. The Zero and Sign statuses are affected.

DEX
CA

The effects of this instruction are the same as those of DEC except that the contents of Index Register X are decremented rather than the contents of a memory location.

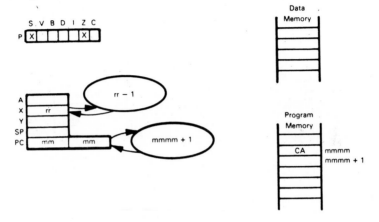

DEY — DECREMENT INDEX REGISTER Y (BY 1)

This instruction decrements by 1 the contents of Index Register Y. The Zero and Sign statuses are affected just as they are by DEC and DEX.

DEY
$\underbrace{}$
88

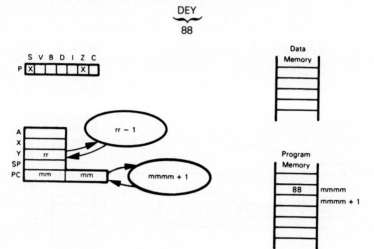

EOR — EXCLUSIVE-OR ACCUMULATOR WITH MEMORY

Exclusive-OR the contents of the Accumulator with the contents of a selected memory byte. This instruction offers the same memory addressing options as the ADC instruction. The first byte of object code selects the addressing mode as follows:

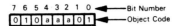

Bit Value for aaa	Hexadecimal Object Code	Addressing Mode	Number of Bytes
000	41	Indirect, pre-indexed with X	2
001	45	Zero page (direct)	2
010	49	Immediate	2
011	4D	Absolute (direct)	3
100	51	Indirect, post-indexed with Y	2
101	55	Zero page indexed with X	2
110	59	Absolute indexed with Y	3
111	5D	Absolute indexed with X	3

We will illustrate the EOR instruction with post-indexed indirect addressing (using Index Register Y). See the discussion of addressing methods and other arithmetic and logical instructions for examples of the other addressing modes.

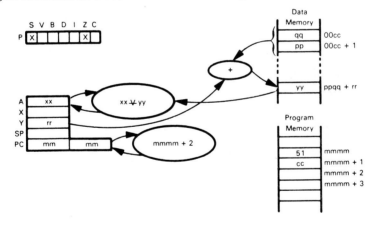

Logically Exclusive-OR the contents of the Accumulator with the contents of the selected memory location, treating both operands as simple binary data. Suppose that $xx = E3_{16}$ and $yy = A0_{16}$. After the instruction

$$EOR \quad (\$40,Y)$$

has executed, the Accumulator will contain 43_{16}. We assume also that $rr = 10_{16}$, $qq = (40_{16}) = 1E_{16}$, $pp = (41_{16}) = 25_{16}$, and $(251E_{16}) = yy = A0_{16}$.

$$
\begin{array}{rl}
E3 = & 1\,1\,1\,0\,0\,0\,1\,1 \\
A0 = & \underline{1\,0\,1\,0\,0\,0\,0\,0} \\
& 0\,1\,0\,0\,0\,0\,1\,1
\end{array}
$$

0 sets S to 0 ◄——┘   └——► Nonzero result sets Z to 0

EOR is used to test for changes in bit status. Note also that the instruction EOR #$FF complements the contents of the Accumulator, changing each '1' bit to a '0' and each '0' bit to a '1'.

INC — INCREMENT MEMORY (BY 1)

This instruction increments by 1 the contents of a selected memory location. The INC instruction uses four data memory addressing options:

1) Zero page (direct) — INC addr
2) Absolute (direct) — INC addr16
3) Zero page indexed with Index Register X — INC addr,X
4) Absolute indexed with Index Register X — INC addr16,X

The first byte of object code determines which addressing mode is selected as follows:

Bit Value for bb	Hexadecimal Object Code	Addressing Mode	Number of Bytes
00	E6	Zero page (direct)	2
01	EE	Absolute (direct)	3
10	F6	Zero page indexed with X	2
11	FE	Absolute indexed with X	3

We will illustrate the INC instruction with absolute (direct) addressing. The other addressing modes are shown elsewhere.

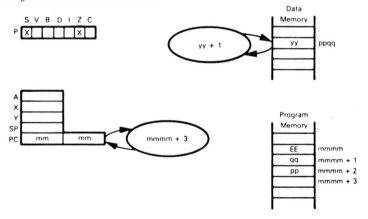

Increment the selected memory byte.

If $pp = 01_{16}$, $qq = A2_{16}$, and $yy = C0_{16}$, then after executing an:

INC $01A2

instruction, the contents of memory location $01A2_{16}$ will be incremented to $C1_{16}$.

```
CO  =  1 1 0 0 0 0 0 0
 1  =  0 0 0 0 0 0 0 1
       ─────────────────
       1 1 0 0 0 0 0 1
```

Sets S to 1 ◄────┘   └────► Nonzero result sets Z to 0

Carry and Overflow are not altered

The INC instruction can be used to provide a counter in a variety of applications such as counting the occurrences of an event or specifying the number of times a task is to be performed.

INX — INCREMENT INDEX REGISTER X (BY 1)

This instruction increments by 1 the contents of Index Register X. The Zero and Sign statuses are affected just as by the INC instruction.

INC
E8

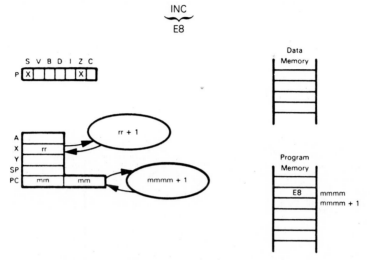

Add 1 to the contents of Index Register X and set the Zero and Sign flags according to the result. Suppose that Index Register X contains $7A_{16}$. After the instruction

INX

has executed, Index Register X will contain $7B_{16}$, the Zero status will be cleared since the result is nonzero, and the Sign status will be cleared since the result has 0 in its most significant bit.

INY — INCREMENT INDEX REGISTER Y (BY 1)

This instruction increments by 1 the contents of Index Register Y. The Zero and Sign statuses are affected just as by the INC instruction.

$$\underbrace{\text{INY}}_{\text{C8}}$$

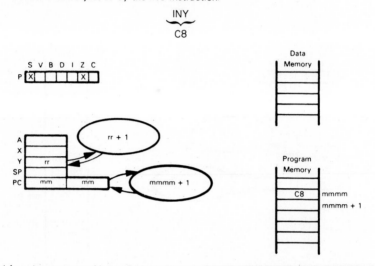

Add 1 to the contents of Index Register Y and set the Zero and Sign flags according to the result. Suppose that Index Register Y contains $0C_{16}$. After the instruction INY has executed, Index Register Y will contain $0D_{16}$, the Zero status will be cleared since the result is nonzero, and the Sign status will be cleared since the result has 0 in its most significant bit.

JMP — JUMP VIA ABSOLUTE OR INDIRECT ADDRESSING

This instruction will be illustrated using indirect addressing. Note that it is the only instruction that has the true indirect addressing mode. The first byte of object code determines the addressing mode as follows:

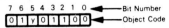

Bit Value for y	Hexadecimal Object Code	Addressing Mode	Number of Bytes
0	4C	Absolute (direct)	3
1	6C	Indirect	3

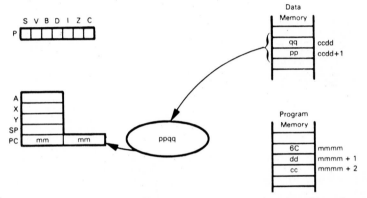

Jump to the instruction specified by the operand by loading the address from the selected memory bytes into the Program Counter.

In the following instruction sequence:

```
CLC
LDA     #BASEL  ;CALCULATE LSB'S OF DESTINATION ADDRESS
ADC     INDXL
STA     JADDR
LDA     #BASEU  ;CALCULATE MSB'S OF DESTINATION ADDRESS
ADC     INDXU
STA     JADDR+1
JMP     (JADDR) ;TRANSFER CONTROL TO DESTINATION
```

The JMP instruction will perform an indexed jump relative to the 16-bit address consisting of BASEU (8 MSBs) and BASEL (8 LSBs). The index here is assumed to be 16 bits long and to be initially stored at addresses INDXL (8 LSBs) and INDXU (8 MSBs). The addresses following the start of the table could then contain absolute JMP instructions that transfer control to the proper routines.

JMP will not work properly if the indirect address crosses a page boundary — that is, if dd = FF_{16} in the illustration above. The discussion of indirect addressing earlier in this chapter discusses this peculiarity in more detail.

The JMP instruction can also use the absolute (direct) addressing mode. In this case, the second byte of the instruction is loaded into the low byte of the Program Counter, and the third byte of the instruction is loaded into the high byte of the Program Counter. Instruction execution continues from this address.

JSR — JUMP TO SUBROUTINE

This instruction pushes the Program Counter onto the Stack and then transfers control to the specified instruction. Only absolute (direct) addressing is allowed. Note that the Stack Pointer is decremented after the storage of each data byte and that the Program Counter value that is saved is the address of the last (third) byte of the JSR instruction: i.e., the initial program counter value plus 2. Remember also that the Stack grows down in memory and that the most significant half of the Program Counter is stored first and thus ends up at the higher address (in the usual 6502 address form).

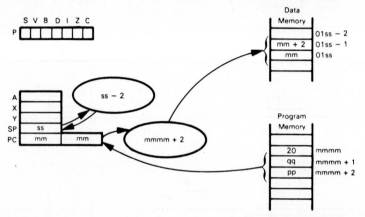

The Program Counter is incremented by 2 and then is pushed onto the Stack. The Stack Pointer is adjusted to point to the next empty location in the Stack. The address part of the instruction is then stored in the Program Counter and execution continues from that point.

Assume that mmmm = $E34F_{16}$ and that ss = $E3_{16}$. Then after the execution of the instruction

$$\text{JSR} \quad \$E100$$

the Program Counter will contain $E100_{16}$, the Stack Pointer will contain $E1_{16}$, and the Stack locations will be as follows:

$$(01ss) = (01E3) = PC(HI) = E3$$
$$(01ss \text{ - } 1) = (01E2) = PC(LO) = 51_{16}$$

The next instruction to be executed will be the one at memory address $E100_{16}$.

LDA — LOAD ACCUMULATOR FROM MEMORY

Load the contents of the selected memory byte into the Accumulator. This instruction offers the same memory addressing options as the ADC instruction and will be illustrated using zero-page indexed addressing with Index Register X. See the discussion of addressing methods and other arithmetic and logical instructions for examples of the other addressing modes. The first byte of object code selects the addressing mode as follows:

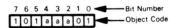

Bit Value for aaa	Hexadecimal Object Code	Addressing Mode	Number of Bytes
000	A1	Indirect, pre-indexed with X	2
001	A5	Zero page (direct)	2
010	A9	Immediate	2
011	AD	Absolute (direct)	3
100	B1	Indirect, post-indexed with Y	2
101	B5	Zero page indexed with X	2
110	B9	Absolute indexed with Y	3
111	BD	Absolute indexed with X	3

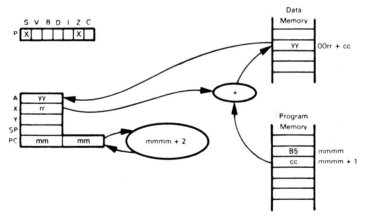

Load the contents of the selected memory byte into the Accumulator.

Suppose that Index Register X contains 10_{16} and $cc = 43_{16}$. If memory location 0053_{16} contains AA_{16}, then after

$$LDA \quad \$43,X$$

has executed, the Accumulator will contain AA_{16}.

$$AA = 1\ 0\ 1\ 0\ 1\ 0\ 1\ 0$$

1 sets S to 1 ◄───┘ └──► Nonzero result sets Z to 0

LDX — LOAD INDEX REGISTER X FROM MEMORY

Load the contents of the selected memory byte into Index Register X. The addressing modes allowed are:

1) Immediate — LDX data
2) Absolute (direct) — LDX addr16
3) Zero page (direct) — LDX addr
4) Absolute indexed with Y — LDX addr16,Y
5) Zero page indexed with Y — LDX addr,Y

Note that there are no indexing modes with Index Register X, and there is no post-indexing. The first byte of object code selects the addressing mode as follows:

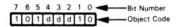

Bit Value for ddd	Hexadecimal Object Code	Addressing Mode	Number of Bytes
000	A2	Immediate	2
001	A6	Zero page (direct)	2
010	AA	Used for TAX instruction	
011	AE	Absolute (direct)	3
100	B2	Not used	
101	B6	Zero page indexed with Y	2
110	BA	Used for TSX instruction	
111	BE	Absolute indexed with Y	3

We will illustrate the LDX instruction with absolute indexed addressing using Index Register Y. See the discussion of addressing methods and other arithmetic and logical instructions for examples of the other addressing modes.

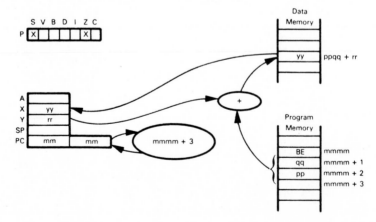

Load the contents of the selected memory byte into Index Register X. Suppose that Index Register Y contains 28_{16}, ppqq = $2E1A_{16}$, and yy = $(2E42_{16}) = 4F_{16}$, then after the execution of the instruction

$$\text{LDX} \quad \$2E1A,Y$$

Index Register X will contain $4F_{16}$.

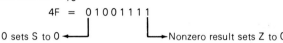

$$4F \ = \ 0\ 1\ 0\ 0\ 1\ 1\ 1\ 1$$

0 sets S to 0 ◄——⌐   ⌐——► Nonzero result sets Z to 0

LDY — LOAD INDEX REGISTER Y FROM MEMORY

Load the contents of the selected memory byte into Index Register Y. The addressing modes allowed are:

1) Immediate — LDY data
2) Absolute (direct) — LDY addr16
3) Zero page (direct) — LDY addr
4) Absolute indexed with X — LDY addr16,X
5) Zero page indexed with X — LDY addr,X

Note that there are no indexing modes with Index Register Y nor is there any pre-indexing.

The first byte of object code selects the addressing mode as follows:

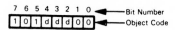

Bit Value for ddd	Hexadecimal Object Code	Addressing Mode	Number of Bytes
000	A0	Immediate	2
001	A4	Zero page (direct)	2
010	A8	Used for TAY instruction	
011	AC	Absolute (direct)	3
100	B0	Used for BCS instruction	
101	B4	Zero page indexed with X	2
110	B8	Used for CLV instruction	
111	BC	Absolute indexed with X	3

We will illustrate the LDY instruction with immediate addressing. See the discussion of addressing methods and other arithmetic and logical instructions for examples of the other addressing modes.

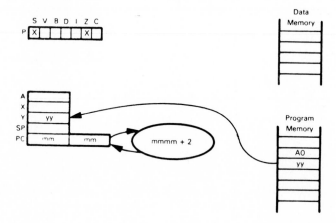

Load the contents of the selected memory byte into Index Register Y. Suppose that $yy = 00_{16}$, then after the execution of the instruction

LDY #0

Index Register Y will contain zero.

$$00 = 00000000$$

0 sets S to 0 ◄———┘   └——►Zero result sets Z to 1

LSR — LOGICAL SHIFT RIGHT OF ACCUMULATOR OR MEMORY

This instruction performs a one-bit logical right shift of the Accumulator or the selected memory byte.

First, consider shifting the Accumulator.

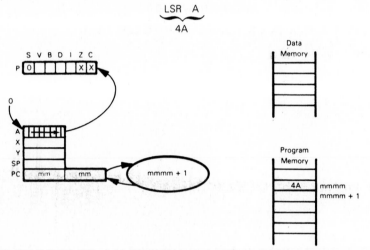

Shift the contents of the Accumulator right one bit. Shift the low-order bit into the Carry status. Shift a zero into the high-order bit.

Suppose the Accumulator contains $7A_{16}$. After the

$$LSR \quad A$$

instruction is executed, the Accumulator will contain $3D_{16}$ and the Carry status will be set to zero.

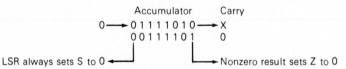

Four methods of addressing data memory are available with the LSR instruction; they are:

1) Zero page (direct) — LSR addr
2) Absolute (direct) — LSR addr16
3) Zero page indexed with Index Register X — LSR addr,X
4) Absolute indexed with Index Register X — LSR addr16,X

The first byte of object code determines which addressing mode is selected as follows:

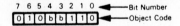

Bit Value for bb	Hexadecimal Object Code	Addressing Mode	Number of Bytes
00	46	Zero page (direct)	2
01	4E	Absolute (direct)	3
10	56	Zero page indexed with X	2
11	5E	Absolute indexed with X	3

We will illustrate the LSR instruction with absolute (direct) addressing. The other addressing modes are shown elsewhere.

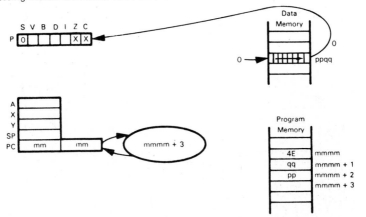

Logically shift the contents of the selected memory location right one bit.

Suppose that ppqq = $04FA_{16}$ and the contents of memory location $04FA_{16}$ are $0D_{16}$. After the instruction

LSR $04FA

has been executed, the Carry status will be 1 and the contents of memory location $04FA_{16}$ will be 06_{16}.

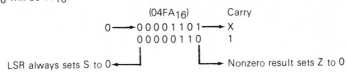

NOP — NO OPERATION

$$\underbrace{\text{NOP}}_{\text{EA}}$$

This is a one-byte instruction which does nothing except increment the Program Counter. This instruction allows you to give a label to an object program byte, to fine tune a delay (each NOP instruction adds two clock cycles), and to replace instruction bytes that are no longer needed because of corrections or changes. NOPs can also be used to replace instructions (such as JSRs) which you may not want to include in debugging runs. NOP is not very frequently used in finished programs, but it is often useful in debugging and testing.

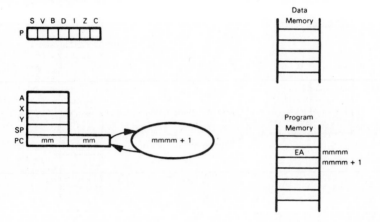

ORA — LOGICALLY OR MEMORY WITH ACCUMULATOR

This instruction logically ORs the contents of a memory location with the contents of the Accumulator. This instruction offers the same memory addressing options as the ADC instruction. The first byte of object code selects the addressing mode as follows:

Bit Value for aaa	Hexadecimal Object Code	Addressing Mode	Number of Bytes
000	01	Indirect, pre-indexed with X	2
001	05	Zero page (direct)	2
010	09	Immediate	2
011	0D	Absolute (direct)	3
100	11	Indirect, post-indexed with Y	2
101	15	Zero page indexed with X	2
110	19	Absolute indexed with Y	3
111	1D	Absolute indexed with X	3

We will illustrate the ORA instruction using absolute indexed addressing with Index Register Y. See the discussion of addressing methods and other arithmetic and logical instructions for examples of the other addressing modes.

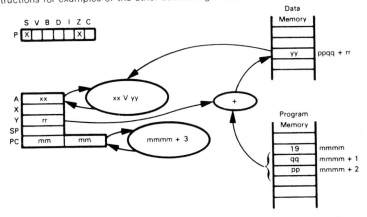

Logically OR the contents of the Accumulator with the contents of the selected memory byte, treating both operands as simple binary data.

Suppose that $ppqq = 1623_{16}$, $rr = 10_{16}$, $xx = E3_{16}$, and $yy = AB_{16}$. After the execution of the instruction

ORA $1623,Y

the Accumulator will contain EB_{16}.

$$\begin{array}{rl}
E3 = & 1 1 1 0 0 0 1 1 \\
AB = & 1 0 1 0 1 0 1 1 \\
\hline
 & 1 1 1 0 1 0 1 1
\end{array}$$

Sets S to 1 ◄─────┘   └───►Nonzero result sets Z to 0

This is a logical instruction; it is often used to turn bits "on", i.e., make them '1's. For example, the instruction

ORA   #$80

will unconditionally set the high-order bit in the Accumulator to 1.

PHA — PUSH ACCUMULATOR ONTO STACK

This instruction stores the contents of the Accumulator on the top of the Stack. The Stack Pointer is then decremented by 1. No other registers or statuses are affected. Note that the Accumulator is stored in the Stack before the Stack Pointer is decremented.

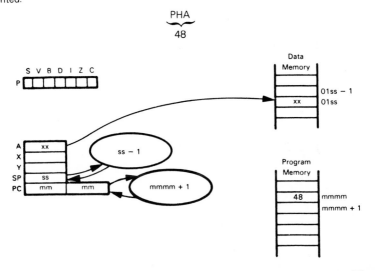

Suppose that the Accumulator contains $3A_{16}$ and the Stack Pointer contains $F7_{16}$. After the instruction PHA has been executed, $3A_{16}$ will have been stored in memory location $01F7_{16}$ and the Stack Pointer will be altered to $F6_{16}$.

The PHA instruction is most frequently used to save Accumulator contents before servicing an interrupt or calling a subroutine.

PHP — PUSH STATUS REGISTER (P) ONTO STACK

This instruction stores the contents of the Status (P) register on the top of the Stack. The Stack Pointer is then decremented by 1. No other registers or statuses are affected. Note that the Status register is stored in the Stack before the Stack Pointer is decremented.

The organization of the status in memory is as follows:

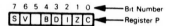

Bit 5 is not used and its value is arbitrary.

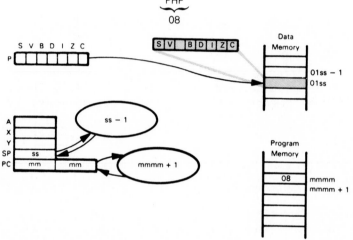

The PHP instruction is generally used to save the contents of the Status register before calling a subroutine. Note that PHP is not necessary before servicing an interrupt since the interrupt response (to $\overline{IRQ}$ or $\overline{NMI}$) and the BRK instruction automatically save the contents of the Status register at the top of the Stack.

PLA — PULL CONTENTS OF ACCUMULATOR FROM STACK

This instruction increments the Stack Pointer by 1 and then loads the Accumulator from the top of the Stack. Note that the Stack Pointer is incremented before the Accumulator is loaded.

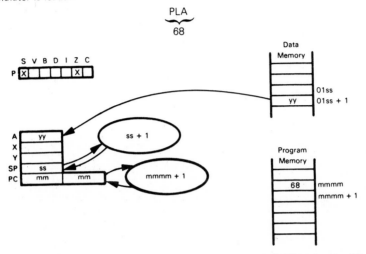

Suppose the Stack Pointer contains $F6_{16}$ and memory location $01F7_{16}$ contains CE_{16}. After the instruction PLA has executed, the Accumulator will contain CE_{16} and the Stack Pointer will contain $F7_{16}$.

The PLA instruction is most frequently used to restore Accumulator contents that have been saved on the Stack: e.g., after servicing an interrupt, or after completing a subroutine.

PLP — PULL CONTENTS OF STATUS REGISTER (P) FROM STACK

This instruction increments the Stack Pointer by 1 and then loads the Status (P) register from the top of the Stack. No other registers are affected but all the statuses may be changed. Note that the Stack Pointer is incremented before the Status register is loaded.

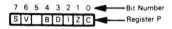

PLP

28

The organization of the status in memory is as follows:

```
7 6 5 4 3 2 1 0 ◄─── Bit Number
S V   B D I Z C ◄─── Register P
```

Bit 5 is not used.

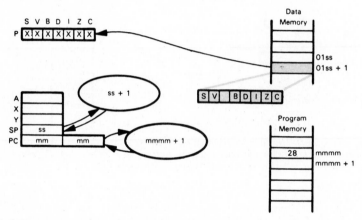

The PLP instruction is generally used to restore the contents of the Status register after completing a subroutine. Thus, it serves to balance the PHP instruction mentioned earlier. Note that PLP is not necessary after servicing an interrupt since the RTI instruction automatically restores the contents of the Status register from the top of the Stack.

ROL — ROTATE ACCUMULATOR OR MEMORY LEFT THROUGH CARRY

This instruction rotates the Accumulator or the selected memory byte one bit to the left through the Carry.

First, consider rotating the Accumulator.

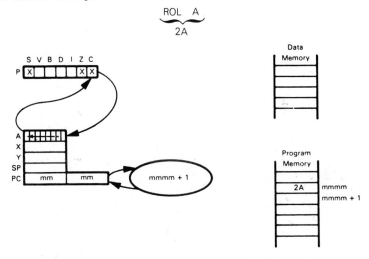

Rotate the Accumulator's contents left one bit through the Carry status.

Suppose the Accumulator contains $7A_{16}$ and the Carry status is set to 1. After the

ROL   A

instruction is executed, the Accumulator will contain $F5_{16}$ and the Carry status will be reset to zero.

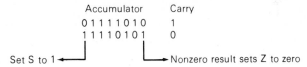

The ROL instruction allows four methods of addressing data memory; they are:

1) Zero page (direct) — ROL addr
2) Absolute (direct) — ROL addr16
3) Zero page indexed with Index Register X — ROL addr,X
4) Absolute indexed with Index Register X — ROL addr16,X

The first byte of object code determines which addressing mode is selected as follows:

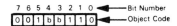

Bit Value for bb	Hexadecimal Object Code	Addressing Mode	Number of Bytes
00	26	Zero page (direct)	2
01	2E	Absolute (direct)	3
10	36	Zero page indexed with X	2
11	3E	Absolute indexed with X	3

We will illustrate the ROL instruction with zero page indexed addressing (using Index Register X). The other addressing modes are shown elsewhere.

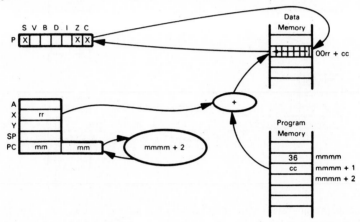

Rotate the selected memory byte left one bit through the Carry status. Suppose that $cc = 34_{16}$, $rr = 16_{16}$, the contents of memory location $004A_{16}$ are $2E_{16}$, and the Carry status is zero. After executing a

ROL $34,X

instruction, memory location $004A_{16}$ will contain $5C_{16}$.

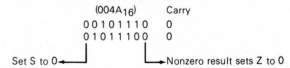

ROR — ROTATE ACCUMULATOR OR MEMORY RIGHT, THROUGH CARRY

This instruction rotates the Accumulator or the selected memory byte one bit to the right through the Carry.

First consider rotating the Accumulator.

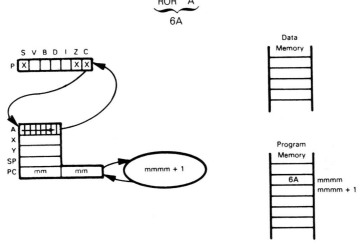

Rotate the Accumulator's contents right one bit through the Carry status. Suppose that the Accumulator contains $7A_{16}$ and the Carry status is set to 1. Execution of the

ROR   A

instruction will produce these results: the Accumulator will contain BD_{16} and the Carry status will be 0.

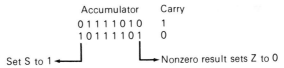

The ROR instruction allows four methods of addressing data memory; they are:

1) Zero page (direct) — ROR addr
2) Absolute (direct) — ROL addr16
3) Zero page indexed with Index Register X — ROR addr,X
4) Absolute indexed with Index Register X — ROR addr16,X

The first byte of object code determines which addressing mode is selected as follows:

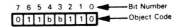

Bit Value for bb	Hexadecimal Object Code	Addressing Mode	Number of Bytes
00	66	Zero page (direct)	2
01	6E	Absolute (direct)	3
10	76	Zero page indexed with X	2
11	7E	Absolute indexed with X	3

We will illustrate the ROR instruction with absolute indexed addressing (using Index Register X). The other addressing modes are shown elsewhere.

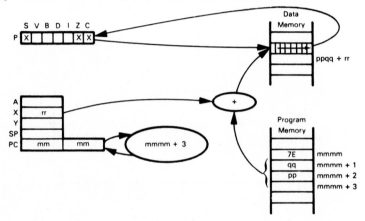

Suppose that rr = 14_{16}, ppqq = 0100_{16}, the contents of memory location 0114_{16} are ED_{16}, and the Carry status is 1. After executing a:

ROR $0100,X

instruction, the Carry status will be 1 and memory location 0114_{16} will contain $F6_{16}$.

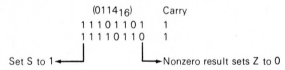

RTI — RETURN FROM INTERRUPT

Pull the Status (P) register and the Program Counter off the top of the Stack. The registers and the corresponding memory locations from which they are loaded are as follows, assuming that the Stack Pointer contains ss at the start of instruction execution:

Memory Location	Register
01ss+1	Status (P) register
01ss+2	Low byte of Program Counter
01ss+3	High byte of Program Counter

The final value of the Stack Pointer is its initial value plus 3. The old values of the Status register and Program Counter are lost.

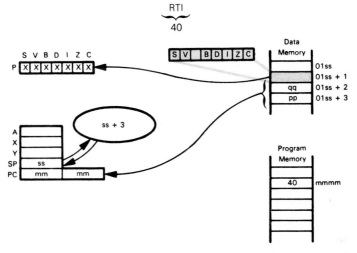

Suppose that the Stack Pointer contains $E8_{16}$, memory location $01E9_{16}$ contains $C1_{16}$, memory location $01EA_{16}$ contains $3E_{16}$, and memory location $01EB_{16}$ contains $D5_{16}$. After the instruction RTI has been executed, the Status register will contain $C1_{16}$, the Stack Pointer will contain EB_{16}, and the Program Counter will contain $D53E_{16}$ (this is the address from which instruction execution will proceed). The statuses will be as follows:

$$C1 = \boxed{\begin{array}{c|c|c|c|c|c|c|c} S & V & & B & D & I & Z & C \\ \hline 1 & 1 & 0 & 0 & 0 & 0 & 0 & 1 \end{array}}$$

Note that the Interrupt Mask bit will be set or reset depending on its value at the time the Status register was stored, assuming that the interrupt service routine did not change it while it was on the Stack.

RTS — RETURN FROM SUBROUTINE

This instruction fetches a new Program Counter value from the top of the Stack and increments it before using it to fetch an instruction. Note that the Stack Pointer is incremented before the loading of each data byte and its final value is thus two greater than its initial value. RTS is normally used at the end of a subroutine to restore the return address that was saved in the Stack by a JSR instruction. Remember that the return address saved by JSR is actually the address of the third byte of the JSR instruction itself; hence, RTS must increment that address before using it to resume the main program. The previous contents of the Program Counter are lost. Every subroutine must contain at least one RTS instruction.

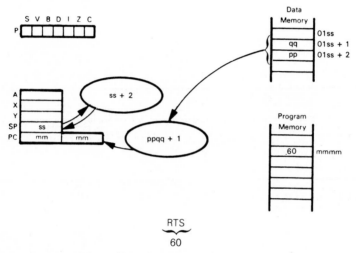

RTS
⌣
60

No statuses are altered by an RTS instruction.

Suppose that the Stack Pointer contains DF_{16}, memory location $01E0_{16}$ contains 08_{16}, and memory location $01E1_{16}$ contains $7C_{16}$. After the instruction RTS has been executed, the Stack Pointer will contain $E1_{16}$ and the Program Counter will contain $7C09_{16}$ (this is the address from which instruction execution will proceed).

SBC — SUBTRACT MEMORY FROM ACCUMULATOR WITH BORROW

Subtract the contents of the selected memory byte and the complement of the Carry status (i.e., 1 − C) from the contents of the Accumulator. This instruction offers the same memory addressing options as does the ADC instruction. The first byte of object code selects the addressing mode as follows:

```
7 6 5 4 3 2 1 0 ◄──── Bit Number
1 1 1 a a a 0 1 ◄──── Object Code
```

Bit Value for aaa	Hexadecimal Object Code	Addressing Mode	Number of Bytes
000	E1	Indirect, pre-indexed with X	2
001	E5	Zero page (direct)	2
010	E9	Immediate	2
011	ED	Absolute (direct)	3
100	F1	Indirect, post-indexed with Y	2
101	F5	Zero page indexed with X	2
110	F9	Absolute indexed with Y	3
111	FD	Absolute indexed with X	3

We will illustrate the SBC instruction using pre-indexed indirect addressing (via Index Register X). See the discussion of addressing methods and other arithmetic and logical instructions for examples of the other addressing modes.

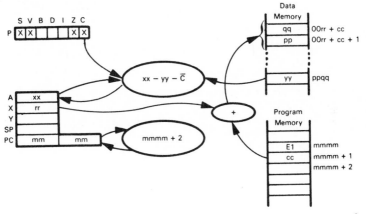

Subtract the contents of the selected memory byte and the complement of the Carry status (1 − C), from the Accumulator, treating all register contents as simple binary data. Note, however, that all data will be treated as decimal (BCD) if the D status is set.

Suppose that $xx = 14_{16}$, $cc = 15_{16}$, $rr = 37_{16}$, $ppqq = 07E2_{16}$, $yy = (07E2_{16}) = 34_{16}$, and $C = 0$. After executing a

$$SBC \quad (\$15,X)$$

instruction, the contents of the Accumulator would be altered to DF_{16}.

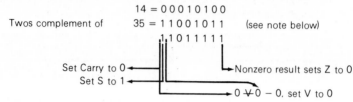

$$14 = 0\,0\,0\,1\,0\,1\,0\,0$$

Twos complement of $\quad 35 = 1\,1\,0\,0\,1\,0\,1\,1 \quad$ (see note below)

$$1\,1\,1\,0\,1\,1\,1\,1\,1$$

Set Carry to 0 ←

Set S to 1 ←

→ Nonzero result sets Z to 0

→ $0 \veebar 0 - 0$, set V to 0

Note: $xx - yy - (1 - C) = xx - (yy + \bar{C})$;

hence, $14_{16} - 34_{16} - (1 - 0) = 14_{16} - (34_{16} + 1) = 14_{16} - 35_{16}$

Note that the resulting Carry is not a borrow. It is, rather, the inverse of a borrow since it is set to 1 if no borrow is required and cleared if a borrow is required. You should be careful of this usage since it differs from that of most other microprocessors, which complement the Carry before it is stored following a subtraction.

SBC is the only binary subtraction instruction. To use it in single-byte operations or to subtract the low-order bytes of two multibyte numbers, a previous instruction (SEC) must explicitly set C to 1 so that it does not affect the operation. Remember that C must be set (not cleared) before a subtraction since its meaning is inverted from the usual borrow. Note also that the 6502 microprocessor, unlike most others, has no subtraction instruction that does not include the Carry.

SEC — SET CARRY

Set the Carry status to 1. No other status or register's contents are affected. Note that this instruction is required as part of a normal subtraction operation since the only subtraction instruction available on the 6502 microprocessor is SBC, which also subtracts the complemented Carry status. This instruction is also required at the start of a multi-byte subtraction since there is never a borrow from the least significant byte.

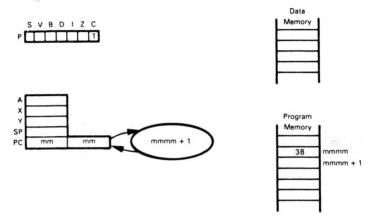

SED — SET DECIMAL MODE

SED

F8

Set the Decimal Mode status to 1. No other status or register's contents are affected. This instruction is used to place the 6502 processor in the decimal mode in which ADC and SBC instructions produce BCD rather than binary results. The programmer should be careful of the fact that the same program will produce different results, depending on the state of the Decimal Mode status. This can lead to puzzling and seemingly random errors if the state of the Decimal Mode status is not carefully monitored.

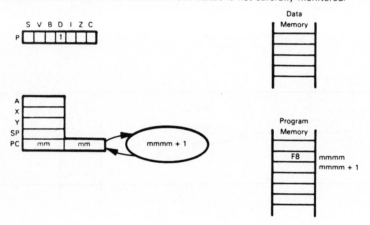

3-94

SEI — SET INTERRUPT MASK (DISABLE INTERRUPTS)

$$\underbrace{\text{SEI}}_{78}$$

Set the interrupt mask in the Status register. This instruction disables the 6502's interrupt service ability, i.e., the 6502 will not respond to the Interrupt Request control line. No other registers or statuses are affected. The Interrupt Mask is bit 2 of the Status (P) register.

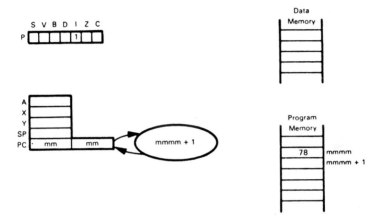

STA — STORE ACCUMULATOR IN MEMORY

Store the contents of the Accumulator into the specified memory location. This instruction offers the same memory addressing modes as the ADC instruction, with the exception that an immediate addressing mode is not available. The first byte of object code selects the addressing mode as follows:

Bit Value for aaa	Hexadecimal Object Code	Addressing Mode	Number of Bytes
000	81	Indirect, pre-indexed with X	2
001	85	Zero page (direct)	2
010	89	Not used	
011	8D	Absolute (direct)	3
100	91	Indirect, post-indexed with Y	2
101	95	Zero page indexed with X	2
110	99	Absolute indexed with Y	3
111	9D	Absolute indexed with X	3

We will illustrate the STA instruction with zero page direct addressing. See the discussion of addressing methods and other arithmetic and logical instructions for examples of the other addressing modes. No statuses are affected.

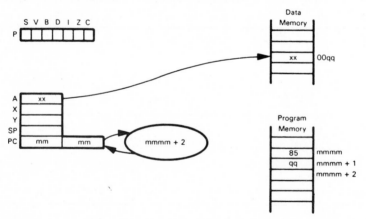

Store the contents of the Accumulator in memory. Suppose that $xx = 63_{16}$ and $qq = 3A_{16}$. After the instruction

$$STA \quad \$3A$$

has been executed, the contents of memory location $003A_{16}$ will be 63_{16}. No registers or statuses are affected.

STX — STORE INDEX REGISTER X IN MEMORY

Store the contents of Index Register X in the selected memory location. The addressing modes allowed are:

1) Zero page (direct) — STX addr
2) Absolute (direct) — STX addr16
3) Zero page indexed with Y — STX addr,Y

Note that there are no indexed modes using Index Register X. There is also no absolute indexed mode. STX and LDX are the only instructions that use the zero page indexed mode with Index Register Y. No statuses are affected.

The first byte of object code selects the addressing mode as follows:

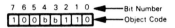

Bit Value for bb	Hexadecimal Object Code	Addressing Mode	Number of Bytes
00	86	Zero page (direct)	2
01	8E	Absolute (direct)	3
10	96	Zero page indexed with Y	2
11	9E	Not used	

We will illustrate the STX instruction using zero page indexed addressing with Index Register Y. See the discussion of addressing methods and other arithmetic and logical instructions for examples of the other addressing modes.

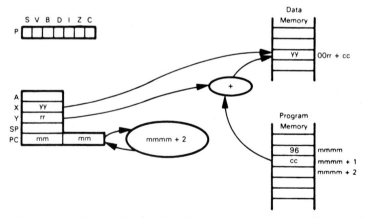

Store the contents of Index Register X in the selected memory byte. Suppose that $cc = 28_{16}$, $rr = 20_{16}$, and $yy = E9_{16}$. After executing the

STX $28,Y

instruction, memory location 0048_{16} will contain $E9_{16}$. No registers or statuses are affected.

STY — STORE INDEX REGISTER Y IN MEMORY

Store the contents of Index Register Y in the selected memory location. The addressing modes allowed are:

1) Zero page (direct) — STY addr
2) Absolute (direct) — STY addr16
3) Zero page indexed with X — STY addr,X

Note that there are no indexed modes using Index Register Y. There is also no absolute indexed mode. No statuses or registers are affected.

The first byte of object code selects the addressing mode as follows:

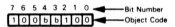

Bit Value for bb	Hexadecimal Object Code	Addressing Mode	Number of Bytes
00	84	Zero page (direct)	2
01	8C	Absolute (direct)	3
10	94	Zero page indexed with X	2
11	9C	Not used	

We will illustrate the STY instruction with absolute direct addressing. See the discussion of addressing methods and other arithmetic and logical instructions for examples of the other addressing modes.

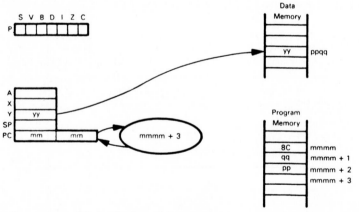

Store the contents of Index Register Y in the selected memory byte. Suppose that $yy = 01_{16}$ and $ppqq = 08F3_{16}$. After the

STY $08F3

instruction has executed, memory location $08F3_{16}$ will contain 01_{16}. No registers or statuses are affected.

TAX — MOVE FROM ACCUMULATOR TO INDEX REGISTER X

TAX
$\underbrace{}$
AA

Move the contents of the Accumulator to Index Register X. Set the Sign and Zero statuses accordingly.

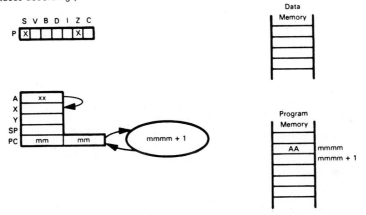

Suppose that $xx = 00_{16}$. After executing the TAX instruction, both the Accumulator and Index Register X will contain 00_{16}.

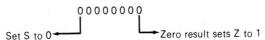

The following instruction sequence will restore the contents of Index Register X from the Stack after completion of a subroutine or interrupt service routine:

```
PLA      ;GET OLD X REGISTER FROM STACK
TAX      ;RESTORE TO X REGISTER
```

TAY — MOVE FROM ACCUMULATOR TO INDEX REGISTER Y

TAY

A8

Move the contents of the Accumulator to Index Register Y. Set the Sign and Zero statuses accordingly.

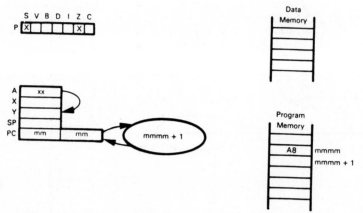

Suppose that xx = F1$_{16}$. After executing the TAY instruction, both the Accumulator and Index Register Y will contain F1$_{16}$.

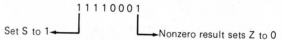

1 1 1 1 0 0 0 1

Set S to 1 ◄——┘   └——► Nonzero result sets Z to 0

The following instruction sequence will restore the contents of Index Register Y from the Stack after completion of a subroutine or interrupt service routine:

```
PLA        ;GET OLD Y REGISTER FROM STACK
TAY        ;RESTORE TO Y REGISTER
```

TSX — MOVE FROM STACK POINTER TO INDEX REGISTER X

TSX

BA

Move the contents of the Stack Pointer to Index Register X. Set the Sign and Zero statuses accordingly. Note that TSX is the only 6502 instruction that allows you to access the value in the Stack Pointer. A typical instruction sequence that saves the value of the Stack Pointer in memory location TEMP is:

```
TSX              ;MOVE STACK POINTER TO X
STX      TEMP    ;SAVE STACK POINTER IN MEMORY
```

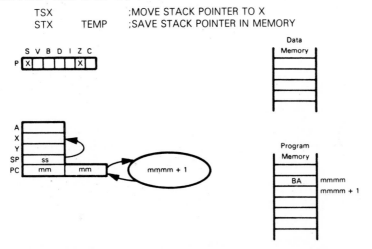

If, for example, the Stack Pointer contains ED_{16}, after executing the TSX instruction, both the Stack Pointer and Index Register X will contain ED_{16}.

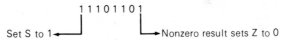

TXA — MOVE FROM INDEX REGISTER X TO ACCUMULATOR

TXA

8A

Move the contents of Index Register X to the Accumulator and set the Sign and Zero statuses accordingly. The following instruction sequence will save the contents of Index Register X in the Stack before execution of a subroutine or interrupt service routine:

```
TXA       ;MOVE X REGISTER TO ACCUMULATOR
PHA       ;SAVE X REGISTER IN STACK
```

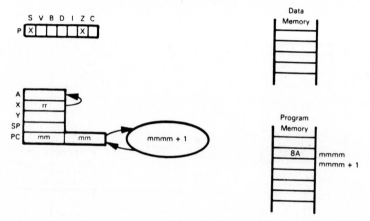

Suppose that $rr = 3B_{16}$. After executing the TXA instruction, both Index Register X and the Accumulator will contain $3B_{16}$.

00111011

Set S to 0 ◄———⌐   ⌐———► Nonzero result sets Z to 0

TXS — MOVE FROM INDEX REGISTER X TO STACK POINTER

$$\underbrace{\text{TXS}}_{\text{9A}}$$

Move the contents of Index Register X to the Stack Pointer. No other registers or statuses are affected. Note that TXS is the only 6502 instruction that allows you to determine the value in the Stack Pointer. A typical instruction sequence that loads the Stack Pointer with the value LAST is:

```
LDX     #LAST    ;GET LOCATION OF STACK ON PAGE 1
TXS              ;PLACE STARTING LOCATION IN STACK POINTER
```

Note that TXS does not affect any statuses, unlike TSX which affects the Zero and Sign statuses.

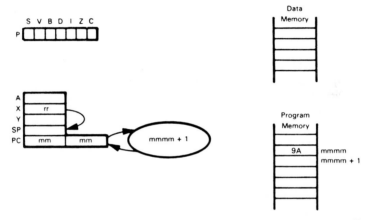

Suppose that $rr = F2_{16}$. After executing the TXS instruction, both Index Register X and the Stack Pointer will contain $F2_{16}$, making $01F2_{16}$ the current Stack location. No statuses or other registers are affected.

TYA — MOVE FROM INDEX REGISTER Y TO ACCUMULATOR

Move the contents of Index Register Y to the Accumulator and set the Sign and Zero statuses accordingly. The following instruction sequence will save the contents of Index Register Y in the Stack before execution of a subroutine or interrupt service routine:

```
TYA     ;MOVE Y REGISTER TO ACCUMULATOR
PHA     ;SAVE Y REGISTER IN STACK
```

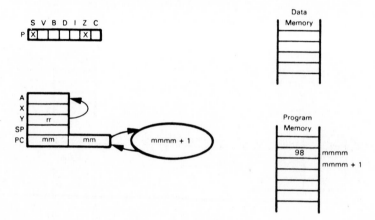

Suppose that rr = AF_{16}. After executing the TYA instruction, both Index Register Y and the Accumulator will contain AF_{16}.

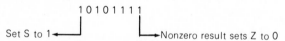

6800/6502 COMPATIBILITY

Although the 6502 microprocessor can certainly be used on its own merits, one of its important characteristics is its similarity to the widely used 6800 microprocessor. This ▐ **6800/6502 SIMILARITY** ▌
similarity is not sufficient to allow programs written for one of these processors at the machine or assembly level to be run on the other, but it is sufficient so that programmers can easily move from one CPU to the other. Most of the external support devices designed for one of these processors can also be used with the other. Chapters 9 and 10 of <u>An Introduction to Microcomputers: Volume 2 — Some Real Microprocessors</u> discuss this hardware compatibility in more detail.

We will briefly describe and compare the 6800 and 6502 microprocessors with regard to their registers, statuses, addressing modes, and instruction sets. You should note that the two processors are far from mirror images, but they are much closer to each other than either is to an 8080, Z80, F8, or 2650 microprocessor. This description should give you some idea as to what problems you would encounter in going from one CPU to the other.

As for registers, both the 6800 and the 6502 have an 8-bit primary Accumulator (A register) and a 16-bit Program Counter (or PC register). The other registers, however, are slightly ▐ **6800/6502 REGISTER COMPARISON** ▌
different. The 6800 has a second 8-bit Accumulator (B register), a 16-bit Index register, and a 16-bit Stack Pointer. The 6502, on the other hand, has two 8-bit Index registers and an 8-bit Stack Pointer. Thus the 6502 Index registers cannot hold a complete 16-bit memory address while the 6800 Index register can. Furthermore the 6800's RAM Stack can be located anywhere in memory because of its 16-bit Stack Pointer while the 6502's RAM Stack is always located on page 1.

As for statuses, the 6800 and 6502 have identical Zero, Overflow, Sign, and Interrupt Mask statuses. The difference in the Carry status is that the 6800 and 6502 version of this flag have opposite meanings after subtraction operations. The ▐ **6800/6502 STATUS COMPARISON** ▌
6800 Carry is set to 1 if a borrow is necessary and to 0 otherwise; the 6502 Carry is set to 0 if a borrow is necessary and to 1 otherwise. This difference means that, before a multi-byte subtraction operation, the programmer must clear the Carry on the 6800 and set the Carry on the 6502. The 6800 and 6502 also differ in how they perform decimal arithmetic; the 6800 has a Half-Carry flag (or carry from bit 3) while the 6502 has a Decimal Mode flag. The 6502 also has a Break flag which is not present in the 6800; it is not necessary in the 6800 because the 6800 Trap or Software Interrupt instruction is automatically vectored separately from the regular interrupt response.

The 6502 microprocessor has many more addressing modes than does the 6800. This is partly necessitated by the fact that the 6502 index registers are only 8 bits long. Table 3-7 compares the addressing modes available on the two processors. The 6800 microprocessor has no indirect modes, no combinations of index- ▐ **6800/6502 ADDRESSING MODE COMPARISON** ▌
ing and indirection, and no absolute indexed modes. There are also some other differences in terms of which modes are available with particular instructions; we will not discuss those differences, but they are enumerated in Table 3-6.

Table 3-7. Memory Addressing Modes Available on the 6800 and 6502 Microprocessors

6800	6502
Immediate	Immediate
Direct (zero-page)	Zero Page (direct)
Extended (absolute direct)	Absolute (direct)
Indexed (absolute)	Absolute Indexed
	Zero Page Indexed
	Post-Indexed Indirect
	Pre-Indexed Indirect
	Indirect
Relative (branches only)	Relative (branches only)

Note that many different variations of indexed addressing are available on the 6502 microprocessor, but remember that the 6502 index registers are only 8 bits long while the 6800 Index register is 16 bits long.

The 6800 and 6502 instruction sets are similar but not identical (see Table 3-6). Table 3-8 compares the two sets, listing first the instructions which are present in both, then the 6800 instructions which have no 6502 equivalent, and finally the 6502 instructions which have no 6800 equivalent. Obviously some of these differences are a direct result of the differences in the statuses and registers. Most of the differences are minor, and involve instructions that are a small part of common applications programs. One noticeable difference is that the 6800 has Add and Subtract instructions that do not involve the Carry status (ADD and SUB) while the 6502 does not. This means that the 6502 assembly language programmer must explicitly clear or set the Carry status when its value should not affect an addition or subtraction operation. Note that this similarity in the instruction sets does not extend to the object code level; the actual machine codes are entirely different on the two microprocessors.

6800/6502
INSTRUCTION
COMPARISON

Table 3-8. Comparison of 6800 and 6502 Assembly Language Instruction Sets

I.	Common Instructions
Instruction	**Meaning**
ADC	Add with Carry
AND	Logical AND
ASL	Arithmetic Shift Left
BCC	Branch if Carry Clear
BCS	Branch if Carry Set
BEQ	Branch if Equal to Zero (Z = 1)
BIT	Bit Test
BMI	Branch if Minus (S = 1)
BNE	Branch if Not Equal to Zero (Z = 0)
BPL	Branch if Plus (S = 0)
BVC	Branch if Overflow Clear
BVS	Branch if Overflow Set
CLC	Clear Carry
CLI	Clear Interrupt Mask (Enable Interrupt)
CLV	Clear Overflow
CMP	Compare Accumulator with Memory
CPX[1] (also CPY on 6502)	Compare Index Register with Memory
DEC	Decrement (by 1)
DEX[1] (also DEY on 6502)	Decrement Index Register (by 1)
EOR	Logical Exclusive-OR
INC	Increment (by 1)
INX[1] (also INY on 6502)	Increment Index Register (by 1)
JMP	Jump to New Location
JSR	Jump to Subroutine
LDA	Load Accumulator
LDX[1] (also LDY on 6502)	Load Index Register
LSR	Logical Shift Right
NOP	No Operation
ORA	Logical (Inclusive) OR
PHA (PSH on 6800)	Push Accumulator onto Stack
PLA (PUL on 6800)	Pull Accumulator from Stack
ROL	Rotate Left through Carry
ROR	Rotate Right through Carry
RTI	Return from Interrupt
RTS	Return from Subroutine
SBC[2]	Subtract with Carry
SEC	Set Carry
SEI	Set Interrupt Mask
STA	Store Accumulator
STX[1] (also STY on 6502)	Store Index Register
TSX	Transfer Stack Pointer to Index Register (X)
TXS	Transfer Index Register (X) to Stack Pointer

[1]Index Register X is 16 bits long on 6800, 8 bits long on 6502 which has Index Register Y as well.

[2]Note that SBC has a different meaning on the 6502 than on the 6800 since, for subtraction operations, the 6800 Carry is the inverse of the 6502 Carry.

Table 3-8. Comparison of 6800 and 6502 Assembly Language Instruction Sets (Continued)

II.	Unique 6800 Instructions
Instruction	**Meaning**
ABA	Add Accumulators
ADD	Add (without Carry)
ASR	Arithmetic Shift Right
BGE	Branch if Greater than or Equal to Zero
BGT	Branch if Greater than Zero
BHI	Branch if Higher
BLE	Branch if Less than or Equal to Zero
BLS	Branch if Lower or Same
BLT	Branch if Less than Zero
BRA	Branch Unconditionally
BSR	Branch to Subroutine
CBA	Compare Accumulators
CLR	Clear
COM	Logical Complement
DAA	Decimal Adjust Accumulator
DES	Decrement Stack Pointer (by 1)
INS	Increment Stack Pointer (by 1)
LDS	Load Stack Pointer
NEG	Negate (Twos Complement)
SBA	Subtract Accumulators
SEV	Set Overflow
STS	Store Stack Pointer
SUB	Subtract (without Carry)
SWI	Software Interrupt (like 6502 BRK)
TAB	Move from Accumulator A to Accumulator B
TAP	Move from Accumulator A to CCR
TBA	Move from Accumulator B to Accumulator A
TPA	Move CCR to Accumulator A
TST	Test Zero or Minus
WAI	Wait for Interrupt

III.	Unique 6502 Instructions
Instruction	**Meaning**
BRK	Break (like 6800 SWI)
CLD	Clear Decimal Mode
PHP	Push Status Register onto Stack
PLP	Pull Status Register from Stack
SED	Set Decimal Mode
TAX (TAY)	Transfer Accumulator to Index Register X (Y)
TXA (TYA)	Transfer Index Register X (Y) to Accumulator

MOS TECHNOLOGY 6502 ASSEMBLER CONVENTIONS

The standard 6502 assembler is available from 6502 manufacturers and on many major time-sharing networks; it is also included in most development systems. Cross-assembler versions are available for most large computers and many minicomputers.

ASSEMBLER FIELD STRUCTURE

The assembly language instructions have the standard field structure (see Table 2-1). The required delimiters are:

1) A space after a label. Note that all labels must start in column 1.
2) A space after the operation code.
3) A comma between operands in the address field, i.e., between the offset address and X or Y to indicate indexing with Index Register X or Y respectively.
4) Parentheses around addresses that are to be used indirectly.
5) A semicolon or exclamation point (we will use the semicolon) before a comment.

Typical 6502 assembly language instructions are:

```
START   LDA     (1000,X)    ;GET LENGTH
        ADC     NEXT
LAST    BRK                 ;END OF SECTION
```

LABELS

The Assembler often allows only six characters in labels and truncates longer ones. The first character must be a letter while subsequent characters must be letters or numbers. The single characters A, X, and Y are reserved for the Accumulator and the two index registers. The use of operation codes as labels is often not allowed and is not good programming practice anyway.

PSEUDO-OPERATIONS

The Assembler has the following explicit pseudo-operations:

.BYTE	— Form Byte-Length Data
.DBYTE	— Form Double-Byte-Length Data with MSBs First
.END	— End of Program
.TEXT	— Form String of ASCII Characters
.WORD	— Form Double-Byte-Length Data with LSBs First
=	— Equate

Other pseudo-operations may be implemented by setting the assembler's location counter (denoted by *) to a new or updated value. Examples are:

```
* = ADDR     — Set Program Origin to ADDR
* = *+N      — Reserve N Bytes for Data Storage
```

.BYTE, .DBYTE, .TEXT, and .WORD are the Data pseudo-operations used to place data in ROM. .BYTE is used for 8-bit data, .TEXT for 7-bit ASCII characters (MSB is zero), .DBYTE for 16-bit data with the most significant bits first, and .WORD for 16-bit addresses or data with the least significant bits first. Note particularly the difference between .DBYTE and .WORD.

.BYTE, .DBYTE,
.TEXT, .WORD
PSEUDO-OPERATIONS

Examples:

ADDR	.WORD	$3165

results in (ADDR) = 65 and (ADDR+1) = 31 (hex).

TCONV	.BYTE	32

This pseudo-operation places the number 32 (20_{16}) in the next byte of ROM and assigns the name TCONV to the address of that byte.

ERROR	.TEXT	/ERROR/

This pseudo-operation places the 7-bit ASCII characters E, R, R, O, and R into the next five bytes of ROM and assigns the name ERROR to the address of the first byte. Any single character (not just /) may be used to surround the ASCII text, but we will always use / for the sake of consistency.

MASK	.DBYTE	$1000

results in (MASK) = 10 and (MASK+1) = 00.

OPERS	.WORD	FADD, FSUB, FMUL,FDIV

This pseudo-operation places the addresses FADD, FSUB, FMUL, and FDIV in the next eight bytes of memory (least significant bits first) and assigns the name OPERS to the address of the first byte.

The operation * = *+N is the Reserve pseudo-operation used to assign locations in RAM; it allocates a specified number of bytes. = is the Equate or Define pseudo-operation used to define names. * = ADDR is the standard Origin pseudo-operation.

SET ORIGIN PSEUDO-OPERATION

6502 programs usually have several origins which are used as follows:

1) To specify the Reset and interrupt service addresses. These addresses must be placed in the highest memory addresses in the system (usually $FFFA_{16}$ through $FFFF_{16}$).

2) To specify the starting addresses of the actual Reset and interrupt service routines. The routines themselves may be placed anywhere in memory.

3) To specify the starting address of the main program.

4) To specify the starting addresses of subroutines.

5) To define areas for RAM storage.

6) To define an area (always on page 1) for the RAM Stack.

7) To specify addresses used for I/O ports and special functions.

Examples:

```
RESET   =$3800
        *=$FFFC
        .WORD   RESET
        *=RESET
```

Note: $ means "hexadecimal".

This sequence places the Reset instruction sequence in memory beginning at address 3800_{16}, and places that address in the memory locations (addresses $FFFC_{16}$ and $FFFD_{16}$) from which the 6502 CPU retrieves the Reset address.

The instruction sequence which follows is stored in memory beginning at location $C000_{16}$.

```
        MAIN    =$C000
                *=MAIN
```

.END simply marks the end of the assembly language program.

LABELS WITH PSEUDO-OPERATIONS

The rules and recommendations for labels with 6502 pseudo-operations are as follows:

1) Simple equates, such as MAIN =$C000, require labels since their purpose is to define the meanings of those labels.

2) .BYTE, .DBYTE, .TEXT, .WORD, and *=*+N pseudo-operations usually have labels.

3) .END should not have a label, since the meaning of such a label is unclear.

ADDRESSES

The 6502 Assembler allows entries in the address field in any of the following forms:

NUMBERS AND CHARACTERS IN ADDRESS FIELD

1) Decimal (the default case)
    Example: 1247

2) Hexadecimal (must start with $)
    Example: $CE00

3) Octal (must start with @)
    Example: @1247

4) Binary (must start with %)
    Example: %11100011

5) ASCII (single character preceded by an apostrophe)
    Example: 'H

6) As an offset from the Program Counter (*)
    Example: *+7

The various 6502 addressing modes are distinguished as follows:

ADDRESSING MODES

- Absolute or Zero Page (direct) are the default modes (the Assembler chooses Zero Page if the address is less than 256, and Absolute otherwise).
- # for immediate mode (precedes the data)
- .X or .Y for indexing (follows the offset address)
- Parentheses around addresses that are used indirectly so that

    (addr,X) indicates pre-indexing (indexed address used indirectly)

    (addr),Y indicates post-indexing (indirect address is indexed)

    (addr) indicates indirection with JMP instruction only

In the indexed modes, as in the direct modes, the Assembler automatically chooses the Zero Page version if it is permitted and if the address is less than 256.

The Assembler also allows expressions in the address field. These expressions consist of numbers and names separated by the arithmetic operators +, −, * (multiplication), or / (integer division).

ASSEMBLER ARITHMETIC EXPRESSIONS

The Assembler evaluates expressions from left to right; no parentheses are allowed to group operations, nor is there any hierarchy of operations. Fractional results are truncated.

We recommend that you avoid expressions within address fields whenever possible. If you must compute an address, comment any unclear expressions and be sure that the evaluation of the expressions never produces a result which is too large for its ultimate use.

OTHER ASSEMBLER FEATURES

The standard 6502 Assembler has neither a conditional assembly capability nor a macro capability. Some 6502 assemblers have one or both of these capabilities, and you should consult your manual for a description. We will not use or refer to either capability again, although both can be quite convenient in actual applications.

Chapter 4
SIMPLE PROGRAMS

The only way to learn assembly language programming is through experience. The next six chapters of this book contain examples of simple programs that perform actual microprocessor tasks. You should read each example carefully and try to execute the program on a 6502-based microcomputer. Finally, you should work the problems at the end of each chapter and run the resulting programs to insure that you understand the material.

This chapter contains some very elementary programs.

GENERAL FORMAT OF EXAMPLES

Each program example contains the following parts:

1) A title that describes the general problem.

```
EXAMPLE
FORMAT
```

2) A statement of purpose that describes the specific task that the program performs and the memory locations that it uses.

3) A sample problem with data and results.

4) A flowchart if the program logic is complex.

5) The source program or assembly language listing.

6) The object program or hexadecimal machine language listing.

7) Explanatory notes that discuss the instructions and methods used in the program.

You should use the examples as guidelines for solving the problems at the end of each chapter. Be sure to run your solutions on a 6502-based microcomputer to insure that they are correct.

The source programs in the examples have been constructed as follows:

1) Standard 6502 assembler notation is used, as summarized in Chapter 3.

```
GUIDELINES
FOR
EXAMPLES
```

2) The forms in which data and addresses appear are selected for clarity rather than for consistency. We use hexadecimal numbers for memory addresses, instruction codes, and BCD data; decimal for numeric constants; binary for logical masks; and ASCII for characters.

3) Frequently used instructions and programming techniques are emphasized.

4) Examples illustrate tasks that microprocessors perform in communications, instrumentation, computers, business equipment, industrial, and military applications.

5) Detailed comments are included.

6) Simple and clear structures are emphasized, but programs are as efficient as possible within this guideline. The notes often describe more efficient procedures.

7) Programs use consistent memory allocations. Each program starts in memory location 0000 and ends with the Break (BRK) instruction. If your microcomputer has no monitor and no interrupts, you may prefer to end programs with an endless loop instruction, e.g.,

HERE   JMP   HERE

Some 6502-based microcomputers may require a JMP or JSR instruction with a specific destination address to return control to the monitor. Other microcomputers may require you to specify the monitor address to be used by the BRK instruction. For example, if you are using the popular KIM-1, you will have to load 1C00 into addresses 17FE and 17FF. Be careful — the 00 must be loaded into address 17FE and the 1C into address 17FF. We will explain later how the 6502 stores addresses and how it implements the BRK instruction (see Chapter 12).

Consult the User's Manual for your microcomputer to determine the required memory allocations and terminating instruction for your particular system.

GUIDELINES FOR SOLVING PROBLEMS

Use the following guidelines in solving the problems at the end of each chapter:

1) Comment each program so that others can understand it. The comments can be brief and ungrammatical; they should explain the purpose of a section or instruction in the program. Comments should not describe the operation of instructions; that description is available in manuals. You do not have to comment each statement or explain the obvious. You may follow the format of the examples but provide less detail.

PROGRAMMING GUIDELINES

2) Emphasize clarity, simplicity, and good structure in programs. While programs should be reasonably efficient, do not worry about saving a single byte of program memory or a few microseconds.

3) Make programs reasonably general. Do not confuse parameters (such as the number of elements in an array) with fixed constants (such as π or ASCII C).

4) Never assume fixed initial values for parameters; i.e., assume that the parameters are already in RAM.

5) Use assembler notation as shown in the examples and defined in Chapter 3.

6) Use hexadecimal notation for addresses. Use the clearest possible form for data.

7) If your microcomputer allows it, start all programs in memory location 0000 and use memory locations starting with 0040_{16} for data and temporary storage. Otherwise, establish equivalent addresses for your microcomputer and use them consistently. Again, consult the user's manual.

8) Use meaningful names for labels and variables: e.g., SUM or CHECK rather than X, Y, or Z.

9) Execute each program on your microcomputer. There is no other way of ensuring that your program is correct. We have provided sample data with each problem. Be sure that the program works for special cases.

We now summarize some useful information that you should keep in mind when writing programs.

Almost all processing instructions (e.g., Add, Subtract, AND, OR) use the contents of the Accumulator as one operand and place the result back in the Accumulator. In most cases, you

USING THE ACCUMULATOR

will load the initial data into the Accumulator with LDA. You will store the result from the Accumulator into memory with STA.

Frequently accessed data and frequently used base addresses or pointers should be placed on page zero of memory. This data can then be accessed with zero-page (direct), pre-indexed, post-indexed, and zero-page indexed addressing. Note in particular that

USING PAGE ZERO OF MEMORY

pre-indexing and post-indexing both assume that an address is stored on page zero. The zero-page direct and indexed modes both require less time and memory than the corresponding absolute addressing modes.

Some instructions, such as shifts, increment (add 1), and decrement (subtract 1) can act directly on data in memory. Such instructions allow you to bypass the user registers but they require extra execution time since the data must actually be loaded into the CPU and the result must be stored back into memory.

PROGRAM EXAMPLES

8-Bit Data Transfer

Purpose: Move the contents of memory location 0040 to memory location 0041.

Sample Problem:

$$(0040) = 6A$$

Result: $(0041) = 6A$

Source Program:

```
LDA    $40        ;GET DATA
STA    $41        ;TRANSFER TO NEW LOCATION
BRK
```

Object Program:

Memory Location (Hex)	Memory Contents (Hex)	Instruction (Mnemonic)	
0000	A5	LDA	$40
0001	40		
0002	85	STA	$41
0003	41		
0004	00	BRK	

The LDA (Load Accumulator) and STA (Store Accumulator) need an address to determine the source or destination of the data. Since the addresses used in the example are on page zero (that is, the eight most significant bits are all zero), the zero page (direct) form of the instructions can be used with the address in the next word. The leading zeros can be omitted. The addresses are really 0040 and 0041, but the shorthand form can be used just as in everyday conversation (e.g., we say "sixty cents" rather than "zero dollars and sixty cents").

BRK (Force Break) is used to end all the examples and return control to the monitor. Remember that you may have to replace this instruction with whatever your microcomputer requires.

8-Bit Addition

Purpose: Add the contents of memory locations 0040 and 0041, and place the result in memory location 0042.

Sample Problem:

$$(0040) = 38$$
$$(0041) = 2B$$

Result: $(0042) = 63$

Source Program:

```
CLC                 ;CLEAR CARRY TO START
LDA     $40         ;GET FIRST OPERAND
ADC     $41         ;ADD SECOND OPERAND
STA     $42         ;STORE RESULT
BRK
```

Object Program:

Memory Address (Hex)	Memory Contents (Hex)	Instruction (Mnemonic)	
0000	18	CLC	
0001	A5	LDA	$40
0002	40		
0003	65	ADC	$41
0004	41		
0005	85	STA	$42
0006	42		
0007	00	BRK	

The only addition instruction on the 6502 microprocessor is ADC (Add with Carry), which results in $(A) = (A) + (M) + (Carry)$ where M is the addressed memory location. Thus, we need the initial CLC (Clear Carry) instruction if the value of Carry is not to affect the addition. Remember that the Carry will be included in all additions and subtractions.

The zero-page (direct) forms of all instructions are used, since all the addresses are in the first 256 bytes of memory.

ADC affects the Carry bit, but LDA and STA do not. Only arithmetic and shift instructions affect the Carry; logical and transfer instructions do not.

LDA and ADC do not affect the contents of memory. STA changes the contents of the addressed memory location but does not affect the contents of the Accumulator.

Be sure that the Decimal Mode (D) flag is cleared when you execute this program. To be absolutely certain of the D flag's state, you could add a CLD instruction ($D8_{16}$) to the start of the program. If you are using the KIM-1 microcomputer, you should clear memory location 00F1 to ensure that the Decimal Mode flag does not interfere with your programs or with the monitor.

Shift Left One Bit

Purpose: Shift the contents of memory location 0040 left one bit and place the result into memory location 0041. Clear the empty bit position.

Sample Problem:

$$(0040) = 6F$$

Result: $(0041) = DE$

Source Program:

```
LDA    $40        ;GET DATA
ASL    A          ;SHIFT LEFT
STA    $41        ;STORE RESULT
BRK
```

Object Program:

Memory Address (Hex)	Memory Contents (Hex)	Instruction (Mnemonic)	
0000	A5	LDA	$40
0001	40		
0002	0A	ASL	A
0003	85	STA	$41
0004	41		
0005	00	BRK	

The instruction ASL A shifts the contents of the Accumulator left one bit and clears the least significant bit. The most significant bit is moved into the Carry. The result is twice the original data (why?).

Note that we could also shift the contents of memory location 0040 one bit with the instruction ASL $40 and then move the result to memory location 0041. This method would, however, change the contents of memory location 0040 as well as the contents of memory location 0041.

Mask Off Most Significant Four Bits

Purpose: Place the least significant four bits of memory location 0040 in the least significant four bits of memory location 0041. Clear the most significant four bits of memory location 0041.

Sample Problem:

$$(0040) = 3D$$

Result: $(0041) = 0D$

Source Program:

```
LDA    $40            ;GET DATA
AND    #%00001111     ;MASK 4 MSB'S
STA    $41            ;STORE RESULT
BRK
```

Note: # means immediate addressing and % means binary constant in standard 6502 Assembler notation.

Object Program:

Memory Address (Hex)	Memory Contents (Hex)	Instruction (Mnemonic)	
0000	A5	LDA	$40
0001	40		
0002	29	AND	#%00001111
0003	0F		
0004	85	STA	$41
0005	41		
0006	00	BRK	

AND #%00001111 logically ANDs the contents of the Accumulator with the number $0F_{16}$ — not the contents of memory location 000F. Immediate addressing (indicated by #) means that the actual data, not the address of the data, is included in the instruction.

The mask (00001111) is written in binary to make its purpose clearer to the reader. Binary notation for masks is clearer than hexadecimal notation since logical operations are performed bit-by-bit rather than digits or bytes at a time. The result, of course, does not depend on the programming notation. Hexadecimal notation should be used for masks longer than eight bits because the binary versions become long and cumbersome. The comments should explain the masking operation.

A logical AND instruction may be used to clear bits that are not in use. For example, the four least significant bits of the data could be an input from a ten-position switch or an output to a numeric display.

Clear a Memory Location

Purpose: Clear memory location 0040.

Source Program:

```
LDA     #0
STA     $40         ;CLEAR LOCATION 40
BRK
```

Object Program:

Memory Address (Hex)	Memory Contents (Hex)	Instruction (Mnemonic)	
0000	A9	LDA	#0
0001	00		
0002	85	STA	$40
0003	40		
0004	00	BRK	

Zero is handled no differently than any other number — the 6502 has no explicit Clear instruction. However, remember that LDA #0 does set the Zero flag to one. Always watch this logic — the Z (Zero) flag is set to <u>one</u> if the last result was <u>zero</u>.

STA does not affect any status flags.

Word Disassembly

Purpose: Divide the contents of memory location 0040 into two 4-bit sections and store them in memory locations 0041 and 0042. Place the four most significant bits of memory location 0040 into the four least significant bit positions of memory location 0041; place the four least significant bits of memory location 0040 into the four least significant bit positions of memory location 0042. Clear the four most significant bit positions of memory locations 0041 and 0042.

Sample Problem:

$$(0040) = 3F$$

Result: $(0041) = 03$
$(0042) = 0F$

Source Program:

```
LDA    $40              ;GET DATA
AND    #%00001111       ;MASK OFF MSB'S
STA    $42              ;STORE LSB'S
LDA    $40              ;RESTORE DATA
LSR    A                ;LOGICALLY SHIFT DATA RIGHT 4 TIMES
LSR    A
LSR    A
LSR    A
STA    $41              ;STORE MSB'S
BRK
```

Object Program:

Memory Address (Hex)	Memory Contents (Hex)	Instruction (Mnemonic)	
0000	A5	LDA	$40
0001	40		
0002	29	AND	#%00001111
0003	0F		
0004	85	STA	$42
0005	42		
0006	A5	LDA	$40
0007	40		
0008	4A	LSR	A
0009	4A	LSR	A
000A	4A	LSR	A
000B	4A	LSR	A
000C	85	STA	$41
000D	41		
000E	00	BRK	

A logical shift right of four positions requires four executions of the LSR A instruction.

Each LSR instruction clears the most significant bit of the result. Thus, the four most significant bits of the Accumulator are all cleared after LSR A has been executed four times.

You might wish to try rewriting the program so that it saves a copy of the data in Index Register X rather than loading the same data twice. Which version do you prefer and why?

Find Larger of Two Numbers

Purpose: Place the larger of the contents of memory locations 0040 and 0041 into memory location 0042. Assume that the contents of memory locations 0040 and 0041 are unsigned binary numbers.

Sample Problems:

a.
$$
\begin{aligned}
(0040) &= 3F \\
(0041) &= 2B
\end{aligned}
$$

Result: (0042) = 3F

b.
$$
\begin{aligned}
(0040) &= 75 \\
(0041) &= A8
\end{aligned}
$$

Result: (0042) = A8

Source Program:

```
         LDA   $40      ;GET FIRST OPERAND
         CMP   $41      ;IS SECOND OPERAND LARGER?
         BCS   STRES
         LDA   $41      ;YES, GET SECOND OPERAND INSTEAD
STRES    STA   $42      ;STORE LARGER OPERAND
         BRK
```

Object Program:

Memory Address (Hex)	Memory Contents (Hex)	Instruction (Mnemonic)		
0000	A5		LDA	$40
0001	40			
0002	C5		CMP	$41
0003	41			
0004	B0		BCS	STRES
0005	02			
0006	A5		LDA	$41
0007	41			
0008	85	STRES	STA	$42
0009	42			
000A	00		BRK	

CMP $41 subtracts the contents of memory location 0041 from the contents of the Accumulator but does not store the result anywhere. The instruction is used merely to set the flags for a subsequent conditional branch.

CMP affects the flags as follows:

1) N takes the value of the most significant bit of the result of the subtraction.

2) Z is set to 1 if the result of the subtraction is zero and to 0 otherwise.

3) C is set to 1 if the subtraction does not require a borrow and to 0 if it does. Note that C is an inverted borrow, not the actual borrow as it is on many other microprocessors.

4) V is not affected.

Note the following cases:

1) If the operands are equal, $Z = 1$; if they are not equal, $Z = 0$.

2) If the contents of the Accumulator are greater than or equal to the contents of the other address (considering both as unsigned binary numbers), $C = 1$, since no borrow would then be needed. Otherwise, $C = 0$.

All 6502 conditional branch instructions use relative addressing, in which the second word of the instruction is an 8-bit twos complement number which the CPU adds to the address of the next instruction to calculate the destination address. In the example, the relative offset is 0008 (destination address) - 0006 (address immediately following the branch) or 02. Obviously, calculating relative offsets is error-prone, particularly if the result is negative; however, if you label all target instructions, the assembler will perform the calculations for you.

BCS causes a branch if the Carry is one. If the Carry is zero, the processor continues executing instructions in their normal sequence as if the Branch instruction did not exist.

STRES is a label, a name that the programmer assigns to a memory address so that it is easier to remember and locate. Note that labels are followed by a space on the line where they are defined. The label makes the destination of the branch clear, particularly when relative addressing is being used. Using a label is preferable to just specifying the offset (i.e., BCS*+4) since the 6502's instructions vary in length. You or another user of the program could easily make an error in determining the offset or the destination.

16-Bit Addition

Purpose: Add the 16-bit number in memory locations 0040 and 0041 to the 16-bit number in memory locations 0042 and 0043. The most significant eight bits are in memory locations 0041 and 0043. Store the result in memory locations 0044 and 0045, with the most significant bits in 0045.

Sample Problem:

$$(0040) = 2A$$
$$(0041) = 67$$
$$(0042) = F8$$
$$(0043) = 14$$

Result=672A + 14F8 = 7C22

$$(0044) = 22$$
$$(0045) = 7C$$

Source Program:

```
CLC                 ;CLEAR CARRY TO START
LDA     $40         ;ADD LEAST SIGNIFICANT BITS
ADC     $42
STA     $44
LDA     $41         ;ADD MOST SIGNIFICANT BITS WITH CARRY
ADC     $43
STA     $45
BRK
```

Object Program:

Memory Address (Hex)	Memory Contents (Hex)	Instruction (Mnemonic)	
0000	18	CLC	
0001	A5	LDA	$40
0002	40		
0003	65	ADC	$42
0004	42		
0005	85	STA	$44
0006	44		
0007	A5	LDA	$41
0008	41		
0009	65	ADC	$43
000A	43		
000B	85	STA	$45
000C	45		
000D	00	BRK	

You must clear the Carry before the first addition since there is never a carry into the least significant bits.

ADC then automatically includes the Carry from the least significant bits in the addition of the most significant bits. Thus the microprocessor can add data of any length; it adds numbers eight bits at a time with the Carry transferring information from one 8-bit section to the next. Note, however, that each 8-bit addition requires the execution of three instructions (LDA, ADC, STA) since there is only one accumulator.

Table of Squares

Purpose: Calculate the square of the contents of memory location 0041 from a table and place the result in memory location 0042. Assume that memory location 0041 contains a number between 0 and 7 inclusive — $0 \leq (0041) \leq 7$.

The table occupies memory locations 0050 to 0057.

Memory Address (Hex)	Entry	
	(Hex)	(Decimal)
0050	00	0 (0^2)
0051	01	1 (1^2)
0052	04	4 (2^2)
0053	09	9 (3^2)
0054	10	16 (4^2)
0055	19	25 (5^2)
0056	24	36 (6^2)
0057	31	49 (7^2)

Sample Problems:

a. $\qquad$ (0041) = 03

$\qquad$ Result: (0042) = 09

b. $\qquad$ (0041) = 06

$\qquad$ Result: (0042) = 24

Remember that the answer is a hexadecimal number.

Source Program:

```
        LDX     $41             ;GET DATA
        LDA     $50,X           ;GET SQUARE OF DATA
        STA     $42             ;STORE SQUARE
        BRK
        *=$50                   ;SQUARES TABLE
SQTAB   .BYTE   0,1,4,9,16,25,36,49
```

Object Program:

Memory Address (Hex)	Memory Contents (Hex)		Instruction (Mnemonic)	
0000	A6		LDX	$41
0001	41			
0002	B5		LDA	$50,X
0003	50			
0004	85		STA	$42
0005	42			
0006	00		BRK	
0050	00	SQTAB	.BYTE	0
0051	01			1
0052	04			4
0053	09			9
0054	10			16
0055	19			25
0056	24			36
0057	31			49

Note that you must also enter the table of squares into memory (the assembler pseudo-operation .BYTE will handle this). The table of squares is constant data, not parameters that may change; that is why you can initialize the table using the .BYTE pseudo-operation, rather than by executing instructions to load values into the table. Remember that, in an actual application, the table would be part of the read-only program memory. The .BYTE pseudo-operation places the specified data in memory in the order in which it appears in the operand field.

The pseudo-operation *= simply determines where the loader (or assembler) will place the next section of code when it is finally entered into the microcomputer's memory for execution. Note that the pseudo-operation does not actually result in any object code being generated.

Indexed addressing (or indexing) means that the actual address used by the instruction (often referred to as the <u>effective address</u>) is the sum of the address included in the instruction and the contents of the Index register. Thus LDA $50,X (,X or ,Y indicates indexed addressing with the specified Index register in 6502 assembly language) is equivalent to LDA $50+(X) or LDA $53 if (X) = 03. In the example program, Index Register X contains the number to be squared and the address included in the instruction is the starting address of the table of squares. Note that there is a special zero-page indexed mode using Index Register X.

Indexing always takes extra time since the microcomputer must perform an addition to calculate the effective address. Thus LDA $50,X requires four clock cycles while LDA $50 requires only three. However, it would clearly take a great deal more time to access the table entry if the microcomputer lacked indexing and the address calculation had to be performed with a series of instructions.

Remember that the Index registers are only 8 bits long so the maximum offset from the base address is 255 (FF_{16}). Note also that the offset is an unsigned number (unlike the offset in relative addressing) so that it can never be negative. However, we do get wrap-around. That is, if the sum of the base address and the contents of the index register exceed the maximum allowed value, the most significant bits of the sum are simply dropped. In the case of zero page indexing, the maximum allowed value is FF_{16}. If, for example, the base address on the zero page is $F0_{16}$ and the index register contains $1B_{16}$, the effective address for zero page indexing is $000B_{16}$; there is no carry to the more significant byte. Thus we can get the effect of a negative offset.

There are a few special instructions that operate on one of the Index registers rather than on the Accumulator. These are:

CPX, CPY - Compare Memory and Index Register
DEX, DEY - Decrement Index Register (by 1)
INX, INY - Increment Index Register (by 1)
LDX, LDY - Load Index Register from Memory
STX, STY - Store Index Register into Memory
TAX, TAY - Transfer Accumulator to Index Register
TXA, TYA - Transfer Index Register to Accumulator

Remember that there are only a few addressing modes available with CPX, CPY, LDX, LDY, STX, and STY. Consult Table 3-4 for more details.

Arithmetic that a microprocessor cannot do directly in a few instructions is often best performed with lookup tables. Lookup tables simply contain all the possible answers to the problem; they are organized so that the answer to a particular problem

ARITHMETIC WITH TABLES

can be found easily. The arithmetic problem now becomes an accessing problem — how do we get the correct answer from the table? We must know two things: the position of the answer in the table (called the index) and the base, or starting, address of the table. The address of the answer is then the base address plus the index.

The base address, of course, is a fixed number for a particular table. How can we determine the index? In simple cases, where a single piece of data is involved, we can organize the table so that the data is the index. In the table of squares, the 0th entry in the table contains zero squared, the first entry one squared, etc. In more complex cases, where the spread of input values is very large or there are several data items involved (e.g., roots of a quadratic equation or number of permutations), we must use more complicated methods to determine indexes.

The basic tradeoff in using a table is time vs. memory. Tables are faster, since no computations are required, and simpler, since no mathematical methods must be devised and tested. However, tables can occupy a large amount of memory if the range of the input data is large. We can often reduce the size of a table by limiting the accuracy of the results, scaling the input data, or organizing the table cleverly. Tables are often used to compute transcendental and trigonometric functions, linearize inputs, convert codes, and perform other mathematical tasks.

Ones Complement

Purpose: Logically complement the contents of memory location 0040 and place the result in memory location 0041.

Sample Problem:

$$(0040) = 6A$$

$$Result = (0041) = 95$$

Source Program:

```
LDA     $40              ;GET DATA
EOR     #%11111111       ;LOGICALLY COMPLEMENT DATA
STA     $41              ;STORE RESULT
BRK
```

Object Program:

Memory Address (Hex)	Memory Contents (Hex)	Instruction (Mnemonic)	
0000	A5	LDA	$40
0001	40		
0002	49	EOR	#%11111111
0003	FF		
0004	85	STA	$41
0005	41		
0006	00	BRK	

The 6502 microprocessor lacks some simple instructions, such as Clear or Complement, that are available in most other sets. However, the required operations are easily accomplished with the existing instructions if the programmer simply gives the matter a little thought.

Exclusive-ORing a bit with '1' complements the bit since

$$1 \veebar 0 = 1$$
$$and \quad 1 \veebar 1 = 0$$

So the Exclusive-OR function turns each '0' bit into a '1' and each '1' bit into a '0', just like a logical complement or inverse. Note, however, that the instruction EOR #%11111111 occupies two bytes of memory, one for the operation code and one for the mask. An explicit Complement instruction would require only one byte.

One problem with this approach is that the purpose of the instructions may not be immediately obvious. A reader would probably have to think about exactly what an Exclusive-OR function with an all-ones word actually does. Adequate documentation is essential here, and the use of macros can also help clarify the situation.

PROBLEMS

1)   16-Bit Data Transfer

Purpose: Move the contents of memory location 0040 to memory location 0042 and the contents of memory location 0041 to memory location 0043.

Sample Problem:

$$
\begin{aligned}
(0040) &= 3E \\
(0041) &= B7
\end{aligned}
$$

Result: $(0042) = 3E$
$(0043) = B7$

2)   8-Bit Subtraction

Purpose: Subtract the contents of memory location 0041 from the contents of memory location 0040. Place the result into memory location 0042.

Sample Problem:

$$
\begin{aligned}
(0040) &= 77 \\
(0041) &= 39
\end{aligned}
$$

Result: $(0042) = 3E$

3)   Shift Left Two Bits

Purpose: Shift the contents of memory location 0040 left two bits and place the result into memory location 0041. Clear the two least significant bit positions.

Sample Problem:

$$(0040) = 5D$$

Result: $(0041) = 74$

4)   Mask Off Least Significant Four Bits

Purpose: Place the four most significant bits of the contents of memory location 0040 into memory location 0041. Clear the four least significant bits of memory location 0041.

Sample Problem:

$$(0040) = C4$$

Result: $(0041) = C0$

5)   Set a Memory Location to All Ones

Purpose: Memory location 0040 is set to all ones (FF_{16}).

6)   Word Assembly

Purpose: Combine the four least significant bits of memory locations 0040 and 0041 into a word and store them in memory location 0042. Place the four least significant bits of memory location 0040 into the four most significant bit positions of memory location 0042; place the four least significant bits of memory location 0041 into the four least significant bit positions of memory location 0042.

Sample Problem:

$$
\begin{aligned}
(0040) &= 6A \\
(0041) &= B3
\end{aligned}
$$

Result: $(0042) = A3$

7) Find Smaller of Two Numbers

Purpose: Place the smaller of the contents of memory locations 0040 and 0041 in memory location 0042. Assume that memory locations 0040 and 0041 contain unsigned binary numbers.

Sample Problems:

a.
$$(0040) = 3F$$
$$(0041) = 2B$$

Result: $(0042) = 2B$

b.
$$(0040) = 75$$
$$(0041) = A8$$

Result: $(0042) = 75$

8) 24-Bit Addition

Purpose: Add the 24-bit number in memory locations 0040, 0041, and 0042 to the 24-bit number in memory locations 0043, 0044, and 0045. The most significant eight bits are in memory locations 0042 and 0045, the least significant eight bits in memory locations 0040 and 0043. Store the result in memory locations 0046, 0047, and 0048 with the most significant bits in 0048 and the least significant bits in 0046.

Sample Problem:

$$(0040) = 2A$$
$$(0041) = 67$$
$$(0042) = 35$$
$$(0043) = F8$$
$$(0044) = A4$$
$$(0045) = 51$$

Result: $(0046) = 22$
$$(0047) = 0C$$
$$(0048) = 87$$

that is,
$$
\begin{array}{r}
35672A \\
+51A4F8 \\
\hline
870C22
\end{array}
$$

9) Sum of Squares

Purpose: Calculate the squares of the contents of memory locations 0040 and 0041 and add them together. Place the result in memory location 0042. Assume that memory locations 0040 and 0041 both contain numbers between 0 and 7 inclusive: i.e., $0 \leq (0040) \leq 7$ and $0 \leq (0041) \leq 7$. Use the table of squares from the example entitled Table of Squares.

Sample Problem:

$$(0040) = 03$$
$$(0041) = 06$$

Result $= (0042) = 2D$

that is, $3^2 + 6^2 = 9 + 36 = 45 = 2D_{16}$

10)   Twos Complement

Purpose: Place the twos complement of the contents of memory location 0040 in memory location 0041. The twos complement is the ones complement plus one.

Sample Problem:

$$(0040) = 3E$$

Result: $(0041) = C2$

The sum of the original number and its twos complement is zero. So the twos complement of X is 0-X. Which approach (calculating the ones complement and adding one, or subtracting from zero) results in a shorter and faster program?

Chapter 5
SIMPLE PROGRAM LOOPS

The program loop is the basic structure that forces the CPU to repeat a sequence of instructions. Loops have four sections:

1) **The initialization section** that establishes the starting values of counters, pointers, indexes, and other variables.

2) **The processing section** where the actual data manipulation occurs. This is the section that does the work.

3) **The loop control section** that updates counters and indexes for the next iteration.

4) **The concluding section** that analyzes and stores the results.

Note that the computer performs Sections 1 and 4 only once while it may perform Sections 2 and 3 many times. Thus, the execution time of the loop will mainly depend on the execution time of Sections 2 and 3. You will want Sections 2 and 3 to execute as quickly as possible; do not worry about the execution time of Sections 1 and 4. A typical program loop can be flowcharted as shown in Figure 5-1, or the positions of the processing and loop control sections may be reversed as shown in Figure 5-2. The processing section in Figure 5-1 is always executed at least once, while the processing section in Figure 5-2 may not be executed at all. Figure 5-1 seems more natural, but Figure 5-2 is often more efficient and avoids the problem of what to do when there is no data (a bugaboo for computers and the frequent cause of silly situations like the computer dunning someone for a bill of $0.00).

The loop structure can be used to process entire blocks of data. To accomplish this, the program must increment an Index register after each iteration so that the effective address of an indexed instruction is the next element in the data block. The next iteration will then perform the same operations on the data in the next memory location. The computer can handle blocks of any length (up to 256, since the Index registers are 8 bits long) with the same set of instructions. Indexed addressing is the key to processing blocks of data with the 6502 microprocessor, since it allows you to vary the actual (or effective) memory address by changing the contents of Index registers. Note that in the direct and immediate addressing modes, the address used is completely determined by the instruction and is therefore fixed if the program memory is read-only.

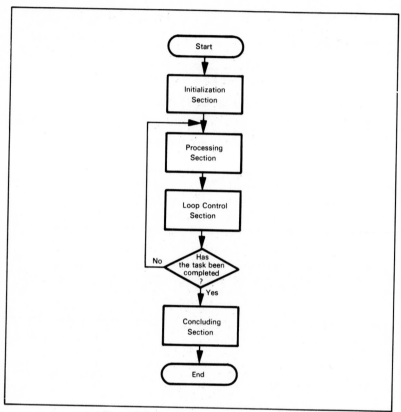

Figure 5-1. Flowchart of a Program Loop

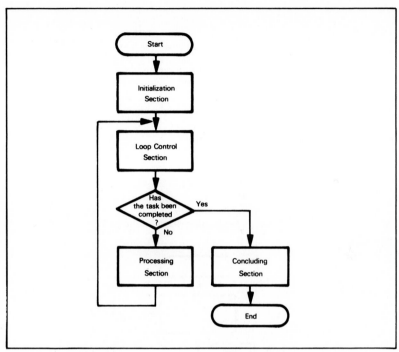

Figure 5-2. A Program Loop that Allows Zero Iterations

EXAMPLES
Sum of Data

Purpose: Calculate the sum of a series of numbers. The length of the series is in memory location 0041, and the series begins in memory location 0042. Store the sum in memory location 0040. Assume that the sum is an 8-bit number so that you can ignore carries.

8-BIT SUMMATION

Sample Problem:

$$
\begin{aligned}
(0041) &= 03 \\
(0042) &= 28 \\
(0043) &= 55 \\
(0044) &= 26
\end{aligned}
$$

Result: $(0040) = (0042) + (0043) + (0044)$
$= 28+55+26$
$= A3$

There are three entries in the sum, since $(0041)=03$.

Flowchart:

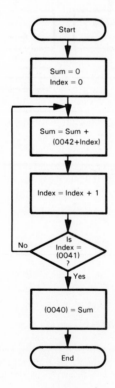

Note: (0042 + Index) is the contents of the memory location whose address is the sum of 0042 and Index. Remember that on the 6502 microprocessor, 0042 is a 16-bit address, Index is an 8-bit offset, and (0042 + Index) is an 8-bit byte of data.

Source Program:

```
          LDA     #0          ;SUM = ZERO
          TAX                 ;INDEX = ZERO
SUMD      CLC                 ;DO NOT INCLUDE CARRY
          ADC     $42,X       ;SUM = SUM + DATA
          INX                 ;INCREMENT INDEX
          CPX     $41         ;HAVE ALL ELEMENTS BEEN SUMMED?
          BNE     SUMD        ;NO, CONTINUE SUMMATION
          STA     $40         ;YES, STORE SUM
          BRK
```

Object Program:

Memory Address (Hex)	Memory Contents (Hex)		Instruction (Mnemonic)	
0000	A9		LDA	#0
0001	00			
0002	AA		TAX	
0003	18	SUMD	CLC	
0004	75		ADC	$42,X
0005	42			
0006	E8		INX	
0007	E4		CPX	$41
0008	41			
0009	D0		BNE	SUMD
000A	F8			
000B	85		STA	$40
000C	40			
000D	00		BRK	

The initialization section of the program is the first two instructions, which set the sum and index to their starting values. Note that TAX transfers the contents of the Accumulator to Index Register X but leaves the Accumulator as it was. The base address of the array and the location of the counter are fixed within the program and need not be initialized.

The processing section of the program consists of the single instruction ADC $42,X, which adds the contents of the effective address (base address plus Index Register X) to the contents of the Accumulator. This instruction does the real work of the program. The CLC instruction simply clears the Carry flag so that it does not affect the summation. Note that each iteration of the loop adds in the contents of a new effective address even though the instructions do not change.

The loop control section of the program consists of the instruction INX. This instruction updates the Index register (by 1) so that the next iteration adds the next number to the sum. Note that (0041) - X tells you how many iterations are left to be done.

The instruction BNE causes a branch if the Zero flag is 0. CPX sets the Zero flag to 1 if Index Register X and the contents of memory location 0041 are the same and to 0 if they are not. The offset is a twos complement number and the count begins from the memory location immediately following the BNE instruction. In this case, the required jump is from memory location 000B to memory location 0003. So the offset is:

$$
\begin{array}{rcl}
0003 & = & 03 \\
-000B & = & +F5 \\
\hline
 & & F8
\end{array}
$$

If the Zero flag is one, the CPU executes the next instruction in sequence (STA $40). Since CPX $41 was the last instruction before BNE to affect the Zero flag, BNE SUMD causes a branch to SUMD if CPX $41 does not produce a zero result; that is,

$$(PC) = \begin{cases} SUMD \text{ if } (X) - (0041) \neq 0 \\ (PC)+2 \text{ if } (X) - (0041) = 0 \end{cases}$$

The 2 is caused by the two-word BNE instruction. A single instruction combining the Decrement and the Jump would be a useful addition to the 6502 instruction set.

The order in which instructions are executed is often very important. INX must come after ADC $42,X or else the first number to be added to the sum will be the contents of memory location 0043 instead of the contents of memory location 0042. CPX $41 must come right before BNE SUMD, since otherwise the Zero status setting produced by CPX could be changed by another instruction.

CPX and CPY are the same as CMP except that the contents of memory are subtracted from an Index register rather than from the Accumulator. Note, however, that CPX and CPY offer limited addressing options (see Table 3-4).

Most computer loops count down rather than up so that the Zero flag can serve as an exit condition, thus eliminating the need for a Compare instruction. This method is a bit awkward for people although it is used occasionally in launch countdowns and in a few other situations. Remember that the Zero flag is set to 1 if the result of an instruction is zero and to 0 if the result is not zero.

We could easily revise the loop so that it works backward through the array (see the next flowchart). The following programs are revised versions.

Source Program:

```
        LDA     #0          ;SUM = ZERO
        LDX     $41         ;INDEX = MAXIMUM COUNT
SUMD    CLC                 ;DO NOT INCLUDE CARRY
        ACD     $41,X       ;SUM = SUM + DATA
        DEX                 ;DECREMENT INDEX
        BNE     SUMD        ;BRANCH BACK IF ALL ELEMENTS NOT SUMMED
        STA     $40         ;STORE SUM
        BRK
```

Note that the addition instruction is now ADC $41,X instead of ADC $42,X; the number in the Index register is one larger than before. Clearly, the net result of subtracting one from the base address and adding one to the index is zero. The reorganized object program is:

Memory Address (Hex)	Memory Contents (Hex)		Instruction (Mnemonic)	
0000	A9		LDA	#0
0001	00			
0002	A6		LDX	$41
0003	41			
0004	18	SUMD	CLC	
0005	75		ADC	$41,X
0006	41			
0007	CA		DEX	
0008	D0		BNE	SUMD
0009	FA			
000A	85		STA	$40
000B	40			
000C	00		BRK	

In most applications, the slight time and memory differences between one implementation of a loop and another do not matter very much. You should therefore select the approach that is the clearest and easiest for you to use. We will discuss program design and efficiency later in Chapters 13 and 15.

You may wish to verify the hexadecimal values for the relative offsets in the last two programs. The final test of any calculations that you make is whether the program runs correctly. If, for whatever reason, you must perform hexadecimal calculations frequently, we suggest that you consider a calculator (like the Texas Instruments Programmer) or one of the numerous manual aids that are available.

Flowchart (of reorganized summation program):

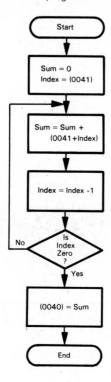

16-Bit Sum of Data

Purpose: Calculate the sum of a series of numbers. The length of the series is in memory location 0042 and the series itself begins in memory location 0043. Store the sum in memory locations 0040 and 0041 (eight least significant bits in 0040).

Sample Problem:

$$(0042) = 03$$
$$(0043) = C8$$
$$(0044) = FA$$
$$(0045) = 96$$

$$\text{Result} = C8 + FA + 96 = 0258_{16}$$

$$(0040) = 58$$
$$(0041) = 02$$

Flowchart:

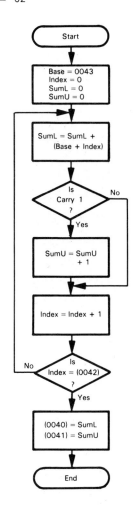

Source Program:

```
          LDA    #0        ;SUM = ZERO
          TAX              ;INDEX = ZERO
          TAY              ;MSB'S OF SUM = ZERO
SUMD      CLC              ;DO NOT INCLUDE CARRY
          ADC    $43,X     ;SUM = SUM + DATA
          BCC    COUNT
          INY              ;ADD CARRY TO MSB'S OF SUM
COUNT     INX
          CPX    $42
          BNE    SUMD      ;CONTINUE UNTIL ALL ELEMENTS SUMMED
          STA    $40       ;STORE LSB'S OF SUM
          STY    $41       ;STORE MSB'S OF SUM
          BRK
```

Object Program:

Memory Address (Hex)	Memory Contents (Hex)	Instruction (Mnemonic)	
0000	A9		LDA	#0
0001	00			
0002	AA		TAX	
0003	A8		TAY	
0004	18	SUMD	CLC	
0005	75		ADC	$43,X
0006	43			
0007	90		BCC	COUNT
0008	01			
0009	C8		INY	
000A	E8	COUNT	INX	
000B	E4		CPX	$42
000C	42			
000D	D0		BNE	SUMD
000E	F5			
000F	85		STA	$40
0010	40			
0011	84		STY	$41
0012	41			
0013	00		BRK	

The structure of this program is the same as the structure of the last example. The most significant bits of the sum must now be initialized and stored. The processing section consists of four instructions (CLC; ADC $43,X; BCC COUNT; and INY), including a condition jump.

BCC COUNT causes a jump to memory location COUNT if Carry = 0. Thus, if there is no carry from the 8-bit addition, the program jumps around the statement that increments the most significant bits of the sum. The relative offset is

$$\begin{array}{r} 000A \\ -0009 \\ \hline 01 \end{array}$$

The relative offset for BNE SUMD is

$$\begin{array}{r} 0004 \\ -000F \end{array} = \begin{array}{r} 0004 \\ +FFF1 \\ \hline F5 \end{array}$$

INY adds 1 to the contents of Index Register Y, which is used here as a temporary register to save the carries from the addition. We could also use a memory location to hold the carries, since the INC instruction can be used to directly increment the contents of a memory location.

You might wish to try reorganizing this program so that it decrements the index down to zero rather than incrementing it. Which version is faster and shorter?

Relative branches are limited to short distances ($7F_{16}$ or $+127$ forward, 80_{16} or -128 backward from the end of the branch instruction). This limitation is seldom important, since most program branches are short. However, if you need a conditional branch with a greater range, you can always invert the condition logic and branch around a JMP instruction. For example, to branch to location FAR if Carry = 0, use the sequence

```
          BCS     NEXT
          JMP     FAR
NEXT
```

NEXT is the address immediately following the last byte of the JMP instruction. JMP allows only absolute (direct) and indirect addressing.

Number of Negative Elements

Purpose: Determine the number of negative elements (most significant bit 1) in a block. The length of the block is in memory location 0041 and the block itself starts in memory location 0042. Place the number of negative elements in memory location 0040.

Sample Problem:

$$
\begin{aligned}
(0041) &= 06 \\
(0042) &= 68 \\
(0043) &= F2 \\
(0044) &= 87 \\
(0045) &= 30 \\
(0046) &= 59 \\
(0047) &= 2A
\end{aligned}
$$

Result: (0040) = 02, since 0043 and 0044 contain numbers with an MSB of 1.

Flowchart:

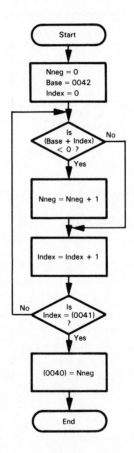

Source Program:

```
            LDX     #0          ;INDEX = ZERO
            LDY     #0          ;NUMBER OF NEGATIVES = ZERO
SRNEG       LDA     $42,X       ;IS NEXT ELEMENT NEGATIVE?
            BPL     CHCNT
            INY                 ;YES, ADD 1 TO NUMBER OF NEGATIVES
CHCNT       INX
            CPX     $41
            BNE     SRNEG       ;CONTINUE UNTIL ALL ELEMENTS EXAMINED
            STY     $40         ;SAVE NUMBER OF NEGATIVES
            BRK
```

Object Program:

Memory Address (Hex)	Memory Contents (Hex)	Instruction (Mnemonic)		
0000	A2		LDX	#0
0001	00			
0002	A0		LDY	#0
0003	00			
0004	B5	SRNEG	LDA	$42,X
0005	42			
0006	10		BPL	CHCNT
0007	01			
0008	C8		INY	
0009	E8	CHCNT	INX	
000A	E4		CPX	$41
000B	41			
000C	D0		BNE	SRNEG
000D	F6			
000E	84		STY	$40
000F	40			
0010	00		BRK	

LDA affects the Sign (S) and Zero (Z) status flags. Therefore, we can immediately check to see if a number that has been loaded is negative or zero.

BPL, Branch-on-Plus, causes a branch over the specified number of locations if the Sign (or Negative) bit is zero. A sign bit of zero may indicate a positive number or may just indicate the value of the most significant bit position; the interpretation depends on what the numbers mean.

The offset for BPL is calculated from the first memory location following the two-byte instruction. Here the offset is simply from 0008 to 0009, or one location (i.e., the INY instruction is skipped if the Negative bit is zero). The Negative bit will be zero if the most significant bit of the data loaded from memory by the LDA $42,X instruction is zero.

Remember that negative-signed numbers all have a most significant bit (bit 7) of 1. All negative numbers are actually larger, in the unsigned sense, than positive numbers.

Maximum Value

Purpose: Find the largest element in a block of data. The length of the block is in memory location 0041 and the block itself begins in memory location 0042. Store the maximum in memory location 0040. Assume that the numbers in the block are all 8-bit unsigned binary numbers.

Sample Problem:

$$
\begin{aligned}
(0041) &= 05 \\
(0042) &= 67 \\
(0043) &= 79 \\
(0044) &= 15 \\
(0045) &= E3 \\
(0046) &= 72
\end{aligned}
$$

Result: (0040) = E3, since this is the largest of the five unsigned numbers.

Flowchart:

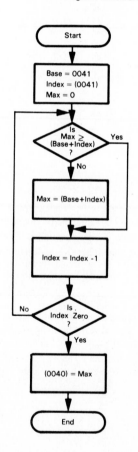

Source Program:

```
        LDX     $41         ;GET ELEMENT COUNT
        LDA     #0          ;MAXIMUM = ZERO (MINIMUM POSSIBLE VALUE)
MAXM    CMP     $41,X       ;IS NEXT ELEMENT ABOVE MAXIMUM?
        BCS     NOCHG       ;NO, KEEP MAXIMUM
        LDA     $41,X       ;YES, REPLACE ,MAXIMUM WITH ELEMENT
NOCHG   DEX
        BNE     MAXM        ;CONTINUE UNTIL ALL ELEMENTS EXAMINED
        STA     $40         ;SAVE MAXIMUM
        BRK
```

Object Program:

Memory Address (Hex)	Memory Contents (Hex)	Instruction (Mnemonic)	
0000	A6	LDX	$41
0001	41		
0002	A9	LDA	#0
0003	00		
0004	D5	MAXM CMP	$41,X
0005	41		
0006	B0	BCS	NOCHG
0007	02		
0008	B5	LDA	$41,X
0009	41		
000A	CA	NOCHG DEX	
000B	D0	BNE	MAXM
000C	F7		
000D	85	STA	$40
000E	40		
000F	00	BRK	

The relative offset for BCS NOCHG is:

$$\begin{array}{r} 000A \\ -0008 \\ \hline 02 \end{array}$$

The relative offset for BNE MAXM is:

$$\begin{array}{r} 0004 \\ -000D \\ \hline \end{array} = \begin{array}{r} 04 \\ +F3 \\ \hline F7 \end{array}$$

The first two instructions of this program form the initialization section.

This program takes advantage of the fact that zero is the smallest 8-bit unsigned binary number. When you set the register that contains the maximum value — in this case, the Accumulator — to the minimum possible value before you enter the loop, then the program will set the Accumulator to a larger value unless all the elements in the array are zeros. The program works properly if there are two elements in the array, but not if there is only one or none at all. Why? How could you solve this problem?

The instruction CMP $41,X sets the Carry flag as follows where ELEMENT is the contents of the effective address and MAX is the contents of the Accumulator:

$$\text{Carry} = 0 \text{ if ELEMENT} > \text{MAX}$$
$$\text{Carry} = 1 \text{ if ELEMENT} \leq \text{MAX}$$

Remember that the carry is an inverted borrow. If Carry = 1, the program proceeds to address NOCHG and does not change the maximum. If Carry = 0, the program replaces the old maximum with the current element by executing the instruction LDA $41,X.

The program does not work if the numbers are signed, because negative numbers will appear to be larger than positive numbers. This problem is somewhat tricky because a twos complement overflow could make the sign of the result incorrect. A further problem is that the CMP instruction does not affect the Overflow flag. A program for signed numbers would therefore have to use the SBC instruction and check both the Sign and the Overflow flags. The Carry flag would have to be set to 1 before the subtraction (remember that Carry is an inverted borrow and the SBC instruction inverts it before subtracting it), and an addition would be required to restore the original value of the maximum. Note how convenient it is in the example that CMP does not actually change the contents of the Accumulator.

Justify a Binary Fraction

Purpose: Shift the contents of memory location 0040 left until the most significant bit of the number is 1. Store the result in memory location 0041 and the number of left shifts required in memory location 0042. If the contents of memory location 0040 are zero, clear both 0041 and 0042.

Note: The process is just like converting a number to a scientific notation; for example:

$$0.0057 = 5.7 \times 10^{-3}$$

Sample Problems:

a.   (0040) = 22

    Result: (0041) = 88
             (0042) = 02

b.   (0040) = 01

    Result: (0041) = 80
             (0042) = 07

c.   (0040) = CB

    Result: (0041) = CB
             (0042) = 00

d.   (0040) = 00

    Result: (0041) = 00
             (0042) = 00

Flowchart:

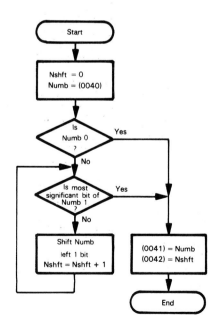

5-17

Source Program:

```
        LDY     #0          ;NUMBER OF SHIFTS =0
        LDA     $40         ;GET DATA
        BEQ     DONE        ;DONE IF DATA IS ZERO
CHKMS   BMI     DONE        ;DONE IF MSB IS ONE
        INY                 ;ADD 1 TO NUMBER OF SHIFTS
        ASL     A           ;SHIFT LEFT ONE BIT
        JMP     CHKMS
DONE    STA     $41         ;SAVE JUSTIFIED DATA
        STY     $42         ;SAVE NUMBER OF SHIFTS
        BRK
```

Object Program:

Memory Address (Hex)	Memory Contents (Hex)		Instruction (Mnemonic)	
0000	A0		LDY	#0
0001	00			
0002	A5		LDA	$40
0003	40			
0004	F0		BEQ	DONE
0005	07			
0006	30	CHKMS	BMI	DONE
0007	05			
0008	C8		INY	
0009	0A		ASL	A
000A	4C		JMP	CHKMS
000B	06			
000C	00			
000D	85	DONE	STA	$41
000E	41			
000F	84		STY	$42
0010	42			
0011	00		BRK	

BMI DONE causes a branch to location DONE if the Sign bit is 1. This condition may mean that the last result was a negative number, or it may just mean that its most significant bit was 1 — the computer only supplies the results; the programmer must provide the interpretation.

ASL A shifts the contents of the Accumulator left one bit and clears the least significant bit.

JMP is an unconditional branch instruction that always places a new value in the Program Counter. It only allows absolute (direct) or indirect addressing. The indirect mode provides flexibility since the actual destination address can be stored in RAM. Note that there is no relative addressing and no special page-zero modes.

The address in the JMP instruction is stored in two successive memory locations with the least significant bits first (at the lower address). This is the standard way in which the 6502 microprocessor expects to find addresses, regardless of whether they are part of instructions or are used indirectly. The same upside-down method is used in the 8080, 8085, and Z80 microprocessors, but the opposite approach (most significant bits first) is used on the 6800 microprocessor. Note that an address occupies two bytes of memory, although there is a single byte of data located at that address.

We could reorganize this program so as to eliminate the extraneous JMP instruction. One reorganized version would be:

```
            LDY     #0          ;NUMBER OF SHIFTS = 0
            LDA     $40         ;GET DATA
            BEQ     DONE        ;DONE IF DATA IS ZERO
CHKMS       INY                 ;ADD 1 TO NUMBER OF SHIFTS
            ASL     A           ;SHIFT LEFT ONE BIT
            BCC     CHKMS       ;CONTINUE IF MSB NOT ONE
            ROR     A           ;OTHERWISE, SHIFT BACK ONCE
            DEY                 ;AND IGNORE EXTRA SHIFT
DONE        STA     $41         ;SAVE JUSTIFIED DATA
            STY     $42         ;SAVE NUMBER OF SHIFTS
            BRK
```

This version shifts the data until the Carry becomes 1. Then it adjusts the data and the number of shifts back one since the last shift was not really necessary. Show that this version is also correct. What are its advantages and disadvantages as compared to the previous program? You might wish to try some other organizations to see how they compare in execution time and memory usage.

Post-Indexed (Indirect) Addressing

We have already noted the additional flexibility provided by the indexed addressing mode. The same instructions can be used to process each element in an array or table. But even more flexibility is provided by the post-indexed addressing mode in which the instruction only specifies the address on

```
POST-INDEXED
(INDIRECT)
ADDRESSING
MODE
```

page zero that contains the base address of the table or array. Now the same program can handle an array or table located anywhere in memory. All that we have to do is place the starting address in the appropriate locations on page zero. Note that the starting address occupies two bytes of memory, with the least significant byte first (at the lower address). Post-indexing requires extra clock cycles (six as compared to four for the zero-page indexed mode) but provides tremendous additional flexibility. Entire arrays need not be moved, nor are repeated versions of the same program required.

Post-indexed (indirect) addressing can only be used with Index Register Y. So the maximum value program with post-indexed addressing is as follows, assuming that the length of the array is in memory location 0041 and its starting address is in memory locations 0042 and 0043.

For example,

```
(0041) = 05
(0042) = 43 (LSBs of starting address minus one)
(0043) = 00 (MSBs of starting address minus one)
(0044) = 67 (first element in array)
(0045) = 79
(0046) = 15
(0047) = E3
(0048) = 72
```

Result = (40) = E3 since this is the largest
of the 5 unsigned numbers.

Source Program:

```
        LDY    $41         ;GET ELEMENT COUNT
        LDA    #0          ;MAXIMUM = ZERO (MINIMUM POSSIBLE VALUE)
MAXM    CMP    ($42),Y     ;IS NEXT ELEMENT ABOVE MAXIMUM?
        BCS    NOCHG       ;NO, KEEP MAXIMUM
        LDA    ($42),Y     ;YES, REPLACE MAXIMUM WITH ELEMENT
NOCHG   DEY
        BNE    MAXM        ;CONTINUE UNTIL ALL ELEMENTS EXAMINED
        STA    $40         ;SAVE MAXIMUM
        BRK
```

Object Program:

Memory Address (Hex)	Memory Contents (Hex)		Instruction (Mnemonic)	
0000	A4		LDY	$41
0001	41			
0002	A9		LDA	#0
0003	00			
0004	D1	MAXM	CMP	($42),Y
0005	42			
0006	B0		BCS	NOCHG
0007	02			
0008	B1		LDA	($42),Y
0009	42			
000A	88	NOCHG	DEY	
000B	D0		BNE	MAXM
000C	F7			
000D	85		STA	$40
000E	40			
000F	00		BRK	

The indirect address (in memory locations 0042 and 0043) is stored in the usual 6502 fashion, with the least significant bits first (at the lower address).

We could use the same program to find the maximum element in an array of 5 entries starting in memory address 25E1. All that we would have to do is change the indirect address to 25E0 before executing the program, that is,

$$(0042) = \text{E0 (LSBs of starting address minus one)}$$
$$(0043) = 25 \text{ (MSBs of starting address minus one)}$$

How would you handle the array starting in memory address 25E1 if the program used ordinary indexed addressing (as in the earlier example)? Assume that the program is in ROM so that you cannot change the addresses in the instructions.

Pre-Indexed (Indirect) Addressing

The pre-indexed addressing mode gives you a different kind of flexibility. This method allows you to choose one address from a table of addresses, rather than being limited to a particular memory address. For example, rather than having memory location 0041 contain the length of the array in the maximum

PRE-INDEXED
(INDIRECT)
ADDRESSING
MODE

problem, we could let it contain the index of the address that contains the length of the array. The table of addresses must be located somewhere on page zero, perhaps starting at memory address 0060, that is

$$(0060) = 2F \brace (0061) = 00 \text{ address in which counter #0 is stored}$$

$$(0062) = 80 \brace (0063) = 00 \text{ address in which counter #1 is stored}$$

$$(0064) = A5 \brace (0065) = 00 \text{ address in which counter #2 is stored}$$

One problem is that addresses occupy two bytes of memory so that you must multiply the counter number by two before applying the pre-indexed addressing mode. Note that all addresses are stored in the usual 6502 manner, with the least significant bits first. Pre-indexed addressing is not as useful as post-indexed addressing, but it does come in handy occasionally.

PROBLEMS

1) Checksum of Data

Purpose: Calculate the checksum of a series of numbers. The length of the series is in memory location 0041 and the series itself begins in memory location 0042. Store the checksum in memory location 0040. The checksum is formed by Exclusive-ORing all the numbers in the series together.

Note: Such checksums are often used in paper tape and cassette systems to ensure that the data has been read correctly. The calculated checksum is compared to the one stored with the data — if the two checksums do not agree, the system will usually either indicate an error to the operator or automatically read the data again.

Sample Problem:

$$(0041) = 03$$
$$(0042) = 28$$
$$(0043) = 55$$
$$(0044) = 26$$

$$
\begin{aligned}
\text{Result:} \quad (0040) &= (0042) \oplus (0043) \oplus (0044) \\
&= 28 \oplus 55 \oplus 26 \\
&= 0\,0\,1\,0\,1\,0\,0\,0 \\
\oplus\ & \underline{0\,1\,0\,1\,0\,1\,0\,1} \\
& 0\,1\,1\,1\,1\,1\,0\,1 \\
\oplus\ & \underline{0\,0\,1\,0\,0\,1\,1\,0} \\
& 0\,1\,0\,1\,1\,0\,1\,1 \\
&= 5B
\end{aligned}
$$

2) Sum of 16-Bit Data

Purpose: Calculate the sum of a series of 16-bit numbers. The length of the series is in memory location 0042 and the series itself begins in memory location 0043. Store the sum in memory locations 0040 and 0041 (eight most significant bits in 0041). Each 16-bit number occupies two memory locations, with the eight most significant bits in the higher address. Assume that the sum can be contained in 16 bits.

Sample Problem:

$$(0042) = 03$$
$$(0043) = F1$$
$$(0044) = 28$$
$$(0045) = 1A$$
$$(0046) = 30$$
$$(0047) = 89$$
$$(0048) = 4B$$

$$
\begin{aligned}
\text{Result:} \quad & 28F1 + 301A + 4B89 = A494 \\
& (0040) = 94 \\
& (0041) = A4
\end{aligned}
$$

3) Number of Zero, Positive, and Negative Numbers

Purpose: Determine the number of zero, positive (most significant bit zero but entire number not zero), and negative (most significant bit 1) elements in a block. The length of the block is in memory location 0043 and the block itself starts in memory location 0044. Place the number of negative elements in memory location 0040, the number of zero elements in memory location 0041, and the number of positive elements in memory location 0042.

Sample Problem:

$$(0043) = 06$$
$$(0044) = 68$$
$$(0045) = F2$$
$$(0046) = 87$$
$$(0047) = 00$$
$$(0048) = 59$$
$$(0049) = 2A$$

Result: 2 negative, 1 zero, and 3 positive, so

$$(0040) = 02$$
$$(0041) = 01$$
$$(0042) = 03$$

4) Find Minimum

Purpose: Find the smallest element in a block of data. The length of the block is in memory location 0041 and the block itself begins in memory location 0042. Store the minimum in memory location 0040. Assume that the numbers in the block are 8-bit unsigned binary numbers.

Sample Problem:

$$(0041) = 05$$
$$(0042) = 67$$
$$(0043) = 79$$
$$(0044) = 15$$
$$(0045) = E3$$
$$(0046) = 72$$

Result: $(0040) = 15$, since this is the smallest of the five unsigned numbers.

5) Count 1 Bits

Purpose: Determine how many bits in memory location 0040 are ones and place the result in memory location 0041.

Sample Problem:

$$(0040) = 3B = 00111011$$

Result: $(0041) = 05$

Chapter 6
CHARACTER-CODED DATA

Microprocessors often handle character-coded data. Not only do keyboards, teletypewriters, communications devices, displays, and computer terminals expect or provide character-coded data, but many instruments, test systems, and controllers also require data in this form. The most commonly used code is ASCII. Baudot and EBCDIC are found less frequently. We will assume all of our character-coded data to be 7-bit ASCII with the most significant bit zero (see Table 6-1).

Some principles to remember in handling ASCII-coded data are:

```
HANDLING
DATA IN
ASCII
```

1) **The codes for the numbers and letters form ordered sub-sequences.** The codes for the decimal numbers are 30_{16} through 39_{16} so that you can convert between decimal and ASCII with a simple additive factor. The codes for the upper case letters are 41_{16} through $5A_{16}$ so that you can do alphabetic ordering by sorting the data in increasing numerical order.

2) **The computer draws no distinction between printing and non-printing characters.** Only the I/O devices make that distinction.

3) **An ASCII device will handle only ASCII data.** To print a 7 on an ASCII printer, the microprocessor must send 37_{16} to the printer; 07_{16} is the 'bell' character. Similarly, the microprocessor will receive the character 9 from an ASCII keyboard as 39_{16}; 09_{16} is the 'tab' character.

4) **Some ASCII devices do not use the full character set.** For example, control characters and lower case letters may be ignored or printed as spaces or question marks.

5) **Some widely used ASCII characters are:**

   $0A_{16}$ - line feed (LF)

   $0D_{16}$ - carriage return (CR)

   20_{16} - space

   $3F_{16}$ - ? (question mark)

   $7F_{16}$ - rubout or delete character

6) **Each ASCII character occupies eight bits.** This allows a large character set but is wasteful when the data is limited to a small subset such as the decimal numbers. An 8-bit byte, for example, can hold only one ASCII-coded decimal digit, while it can hold two BCD-coded digits.

Table 6-1. Hex-ASCII Table

Hex LSD / Hex MSD	0	1	2	3	4	5	6	7
0	NUL	DLE	SP	0	@	P	`	p
1	SOH	DC1	!	1	A	Q	a	q
2	STX	DC2	"	2	B	R	b	r
3	ETX	DC3	#	3	C	S	c	s
4	EOT	DC4	$	4	D	T	d	t
5	ENQ	NAK	%	5	E	U	e	u
6	ACK	SYN	&	6	F	V	f	v
7	BEL	ETB	'	7	G	W	g	w
8	BS	CAN	(	8	H	X	h	x
9	HT	EM	)	9	I	Y	i	y
A	LF	SUB	*	:	J	Z	j	z
B	VT	ESC	+	;	K	[	k	{
C	FF	FS	,	<	L	\	l	|
D	CR	GS	-	=	M	]	m	}
E	SO	RS	.	>	N	^	n	~
F	SI	US	/	?	O	_	o	DEL

EXAMPLES
Length of a String of Characters

Purpose: Determine the length of a string of ASCII characters (seven bits with most significant bit zero). The string starts in memory location 0041; the end of the string is marked by a carriage return character ('CR', $0D_{16}$). Place the length of the string (excluding the carriage return) into memory location 0040.

Sample Problems:

a.   (0041) = 0D

Result: (0040) = 00 since the first character is a carriage return.

b.   (0041) = 52 'R'
      (0042) = 41 'A'
      (0043) = 54 'T'
      (0044) = 48 'H'
      (0045) = 45 'E'
      (0046) = 52 'R'
      (0047) = 0D CR

Result: (0040) = 06

Flowchart:

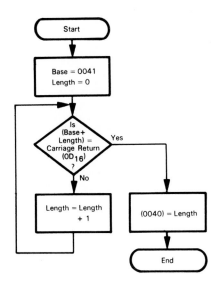

Source Program:

```
        LDX     #0          ;STRING LENGTH = ZERO
        LDA     #$0D        ;GET ASCII CARRIAGE RETURN TO COMPARE
CHKCR   CMP     $41,X       ;IS CHARACTER A CARRIAGE RETURN?
        BEQ     DONE        ;YES, DONE
        INX                 ;NO, ADD 1 TO STRING LENGTH
        JMP     CHKCR
DONE    STX     $40         ;SAVE STRING LENGTH
        BRK
```

Object Program:

Memory Address (Hex)	Memory Contents (Hex)	Instruction (Mnemonic)		
0000	A2		LDX	#0
0001	00			
0002	A9		LDA	#$0D
0003	0D			
0004	D5	CHKCR	CMP	$41,X
0005	41			
0006	F0		BEQ	DONE
0007	04			
0008	E8		INX	
0009	4C		JMP	CHKCR
000A	04			
000B	00			
000C	86	DONE	STX	$40
000D	40			
000E	00		BRK	

The carriage return character, 'CR', is just another ASCII code ($0D_{16}$) as far as the computer is concerned. The fact that this character causes an output device to perform a control function rather than print a symbol does not affect the computer.

The Compare instruction, CMP, sets the flags as if a subtraction had been performed but leaves the carriage return character in the Accumulator for later comparisons. The Zero (Z) flag is affected as follows:

$Z = 1$ if the character in the string is a carriage return

$Z = 0$ if it is not a carriage return

The instruction INX adds 1 to the string length counter in Index Register X. LDX #0 initializes this counter to zero before the loop begins. Remember to initialize variables before using them in a loop.

This loop does not terminate because a counter is decremented to zero or reaches a maximum value. The computer will simply continue examining characters until it finds a carriage return. It is good programming practice to place a maximum count in a loop like this to avoid problems with erroneous strings that do not contain a carriage return. What would happen if the example program were used with such a string?

Note that by rearranging the logic and changing the initial conditions, you can shorten the program and decrease its execution time. If we adjust the flowchart so that the program increments the string length before it checks for the carriage return, only one Jump instruction is necessary instead of two. The new flowchart and program are as follows:

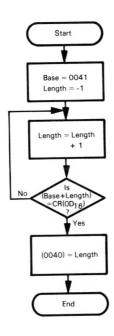

Source Program:

```
            LDX    #$FF        ;STRING LENGTH = -1
            LDA    #$0D        ;GET ASCII CARRIAGE RETURN TO COMPARE
CHKCR       INX                ;ADD 1 TO STRING LENGTH
            CMP    $41,X       ;IS CHARACTER A CARRIAGE RETURN?
            BNE    CHKCR       ;NO, CHECK NEXT CHARACTER
            STX    $40         ;YES, SAVE STRING LENGTH
            BRK
```

This version is not only shorter and faster, but it also contains no absolute destination addresses; thus it can easily be placed anywhere in memory. The earlier version contains a JMP instruction with a specific absolute address, while this version has only branch instructions with relative addresses.

Object Program:

Memory Address (Hex)	Memory Contents (Hex)		Instruction (Mnemonic)	
0000	A2		LDX	#$FF
0001	FF			
0002	A9		LDA	#$0D
0003	0D			
0004	E8	CHKCR	INX	
0005	D5		CMP	$41,X
0006	41			
0007	D0		BNE	CHKCR
0008	FB			
0009	86		STX	$40
000A	40			
000B	00		BRK	

Find First Non-Blank Character

Purpose: Search a string of ASCII characters (seven bits with most significant bit zero) for a non-blank character. The string starts in memory location 0042. Place the index of the first non-blank character in memory location 0040. A blank character is 20_{16} in ASCII.

Sample Problems:

a.   (0042) = 37   ASCII 7

    Result: (0040) = 00, since memory location 0042 contains a non-blank character.

b.   (0042) = 20   SP
                         (0043) = 20   SP
                         (0044) = 20   SP
                         (0045) = 46   'F'
                         (0046) = 20   SP

    Result: (0040) = 03, since the three previous memory locations all contain blanks.

Flowchart:

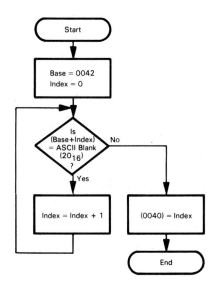

Source Program:

```
        LDX    #0           ;START WITH INDEX = ZERO
        LDA    #'           ;GET ASCII SPACE FOR COMPARISON
CHBLK   CMP    $42,X        ;IS CHARACTER AN ASCII SPACE?
        BNE    DONE         ;NO, DONE
        INX                 ;YES, EXAMINE NEXT CHARACTER
        JMP    CHBLK
DONE    STX    $40          ;SAVE INDEX OF FIRST NON-BLANK
                            ;   CHARACTER
        BRK
```

Note the use of an apostrophe (') or single quotation mark before an ASCII character.

Object Program:

Memory Address (Hex)	Memory Contents (Hex)	Instruction (Mnemonic)		
0000	A2		LDX	#0
0001	00			
0002	A9		LDA	#'
0003	20			
0004	D5	CHBLK	CMP	$42,X
0005	42			
0006	D0		BNE	DONE
0007	04			
0008	E8		INX	
0009	4C		JMP	CHBLK
000A	04			
000B	00			
000C	86	DONE	STX	$40
000D	40			
000E	00		BRK	

Looking for spaces in strings is a common task. Spaces often are eliminated from strings when they are used simply to increase readability or to fit particular formats. It is obviously wasteful to store and transmit beginning, ending, or extra spaces, particularly if you are paying for the communications capability and memory required. Data and program entry, however, are much simpler if extra spaces are tolerated. Microcomputers are often used in situations like this to convert data between forms that are easy for humans to use and forms that are efficiently handled on computers and communications lines.

Again, if we alter the initial conditions so that the loop control section precedes the processing section, we can reduce the number of bytes in the program and decrease the loop's execution time. The rearranged flowchart is:

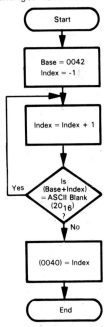

Source Program:

```
        LDX     #$FF        ;START WITH INDEX = -1
        LDA     #'          ;GET ASCII SPACE FOR COMPARISON
CHBLK   INX                 ;INCREMENT INDEX
        CMP     $42,X       ;IS CHARACTER AN ASCII SPACE?
        BEQ     CHBLK       ;YES, EXAMINE NEXT CHARACTER
        STX     $40         ;NO, SAVE INDEX OF FIRST NON-BLANK
                            ;   CHARACTER
        BRK
```

Object Program:

Memory Address (Hex)	Memory Contents (Hex)	Instruction (Mnemonic)	
0000	A2	LDX	#$FF
0001	FF		
0002	A9	LDA	#'
0003	20		
0004	E8	CHBLK INX	
0005	D5	CMP	$42,X
0006	42		
0007	F0	BEQ	CHBLK
0008	FB		
0009	86	STX	$40
000A	40		
000B	00	BRK	

Replace Leading Zeros with Blanks

Purpose: Edit a string of ASCII decimal characters by replacing all leading zeros with blanks. The string starts in memory location 0041; assume that it consists entirely of ASCII-coded decimal digits. The length of the string is in memory location 0040.

Sample Problems:

a.

$$(0040) = 02$$
$$(0041) = 36 \quad \text{ASCII 6}$$

The program leaves the string unchanged, since the leading digit is not zero.

b.

$$(0040) = 08$$
$$(0041) = 30 \quad \text{ASCII 0}$$
$$(0042) = 30 \quad \text{ASCII 0}$$
$$(0043) = 38 \quad \text{ASCII 8}$$

Result:
$$(0041) = 20 \quad \text{SP}$$
$$(0042) = 20 \quad \text{SP}$$

The two leading ASCII zeros have been replaced by ASCII blanks.

Flowchart:

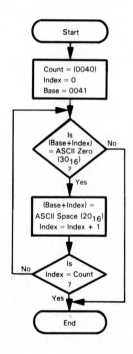

6-10

Source Program:

```
        LDX     #0          ;INDEX = ZERO TO START
        LDY     #'          ;GET ASCII SPACE FOR REPLACEMENT
        LDA     #'0         ;GET ASCII ZERO FOR COMPARISON
CHKZ    CMP     $41,X       ;IS LEADING DIGIT ZERO?
        BNE     DONE        ;NO, END REPLACEMENT PROCESS
        STY     $41,X       ;IS LEADING DIGIT ZERO?
        INX
        CPX     $40
        BNE     CHKZ        ;EXAMINE NEXT DIGIT IF ANY
DONE    BRK
```

Single quotation mark in front of a character indicates that the operand is an ASCII code.

Object Program:

Memory Address (Hex)	Memory Contents (Hex)	Instruction (Mnemonic)		
0000	A2		LDX	#0
0001	00			
0002	A0		LDY	#'
0003	20			
0004	A9		LDA	#'0
0005	30			
0006	D5	CHKZ	CMP	$41,X
0007	41			
0008	D0		BNE	DONE
0009	07			
000A	94		STY	$41,X
000B	41			
000C	E8		INX	
000D	E4		CPX	$40
000E	40			
000F	D0		BNE	CHKZ
0010	F5			
0011	00	DONE	BRK	

You will frequently want to edit decimal strings before they are printed or displayed to improve their appearance. Common editing tasks include eliminating leading zeros, justifying numbers, adding signs or other identifying markers, and rounding. Clearly, printed numbers like 0006 or $27.34382 can be confusing and annoying.

Here the loop has two exits — one if the processor finds a nonzero digit and the other if it has examined the entire string.

The instruction STY $41,X places an ASCII space character (20 hex) in a memory location that previously contained an ASCII zero. Note that STY has only a limited number of addressing modes (see Table 3-4); there are no indexing modes with Register Y, no pre-indexing, and no absolute indexing. The only indexed addressing mode is the zero-page mode with Index Register X.

All digits in the string are assumed to be ASCII; that is, the digits are 30_{16} through 39_{16} rather than the ordinary decimal 0 to 9. The conversion from decimal to ASCII is simply a matter of adding 30_{16} to the decimal digit.

You can place a single ASCII character in a 6502 assembly language program by preceding it with an apostrophe ('). You can place a string of ASCII characters in program memory by using the .TEXT (Store ASCII Text) pseudo-operation on the 6502 assembler. A delimiter character (usually /) must surround the text; the usual form is:

Label	Operation Code	Operand
EMSG	.TEXT	/ERROR/

You may have to be careful, when blanking zeros, to leave one zero in the event that all the digits are zero. How would you do this?

Note that each ASCII digit requires eight bits, as compared to four for a BCD digit. Therefore, ASCII is an expensive format in which to store or transmit numerical data.

Add Even Parity to ASCII Characters

Purpose: Add even parity to a string of 7-bit ASCII characters. The length of the string is in memory location 0040 and the string itself begins in memory location 0041. Place even parity in the most significant bit of each character by setting the most significant bit to 1 if that makes the total number of 1 bits in the word an even number.

Sample Problem:

$$
\begin{array}{llll}
& (0040) & = & 06 \\
& (0041) & = & 31 \\
& (0042) & = & 32 \\
& (0043) & = & 33 \\
& (0044) & = & 34 \\
& (0045) & = & 35 \\
& (0046) & = & 36 \\
\\
\text{Result:} & (0041) & = & B1 \\
& (0042) & = & B2 \\
& (0043) & = & 33 \\
& (0044) & = & B4 \\
& (0045) & = & 35 \\
& (0046) & = & 36 \\
\end{array}
$$

Flowchart:

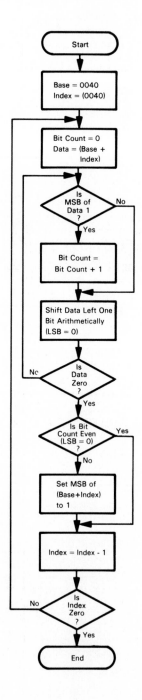

Source Program:

```
          LDX     $40            ;INDEX = MAXIMUM COUNT
GTDATA    LDY     #0             ;BIT COUNT = ZERO FOR DATA
          LDA     $40,X          ;GET DATA FROM BLOCK
CHBIT     BPL     CHKZ           ;IS NEXT DATA BIT 1?
          INY                    ;YES, ADD 1 TO BIT COUNT
CHKZ      ASL     A              ;EXAMINE NEXT BIT POSITION
          BNE     CHBIT          ;UNLESS ALL BITS ARE ZEROS
          TYA
          LSR     A              ;DID DATA HAVE EVEN NUMBER OF '1' BITS?
          BCC     NEXTE
          LDA     $40,X          ;NO, SET PARITY BIT
          ORA     #%10000000
          STA     $40,X
NEXTE     DEX
          BNE     GTDATA         ;CONTINUE THROUGH DATA BLOCK
          BRK
```

Object Program:

Memory Address (Hex)	Memory Contents (Hex)	Instruction (Mnemonic)	
0000	A6	LDX	$40
0001	40		
0002	A0	GTDATA LDY	#0
0003	00		
0004	B5	LDA	$40,X
0005	40		
0006	10	CHBIT BPL	CHKZ
0007	01		
0008	C8	INY	
0009	0A	CHKZ ASL	A
000A	D0	BNE	CHBIT
000B	FA		
000C	98	TYA	
000D	4A	LSR	A
000E	90	BCC	NEXTE
000F	06		
0010	B5	LDA	$40,X
0011	40		
0012	09	ORA	#%10000000
0013	80		
0014	95	STA	$40,X
0015	40		
0016	CA	NEXTE DEX	
0017	D0	BNE	GTDATA
0018	E9		
0019	00	BRK	

Parity is often added to ASCII characters before they are transmitted on noisy communications lines; this provides a simple error-checking facility. Parity detects all single-bit errors but does not allow for error correction; that is, you can tell by checking the parity of the data that an error has occurred, but you cannot tell which bit was received incorrectly. All that the receiver can do is request retransmission.

The procedure for calculating parity is to count the number of '1' bits in the data words. If that number is odd, the MSB of the data word is set to 1 to make the parity even.

ASL clears the least significant bit of the number being shifted. Therefore, the result of a series of ASL instructions will eventually be zero, regardless of the original value of the data (try it!). The bit counting section of the example program not only does not need a counter, but also stops examining the data as soon as all remaining bits are zeros. This procedure saves execution time in many cases.

The MSB of the data is set to '1' by logically ORing it with a pattern that has a '1' in its most significant bit and zeros elsewhere. Logically ORing a bit with one produces a result of one regardless of the original value, while logically ORing a bit with zero does not change the original value.

Pattern Match

Purpose: Compare two strings of ASCII characters to see if they are the same. The length of the strings is in memory location 0041; one string starts in memory location 0042 and the other in memory location 0052. If the two strings match, clear memory location 0040; otherwise, set memory location 0040 to FF_{16} (all ones).

Sample Problems:

a.   (0041) = 03

                    (0042) = 43 'C'
                    (0043) = 41 'A'
                    (0044) = 54 'T'

                    (0052) = 43 'C'
                    (0053) = 41 'A'
                    (0054) = 54 'T'

    Result: (0040) = 00, since the two strings are the same.

b.   (0041) = 03

                    (0042) = 52 'R'
                    (0043) = 41 'A'
                    (0044) = 54 'T'

                    (0052) = 43 'C'
                    (0053) = 41 'A'
                    (0054) = 54 'T'

    Result: (0040) = FF, since the first characters in the strings differ.

Note: The matching process ends as soon as the CPU finds a difference — the rest of the strings need not be examined.

Flowchart:

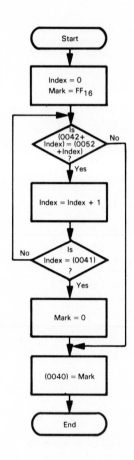

Source Program:

```
            LDX     #0          ;START WITH FIRST ELEMENT IN STRINGS
            LDY     #$FF        ;MARKER FOR NO MATCH
CHCAR       LDA     $42,X       ;GET CHARACTER FROM STRING 1
            CMP     $52,X       ;IS THERE A MATCH WITH STRING 2?
            BNE     DONE        ;NO, DONE
            INX
            CPX     $41
            BNE     CHCAR       ;CHECK NEXT PAIR IF ANY LEFT
            LDY     #0          ;IF NONE LEFT, MARK MATCH
DONE        STY     $40         ;SAVE MATCH MARKER
            BRK
```

Object Program:

Memory Address (Hex)	Memory Contents (Hex)	Instruction (Mnemonic)		
0000	A2		LDX	#0
0001	00			
0002	A0		LDY	#$FF
0003	FF			
0004	B5	CHCAR	LDA	$42,X
0005	42			
0006	D5		CMP	$52,X
0007	52			
0008	D0		BNE	DONE
0009	07			
000A	E8		INX	
000B	E4		CPX	$41
000C	41			
000D	D0		BNE	CHCAR
000E	F5			
000F	A0		LDY	#0
0010	00			
0011	84	DONE	STY	$40
0012	40			
0013	00		BRK	

Matching strings of ASCII characters is an essential part of recognizing names or commands, identifying variables or operation codes in assemblers and compilers, finding files, and many other tasks.

Index Register X is used to access both strings — only the base addresses are different. This method allows the strings to be located anywhere in memory, although we would have to use the absolute indexed addressing modes if the strings were not on page zero. We could also use the post-indexed mode (with Index Register Y) if we had two different base addresses stored somewhere on page zero.

The instruction CMP $52,X compares the Accumulator to the contents of the indexed memory location. We could replace the LDY #0 instruction with INY. Why? Compare the time and memory requirements of the two alternatives. Which version do you think is clearer? The replacement would also allow you to use a memory location for the marker rather than a register (why?).

PROBLEMS

1) Length of a Teletypewriter Message

Purpose: Determine the length of an ASCII message. All characters are 7-bit ASCII with MSB = 0. The string of characters in which the message is embedded starts in memory location 0041. The message itself starts with an ASCII STX character (02_{16}) and ends with ETX (03_{16}). Place the length of the message (the number of characters between the STX and the ETX but including neither) into memory location 0040.

Sample Problem:

$$
\begin{aligned}
(0041) &= 40 \\
(0042) &= 02 \quad \text{STX} \\
(0043) &= 47 \quad \text{'G'} \\
(0044) &= 4F \quad \text{'O'} \\
(0045) &= 03 \quad \text{ETX}
\end{aligned}
$$

Result: (0040) = 02, since there are two characters between the STX in location 0042 and ETX in location 0045.

2) Find Last Non-Blank Character

Purpose: Search a string of ASCII characters for the last non-blank character. The string starts in memory location 0042 and ends with a carriage return character ($0D_{16}$). Place the index of the last non-blank character in memory location 0040.

Sample Problems:

a.

$$
\begin{aligned}
(0042) &= 37 \quad \text{ASCII 7} \\
(0043) &= 0D \quad \text{CR}
\end{aligned}
$$

Result: (0040) = 00, since the last (and only) non-blank character is in memory location 0042.

b.

$$
\begin{aligned}
(0042) &= 41 \quad \text{'A'} \\
(0043) &= 20 \quad \text{SP} \\
(0044) &= 48 \quad \text{'H'} \\
(0045) &= 41 \quad \text{'A'} \\
(0046) &= 54 \quad \text{'T'} \\
(0047) &= 20 \quad \text{SP} \\
(0048) &= 20 \quad \text{SP} \\
(0049) &= 0D \quad \text{CR}
\end{aligned}
$$

Result: (0040) = 04

3) Truncate Decimal String to Integer Form

Purpose: Edit a string of ASCII decimal characters by replacing all digits to the right of the decimal point with ASCII blanks (20_{16}). The string starts in memory location 0041 and is assumed to consist entirely of ASCII-coded decimal digits and a possible decimal point ($2E_{16}$). The length of the string is in memory location 0040. If no decimal point appears in the string, assume that the decimal point is implicitly at the far right.

Sample Problems:

a.

	(0040)	=	04	
	(0041)	=	37	ASCII 7
	(0042)	=	2E	ASCII .
	(0043)	=	38	ASCII 8
	(0044)	=	31	ASCII 1
Result:	(0041)	=	37	ASCII 7
	(0042)	=	2E	ASCII .
	(0043)	=	20	SP
	(0044)	=	20	SP

b.

	(0040)	=	03	
	(0041)	=	36	ASCII 6
	(0042)	=	37	ASCII 7
	(0043)	=	31	ASCII 1

Result: Unchanged, as number is assumed to be 671.

4) Check Even Parity in ASCII Characters

Purpose: Check even parity in a string of ASCII characters. The length of the string is in memory location 0041, and the string itself begins in memory location 0042. If the parity of all the characters in the string is correct, clear memory location 0040; otherwise, place FF_{16} (all ones) into memory location 0040.

Sample Problems:

a.

	(0041)	=	03
	(0042)	=	B1
	(0043)	=	B2
	(0044)	=	33

Result: (0040) = 00, since all the characters have even parity.

b.

	(0041)	=	03
	(0042)	=	B1
	(0043)	=	B6
	(0044)	=	33

Result: (0040) = FF, since the character in memory location 0043 does not have even parity.

5) String Comparison

Purpose: Compare two strings of ASCII characters to see which is larger (i.e., which follows the other in alphabetical ordering). The length of the strings is in memory location 0041; one string starts in memory location 0042 and the other in memory location 0052. If the string starting in memory location 0042 is greater than or equal to the other string, clear memory location 0040; otherwise, set memory location 0040 to FF_{16} (all ones).

Sample Problems:

a.

$$(0041) = 03$$

(0042) = 43	'C'
(0043) = 41	'A'
(0044) = 54	'T'
(0052) = 42	'B'
(0053) = 51	'A'
(0054) = 54	'T'

Result: (0040) = 00, since CAT is 'larger' than BAT.

b.

$$(0041) = 03$$

(0042) = 43	'C'
(0043) = 41	'A'
(0044) = 54	'T'
(0052) = 43	'C'
(0053) = 41	'A'
(0054) = 54	'T'

Result: (0040) = 00, since the two strings are equal.

c.

$$(0041) = 03$$

(0042) = 43	'C'
(0043) = 41	'A'
(0044) = 54	'T'
(0052) = 43	'C'
(0053) = 55	'U'
(0054) = 54	'T'

Result: (0040) = FF, since CUT is 'larger' than CAT.

Chapter 7
CODE CONVERSION

Code conversion is a continual problem in most microcomputer applications. Peripherals provide data in ASCII, BCD, or various special codes. The system must convert the data into some standard form for processing. Output devices may require data in ASCII, BCD, seven-segment, or other codes. Therefore, the system must convert the results to a suitable form after the processing is completed.

There are several ways to approach code conversion:

1) **Some conversions can easily be handled by algorithms involving arithmetic or logical functions.** The program may, however, have to handle some special cases separately.

2) **More complex conversions can be handled with lookup tables.** The lookup table method requires little programming and is easy to apply. However, the table may occupy a large amount of memory if the range of input values is large.

3) **Hardware is readily available for some conversion tasks.** Typical examples are decoders for BCD to seven-segment conversion and Universal Asynchronous Receiver/Transmitters (UARTs) for conversion between parallel (ASCII) and serial (teletypewriter) formats.

In most applications, the program should do as much as possible of the code conversion work. This results in a savings in parts and board space as well as in increased reliability. Furthermore, most code conversions are easy to program and require little execution time.

EXAMPLES

Hex to ASCII

Purpose: Convert the contents of memory location 0040 to an ASCII character. Memory location 0040 contains a single hexadecimal digit (the four most significant bits are zero). Store the ASCII character in memory location 0041.

Sample Problems:

a.   (0040) = 0C

   Result: (0041) = 43   'C'

b.   (0040) = 06

   Result: (0041) = 36   '6'

Flowchart:

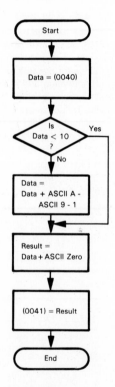

Source Program:

```
        LDA   $40        ;GET DATA
        CMP   #10        ;IS DATA LESS THAN 10?
        BCC   ASCZ
        ADC   #'A-'9-2   ;NO, ADD OFFSET FOR LETTERS (CARRY = 1)
ASCZ    ADC   #'0        ;ADD OFFSET FOR ASCII
        STA   $41        ;STORE ASCII DIGIT
        BRK
```

Object Program:

Memory Address (Hex)	Memory Contents (Hex)		Instruction (Mnemonic)	
0000	A5		LDA	$40
0001	40			
0002	C9		CMP	#10
0003	0A			
0004	90		BCC	ASCZ
0005	02			
0006	69		ADC	#'A-'9-2
0007	06			
0008	69	ASCZ	ADC	#'0
0009	30			
000A	85		STA	$41
000B	41			
000C	00		BRK	

The basic idea of this program is to add ASCII zero (30_{16}) to all the hexadecimal digits. This addition converts the decimal digits to ASCII correctly; however, there is a break between ASCII 9 (39_{16}) and ASCII A (41_{16}) which must be considered. This break must be added to the non-decimal digits A, B, C, D, E, and F. The first ADC instruction accomplishes this by adding the offset 'A-'9-2 to the contents of the Accumulator. Can you explain why the offset is 'A-'9-2?

The problem here is that the letters do not follow immediately after the decimal digits in ASCII. There is a gap occupied by the ASCII codes for such characters as : ($3A_{16}$), = ($3D_{16}$), and @ (40_{16}). To bridge this gap, we must add a constant factor determined by the distance between the actual value of ASCII A (41_{16}) and the value it would have if there were no gap ($3A_{16}$). There is also an extra factor of 1 provided by the Carry flag. You can compare this situation to the problem of walking from one address to another on a street that is divided into two discontinuous sections by a canyon or a river.

Remember that the ADC instruction always adds in the Carry bit. After the BCC instruction, we know that the Carry contains one (otherwise a branch would have occurred). So we simply reduce the additive factor by 1 to account for the Carry. As for the second ADC instruction, the Carry will be zero if the program branched after the CMP instruction (since the BCC instruction was used) or if the Accumulator contained a valid hexadecimal digit (10 through 15) since the additive factor is only 7. Therefore, we do not have to worry about the Carry in any reasonable case.

This routine could be used in a variety of programs; for example, monitor programs must convert hexadecimal digits to ASCII in order to display the contents of memory locations in hexadecimal on an ASCII printer or CRT display.

Another (quicker) conversion method that requires no conditional jumps at all is the following program, described by Allison.[1]

```
SED                 ;MAKE ADDITIONS DECIMAL
CLC                 ;CLEAR CARRY TO START
LDA     $40         ;GET HEXADECIMAL DIGIT
ADC     #$90        ;DEVELOP EXTRA 6 AND CARRY
ADC     #$40        ;ADD IN CARRY, ASCII OFFSET
STA     $41         ;STORE ASCII DIGIT
CLD                 ;CLEAR DECIMAL MODE BEFORE ENDING
BRK
```

Try this program on some digits. Can you explain why it works? Note that you must be careful to clear the decimal mode flag when you have completed all decimal arithmetic. Otherwise, you will get decimal results in programs (including the monitor) where they are not wanted.

Decimal to Seven-Segment

Purpose: Convert the contents of memory location 0041 to a seven-segment code in memory location 0042. If memory location 0041 does not contain a single decimal digit, clear memory location 0042.

Seven-segment table: The following table can be used to convert decimal numbers to seven-segment code. The seven-segment code is organized with the most significant bit always zero followed by the code (1 = on, 0 = off) for segments g, f, e, d, c, b, and a (see Figure 7-1 for the positions of the segments). The segment names are standard but the organization that we have chosen is arbitrary. In actual applications, the hardware determines the assignment of data bits to segments.

Note that the table uses 7D for 6 rather than the alternative 7C (top bar off) to avoid confusion with lower case b, and 6F for 9 rather than 67 (bottom bar off), for no particular reason.

Digit	Code
0	3F
1	06
2	5B
3	4F
4	66
5	6D
6	7D
7	07
8	7F
9	6F

Figure 7-1. Seven-segment Arrangement

Sample Problems:

a.   (0041) = 03

    Result: (0042) = 4F

b.   (0041) = 28

    Result: (0042) = 00

Flowchart:

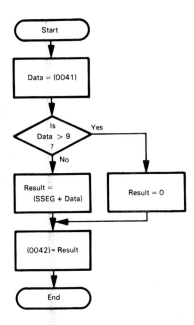

Note that the addition of base address (SSEG) and index (DATA) produces the address that contains the answer.

Source Program:

```
        LDA    #0            ;GET ERROR CODE TO BLANK DISPLAY
        LDX    $41           ;GET DATA
        CPX    #10           ;IS DATA A DECIMAL DIGIT?
        BCS    DONE          ;NO, KEEP ERROR CODE
        LDA    SSEG,X        ;YES, GET SEVEN-SEGMENT CODE FROM
                             ;  TABLE
DONE    STA    $42           ;SAVE SEVEN-SEGMENT CODE OR ERROR
                             ;  CODE

        BRK
        *=$20                ;SEVEN-SEGMENT CODE TABLE
SSEG    .BYTE  $3F,$06,$5B,$4F,$66
        .BYTE  $6D,$7D,$07,$7F,$6F
```

Object Program:

Memory Address (Hex)	Memory Contents (Hex)		Instruction (Mnemonic)	
0000	A9		LDA	#0
0001	00			
0002	A6		LDX	$41
0003	41			
0004	E0		CPX	#10
0005	0A			
0006	B0		BCS	DONE
0007	02			
0008	B5		LDA	SSEG,X
0009	20			
000A	85	DONE	STA	$42
000B	42			
000C	00		BRK	
0020	3F	SSEG	.BYTE	$3F
0021	06			$06
0022	5B			$5B
0023	4F			$4F
0024	66			$66
0025	6D		.BYTE	$6D
0026	7D			$7D
0027	07			$07
0028	7F			$7F
0029	6F			$6F

The program calculates the memory address of the desired code by adding the index (i.e., the digit to be displayed) to the base address of the seven-segment code table. This procedure is known as a table lookup. No explicit instructions are required for the addition, since it is performed automatically in the indexed addressing modes.

The assembly language pseudo-operation .BYTE (define byte-length data) places constant data in program memory. Such data may include tables, headings, error messages, priming messages, format characters, thresholds, etc. The label attached to a .BYTE pseudo-operation is assigned the value of the address into which the first byte of data is placed.

Tables are often used to perform code conversions that are more complex than the previous example. Such tables typically contain all the results organized according to the input data; e.g., the first entry is the code corresponding to the number zero.

Seven-segment displays provide recognizable forms of the decimal digits and a few letters and other characters. Calculator-type seven-segment displays are inexpensive, easy to multiplex, and use little power. However, the seven-segment coded digits are somewhat difficult to read.

The assembler simply places the data for the table in memory. Note that one .BYTE pseudo-operation can fill many memory locations. We have left some memory space between the program and the table to allow for later additions or corrections.

The table can be placed anywhere in memory, although the absolute indexed addressing mode would have to be used if it was not on page zero. We could also use post-indexing (with Index Register Y) and have the base address saved in two memory locations on page zero. The same program could then be used with any table since the base address would be specified in RAM rather than in ROM.

ASCII to Decimal

Purpose: Convert the contents of memory location 0040 from an ASCII character to a decimal digit and store the result in memory location 0041. If the contents of memory location 0040 are not the ASCII representation of a decimal digit, set the contents of memory location 0041 to FF_{16}.

Sample Problems:

a.
$$(0040) = 37 \quad (ASCII\ 7)$$
Result: $(0041) = 07$

b.
$$(0040) = 55 \quad \text{(an invalid code, since it is not an ASCII decimal digit)}$$
Result: $(0041) = FF$

Flowchart:

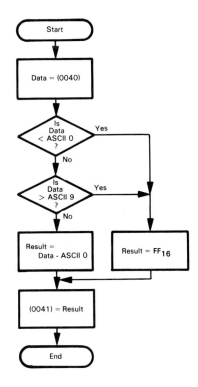

Source Program:

```
        LDX     #$FF    ;GET ERROR MESSAGE
        LDA     $40     ;GET DATA
        SEC             ;IGNORE CARRY IN SUBTRACTION
        SBC     #'0     ;IS DATA BELOW ASCII ZERO?
        BCC     DONE    ;YES, NOT A DIGIT
        CMP     #10     ;IS DATA ABOVE ASCII NINE?
        BCS     DONE    ;YES, NOT A DIGIT
        TAX             ;SAVE DIGIT IF VALID
DONE    STX     $41     ;SAVE DIGIT OR ERROR MARKER
        BRK
```

Object Program:

Memory Address (Hex)	Memory Contents (Hex)	Instruction (Mnemonic)	
0000	A2	LDX	#$FF
0001	FF		
0002	A5	LDA	$40
0003	40		
0004	38	SEC	
0005	E9	SBC	#'0
0006	30		
0007	90	BCC	DONE
0008	05		
0009	C9	CMP	#10
000A	0A		
000B	B0	BCS	DONE
000C	01		
000D	AA	TAX	
000E	86	DONE	STX	$41
000F	41		
0010	00	BRK	

This program handles ASCII-coded characters just like ordinary numbers. Note that the decimal digits and the letters form groups of consecutive codes. Strings of letters (like names) can be alphabetized by placing their ASCII representations in increasing numerical order (ASCII B = ASCII A + 1 for example).

Subtracting ASCII zero (30_{16}) from any ASCII decimal digit gives the BCD representation of that digit.

The Carry must be set before a subtraction if it is not to affect the result since SBC produces (A) = (A) - (M) - (1 - Carry) where M is the contents of the addressed memory location. Compare instructions, on the other hand, do not include the Carry in their implied subtractions.

ASCII-to-decimal conversion is necessary when decimal numbers are being entered from an ASCII device like a teletypewriter or CRT terminal.

The basic idea of the program is to determine if the character is between ASCII 0 and ASCII 9, inclusive. If so, the character is an ASCII decimal digit since the digits form a sequence. It may then be converted to decimal simply by subtracting 30_{16} (ASCII 0): e.g., ASCII 7 - ASCII 0 = 37 - 30 = 7.

Note that one comparison is done with an actual subtraction (SBC #'0) since the subraction is necessary to convert ASCII to decimal. The other comparison is done with an implied subtraction (CMP #10) since the final result is now in the Accumulator if the original number was valid.

BCD to Binary

Purpose: Convert two BCD digits in memory locations 0040 and 0041 to a binary number in memory location 0042. The most significant BCD digit is in memory location 0040.

Sample Problems:

a.
$$(0040) = 02$$
$$(0041) = 09$$

Result: $(0042) = 1D_{16} = 29_{10}$

b.
$$(0040) = 07$$
$$(0041) = 01$$

Result: $(0042) = 47_{16} = 71_{10}$

Note: We include no flowchart because the program multiplies the most significant digit by 10 simply by using the formula $10x = 8x + 2x$. Multiplying by 2 requires one arithmetic left shift and multiplying by 8 requires three such shifts.

Source Program:

```
LDA     $40         ;GET MOST SIGNIFICANT DIGIT (MSD)
ASL     A           ;MSD TIMES TWO
STA     $42         ;SAVE MSD TIMES TWO
ASL     A           ;MSD TIMES FOUR
ASL     A           ;MSD TIMES EIGHT
CLC
ADC     $42         ;MSD TIMES TEN (NO CARRY)
ADC     $41         ;ADD LEAST SIGNIFICANT DIGIT
STA     $42         ;STORE BINARY EQUIVALENT
BRK
```

Object Program:

Memory Address (Hex)	Memory Contents (Hex)	Instruction (Mnemonic)	
0000	A5	LDA	$40
0001	40		
0002	0A	ASL	A
0003	85	STA	$42
0004	42		
0005	0A	ASL	A
0006	0A	ASL	A
0007	18	CLC	
0008	65	ADC	$42
0009	42		
000A	65	ADC	$41
000B	41		
000C	85	STA	$42
000D	42		
000E	00	BRK	

BCD entries are converted to binary in order to save on storage and to simplify calculations. However, the need for conversion may offset some of the advantages of binary storage and arithmetic.

This program multiplies the BCD digit in memory location 0040 by 10 using left shifts and additions.[2] Note that ASL A multiplies the contents of the Accumulator by 2. This allows you to multiply the contents of the Accumulator by small decimal numbers in a few instructions. How would you use this procedure to multiply by 16? by 12? by 7?

BCD numbers require about 20% more storage than do binary numbers. Representing 0 to 999 requires 3 BCD digits (12 bits) and 10 bits in binary (since $2^{10} = 1024 \approx 1000$).

Convert Binary Number to ASCII String

Purpose: Convert the 8-bit binary number in memory location 0041 to eight ASCII characters (either ASCII 0 or ASCII 1) in memory locations 0042 through 0049 (the most significant bit is in 0042).

Sample Problem:

$$(0041) = D2 = 11010010$$

Result:
(0042)	=	31	ASCII 1
(0043)	=	31	ASCII 1
(0044)	=	30	ASCII 0
(0045)	=	31	ASCII 1
(0046)	=	30	ASCII 0
(0047)	=	30	ASCII 0
(0048)	=	31	ASCII 1
(0049)	=	30	ASCII 0

Flowchart:

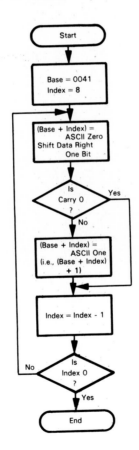

Source Program:

```
        LDA    $41        ;GET DATA
        LDX    #8         ;NUMBER OF BITS = 8
        LDY    #'0        ;GET ASCII ZERO TO STORE IN STRING
CONV    STY    $41,X      ;STORE ASCII ZERO IN STRING
        LSR    A          ;IS NEXT BIT OF DATA ZERO?
        BCC    COUNT
        INC    $41,X      ;NO, MAKE STRING ELEMENT ASCII ONE
COUNT   DEX               ;COUNT BITS
        BNE    CONV
        BRK
```

Object Program:

Memory Address (Hex)	Memory Contents (Hex)	Instruction (Mnemonic)		
0000	A5		LDA	$41
0001	41			
0002	A2		LDX	#8
0003	08			
0004	A0		LDY	#'0
0005	30			
0006	94	CONV	STY	$41,X
0007	41			
0008	4A		LSR	A
0009	90		BCC	COUNT
000A	02			
000B	F6		INC	$41,X
000C	41			
000D	CA	COUNT	DEX	
000E	D0		BNE	CONV
000F	F6			
0010	00		BRK	

The ASCII digits form a sequence so ASCII 1 = ASCII 0 + 1. The INX instruction can be used to directly increment the contents of a memory location. The savings here are that no explicit instructions are required to load the data from memory or to store the result back into memory. Nor are any of the user registers (A, X, and Y) disturbed. However, the CPU must actually load the data from memory, save it in a temporary register, increment it, and store the result back into memory. All data processing actually takes place inside the CPU.

Be careful of the difference between INX and an instruction like INC $41,X. The INC instruction adds one to the contents of Index Register X; INC $41,X adds one to the contents of the indexed memory location — it has no effect on Index Register X.

Binary-to-ASCII conversion is necessary when numbers are printed in binary form on an ASCII device.

The conversion to ASCII simply involves adding ASCII zero (30_{16}).

PROBLEMS

1) ASCII to Hex

Purpose: Convert the contents of memory location 0040 to a hexadecimal digit and store the result in memory location 0041. Assume that memory location 0040 contains the ASCII representation of a hexadecimal digit (7 bits with MSB 0).

Sample Problems:

a.
$\qquad$ (0040) = 43 ASCII C

Result: (0041) = 0C

b.
$\qquad$ (0040) = 36 ASCII 6

Result: (0041) = 06

2) Seven-Segment to Decimal

Purpose: Convert the contents of memory location 0040 from a seven-segment code to a decimal number in memory location 0041. If memory location 0040 does not contain a valid seven-segment code, set memory location 0041 to FF_{16}. Use the seven-segment table given under the Decimal to Seven-Segment example and try to match codes.

Sample Problems:

a.
$\qquad$ (0040) = 4F

Result: (0041) = 03

b.
$\qquad$ (0040) = 28

Result: (0041) = FF

3) Decimal to ASCII

Purpose: Convert the contents of memory location 0040 from a decimal digit to an ASCII character and store the result in memory location 0041. If the number in memory location 0040 is not a decimal digit, set the contents of memory location 0041 to an ASCII blank character (20_{16}).

Sample Problems:

a.
$\qquad$ (0040) = 07

Result: (0041) = 37 ASCII 7

b.
$\qquad$ (0040) = 55

Result: (0041) = 20 ASCII SPACE

4) Binary to BCD

Purpose: Convert the contents of memory location 0040 to two BCD digits in memory locations 0041 and 0042 (most significant digit in 0041). The number in memory location 0040 is unsigned and less than 100.

Sample Problems:

a.
$\qquad$ (0040) = 1D (29 decimal)

Result: (0041) = 02
(0042) = 09

b.
$\qquad$ (0040) = 47 (71 decimal)

Result: (0041) = 07
(0042) = 01

5) ASCII String to Binary Number

Purpose: Convert the eight ASCII characters in memory locations 0042 through 0049 to an 8-bit binary number in memory location 0041 (the most significant bit is in 0042). Clear memory location 0040 if all the ASCII characters are either ASCII 1 or ASCII 0 and set it to FF_{16} otherwise.

Sample Problems:

a.
	(0042)	=	31	ASCII 1
	(0043)	=	31	ASCII 1
	(0044)	=	30	ASCII 0
	(0045)	=	31	ASCII 1
	(0046)	=	30	ASCII 0
	(0047)	=	30	ASCII 0
	(0048)	=	31	ASCII 1
	(0049)	=	30	ASCII 0
Result:	(0041)	=	D2	
	(0040)	=	00	

b. same as 'a' except:

	(0045)	=	37	ASCII 7
Result:	(0040)	=	FF	

REFERENCES

1. D. R. Allison, "A Design Philosophy for Microcomputer Architectures," Computer, February 1977, pp. 35-41. This is an excellent article which we recommend highly.

2. Other BCD-to-binary conversion methods are discussed in J.A. Tabb and M.L. Roginsky, "Microprocessor Algorithms Make BCD-Binary Conversions Super-fast," EDN, January 5, 1977, pp. 46-50 and in J.B. Peatman, Microcomputer-based Design, (New York: McGraw-Hill, 1977, pp. 400-406.

Chapter 8
ARITHMETIC PROBLEMS

Most arithmetic in microprocessor applications consists of multiple-word binary or decimal manipulations. A decimal correction (decimal adjust) or some other means for performing decimal arithmetic is frequently the only arithmetic instruction provided besides basic addition and subtraction. You must implement other arithmetic operations with sequences of instructions.

Multiple-precision binary arithmetic requires simple repetitions of the basic single-word instructions. The Carry bit transfers information between words. Add with Carry and Subtract with Carry use the information from the previous arithmetic operations. You must be careful to clear the Carry before operating on the first words (obviously there is no carry into or borrow from the least significant bits).

Decimal arithmetic is a common enough task for microprocessors that most have special instructions for this purpose. These instructions may either perform decimal operations directly or correct the results of binary operations to the proper decimal form. Decimal arithmetic is essential in such applications as point-of-sale terminals, calculators, check processors, order entry systems, and banking terminals.

You can implement multiplication and division as series of additions and subtractions respectively, much as they are done by hand. Double-word operations are necessary since a multiplication produces a result twice as long as the operands, while a division similarly contracts the length of the result. Multiplications and divisions are time-consuming when done in software because of the repeated arithmetic and shift operations that are necessary. Of course, multiplying or dividing by a power of 2 is simple because such operations can be implemented with an appropriate number of left or right arithmetic shifts.

EXAMPLES

Multiple-Precision Binary Addition

Purpose: Add two multiple-word binary numbers. The length of the numbers (in bytes) is in memory location 0040, the numbers themselves start (most significant bits first) in memory locations 0041 and 0051, respectively, and the sum replaces the number starting in memory location 0041.

Sample Problem:

$$(0040) = 04$$

$$(0041) = 2F$$
$$(0042) = 5B$$
$$(0043) = A7$$
$$(0044) = C3$$

$$(0051) = 14$$
$$(0052) = DF$$
$$(0053) = 35$$
$$(0054) = B8$$

Result:
$$(0041) = 44$$
$$(0042) = 3A$$
$$(0043) = DD$$
$$(0044) = 7B$$

that is,

```
  2F5BA7C3
+ 14DF35B8
  443ADD7B
```

Flowchart:

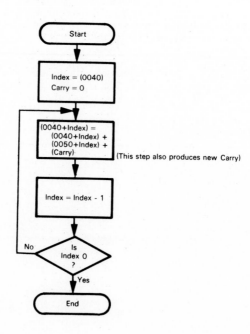

Source Program:

```
        LDX    $40      ;INDEX = LENGTH OF STRINGS
        CLC             ;CLEAR CARRY TO START
ADDW    LDA    $40,X    ;GET BYTE FROM STRING 1
        ADC    $50,X    ;ADD BYTE FROM STRING 2
        STA    $40,X    ;STORE RESULT IN STRING 1
        DEX
        BNE    ADDW     ;CONTINUE UNTIL ALL BYTES ADDED
        BRK
```

Object Program:

Memory Address (Hex)	Memory Contents (Hex)	Instruction (Mnemonic)	
0000	A6		LDX $40
0001	40		
0002	18		CLC
0003	B5	ADDW	LDA $40,X
0004	40		
0005	75		ADC $50,X
0006	50		
0007	95		STA $40,X
0008	40		
0009	CA		DEX
000A	D0		BNE ADDW
000B	F7		
000C	00		BRK

The relative address for BNE ADDW is:

$$\begin{array}{r} 0003 \\ -000C \\ \hline \end{array} = \begin{array}{r} 03 \\ +F4 \\ \hline F7 \end{array}$$

The instruction CLC is used to clear the Carry bit since there is no carry involved in the addition of the least significant bytes.

The instruction ADC, Add with Carry, includes the Carry from the previous words in the addition. ADC is the only instruction in the loop that affects the Carry. In particular, note that increment and decrement instructions (DEC, DEX, DEY, INC, INX, INY) do not affect the Carry.

This program uses the same index with two different base addresses to handle the two strings. The strings can be located anywhere in memory. Furthermore, there would be no difficulty in storing the result in a third string.

DECIMAL ACCURACY IN BINARY

This procedure can add binary numbers of any length. Note that ten binary bits correspond to three decimal digits since $2^{10} = 1024 \approx 1000$. So, you can calculate the number of bits required to give a certain accuracy in decimal digits. For example, twelve decimal digit accuracy requires:

$$12 \times \frac{10}{3} = 40 \text{ bits}$$

Decimal Addition

Purpose: Add two multi-byte decimal (BCD) numbers. The length of the numbers (in bytes) is in memory location 0040, the numbers themselves start (most significant bits first) in memory locations 0041 and 0051, respectively, and the sum replaces the number starting in memory location 0041.

Sample Problem:

$$(0040) = 04$$

$$(0041) = 36$$
$$(0042) = 70$$
$$(0043) = 19$$
$$(0044) = 85$$

$$(0051) = 12$$
$$(0052) = 66$$
$$(0053) = 34$$
$$(0054) = 59$$

Result:
$$(0041) = 49$$
$$(0042) = 36$$
$$(0043) = 54$$
$$(0044) = 44$$

that is,

```
  36701985
+ 12663459
----------
  49365444
```

Flowchart:

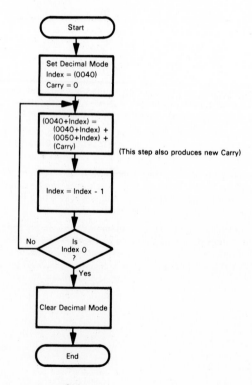

Source Program:

```
        SED             ;MAKE ALL ARITHMETIC DECIMAL
        LDX     $40     ;INDEX = LENGTH OF STRINGS
        CLC             ;CLEAR CARRY TO START
ADDW    LDA     $40,X   ;GET TWO DIGITS FROM STRING 1
        ADC     $50,X   ;ADD TWO DIGITS FROM STRING 2
        STA     $40,X   ;STORE RESULT IN STRING 1
        DEX
        BNE     ADDW    ;CONTINUE UNTIL ALL DIGITS ADDED
        CLD             ;RETURN TO BINARY MODE
        BRK
```

Object Program:

Memory Address (Hex)	Memory Contents (Hex)	Instruction (Mnemonic)		
0000	F8		SED	
0001	A6		LDX	$40
0002	40			
0003	18		CLC	
0004	B5	ADDW	LDA	$40,X
0005	40			
0006	75		ADC	$50,X
0007	50			
0008	95		STA	$40,X
0009	40			
000A	CA		DEX	
000B	D0		BNE	ADDW
000C	F7			
000D	D8		CLD	
000E	00		BRK	

The Decimal mode automatically takes care of the following situations in which binary and BCD addition differ:

```
6502
DECIMAL
MODE
```

1) The sum of two digits is between 10 and 15 inclusive. In this case, six must be added to the sum to give the right result, i.e.,

$$
\begin{array}{ll}
& 0101 \quad (5) \\
+ & 1000 \quad (8) \\
\hline
& 1101 \quad (D) \\
+ & 0110 \\
\hline
0001 & 0011 \quad (\text{BCD 13, which is correct})
\end{array}
$$

2) The sum of two digits is 16 or more. In this case, the result is a proper BCD digit but six less than it should be, i.e.,

$$
\begin{array}{ll}
& 1000 \quad (8) \\
+ & 1001 \quad (9) \\
\hline
0001 & 0001 \quad (\text{BCD 11}) \\
+ & 0110 \\
\hline
0001 & 0111 \quad (\text{BCD 17, which is correct})
\end{array}
$$

Six must be added in both situations. However, case 1 can be recognized by the fact that the sum is not a BCD digit, i.e., it is between 10 and 15 (or A and F hexadecimal). Case 2 can only be recognized by the fact that the carry from the digit addition is one since the result is a valid BCD number.

When the Decimal Mode flag is set, all arithemtic is carried out in the decimal form. This includes subtractions as well as additions, regardless of which addressing mode is employed.

However, the Increment and Decrement instructions produce binary results even when the Decimal Mode flag is set. Thus DEC, DEX, DEY, INC, INX, and INY can only be used to maintain binary counters. For example, to increment a decimal counter in memory location 0040, you must use the sequence:

```
SED                 ;MAKE ARITHMETIC DECIMAL
LDA    $40          ;GET COUNTER
CLC                 ;KEEP CARRY FROM AFFECTING ADDITION
ADC    #1           ;INCREMENT COUNTER (DECIMAL)
STA    $40
CLD                 ;RETURN TO BINARY MODE
```

The SED, CLC, and CLD instructions may not be necessary if other parts of the program set the status flags appropriately.

Subtractions in the decimal mode produce correct BCD results with the Carry being an inverted borrow. For example, if the Accumulator contains 03, the addressed memory location contains 27, and the Carry contains 1, after the execution of an SBC instruction the Accumulator will contain 76 and the Carry will be 0. As in the binary mode, a Carry of zero means that a borrow has been generated.

The Sign bit is not meaningful after additions and subtractions when the Decimal Mode flag is set. It reflects the result of the binary operation, not of the decimal operation. In the most recently mentioned situation (03-27), the Sign bit will be set (as it would be if the numbers were binary) even though the decimal result (76) has a most significant bit of zero.

This procedure can add decimal (BCD) numbers of any length. Here four binary bits are required for each decimal digit, so twelve-digit accuracy requires

ACCURACY IN BINARY AND BCD

$$12 \times 4 = 48 \text{ bits}$$

as opposed to 40 bits in the binary case. This is six 8-bit words instead of five.

The program for decimal addition is the same as that for binary addition except for the surrounding CLD and SED instructions. Thus a single sequence of instructions can produce two entirely different results depending on the value of a flag that is not even mentioned explicitly. Can you suggest some problems this might create in connecting programs written at different times or by different people?

8-6

8-Bit Binary Multiplication

Purpose: Multiply the 8-bit unsigned number in memory location 0040 by the 8-bit unsigned number in memory location 0041. Place the eight least significant bits of the result into memory location 0042 and the eight most significant bits into memory location 0043.

Sample Problems:

a.
$$
\begin{aligned}
(0040) &= 03 \\
(0041) &= 05
\end{aligned}
$$

Result:
$$
\begin{aligned}
(0042) &= 0F \\
(0043) &= 00
\end{aligned}
$$

or in decimal 3 x 5 = 15

b.
$$
\begin{aligned}
(0040) &= 6F \\
(0041) &= 61
\end{aligned}
$$

Result:
$$
\begin{aligned}
(0042) &= 0F \\
(0043) &= 2A
\end{aligned}
$$

or 111 x 97 = 10,767

You can perform multiplication on a computer in the same way that you do long multiplication by hand. Since the numbers are binary, the only problem is whether to multiply by 0 or 1; multiplying by zero obviously gives zero as a result, while multiplying by one produces the same number that you started with (the multiplicand). So, each step in a binary multiplication can be reduced to the following operation.

If the current bit in the multiplier is 1, add the multiplicand to the partial product. | **MULTIPLICATION ALGORITHM**

The only remaining problem is to ensure that you line everything up correctly each time. The following operations perform this task.

1) Shift the multiplier left one bit so that the bit to be examined is placed in the Carry.

2) Shift the product left one bit so that the next addition is lined up correctly.

The complete process for binary multiplication is as follows:

Step 1 - Initialization
   Product = 0
   Counter = 8

Step 2 - Shift Product so as to line up properly
   Product = 2 x Product (LSB = 0)

Step 3 - Shift Multiplier so bit goes to Carry
   Multiplier = 2 x Multiplier

Step 4 - Add Multiplicand to Product if Carry is 1
   If Carry = 1, Product = Product + Multiplicand

Step 5 - Decrement Counter and check for zero
   Counter = Counter - 1
   If Counter $\neq$ 0 go to Step 2

In the case of Sample Problem b. where the multiplier is 61_{16} and the multiplicand is $6F_{16}$ the process works as follows:

Initialization:

Product	0000
Multiplier	61
Multiplicand	6F
Counter	08

After first iteration of steps 2-5:

Product	0000
Multiplier	C2
Multiplicand	6F
Counter	07
Carry from Multiplier	0

After second iteration:

Product	006F
Multiplier	84
Multiplicand	6F
Counter	06
Carry from Multiplier	1

After third iteration:

Product	014D
Multiplier	08
Multiplicand	6F
Counter	05
Carry from Multiplier	1

After fourth iteration:

Product	029A
Multiplier	10
Multiplicand	6F
Counter	04
Carry from Multiplier	0

After fifth iteration:

Product	0534
Multiplier	20
Multiplicand	6F
Counter	03
Carry from Multiplier	0

After sixth iteration:

Product	0A68
Multiplier	40
Multiplicand	6F
Counter	02
Carry from Multiplier	0

After seventh iteration:

Product	14D0
Multiplier	80
Multiplicand	6F
Counter	01
Carry from Multiplier	0

After eighth iteration:

Product	2A0F
Multiplier	00
Multiplicand	6F
Counter	00
Carry from Multiplier	1

Flowchart:

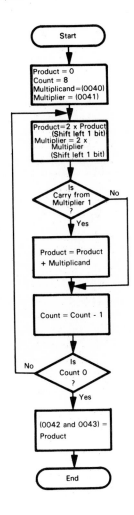

Source Program:

```
            LDA     #0          ;LSB'S OF PRODUCT = ZERO
            STA     $43         ;MSB'S OF PRODUCT = ZERO
            LDX     #8          ;NUMBER OF BITS IN MULTIPLIER = 8
SHIFT       ASL     A           ;SHIFT PRODUCT LEFT ONE BIT
            ROL     $43
            ASL     $41         ;SHIFT MULTIPLIER LEFT
            BCC     CHCNT       ;NO ADDITION IF NEXT BIT IS ZERO
            CLC                 ;ADD MULTIPLICAND TO PRODUCT
            ADC     $40
            BCC     CHCNT
            INC     $43         ;WITH CARRY IF NECESSARY
CHCNT       DEX                 ;LOOP UNTIL 8 BITS ARE MULTIPLIED
            BNE     SHIFT
            STA     $42         STORE LSB'S OF PRODUCT
            BRK
```

Object Program:

Memory Address (Hex)	Memory Contents (Hex)	Instruction (Mnemonic)		
0000	A9		LDA	#0
0001	00			
0002	85		STA	$43
0003	43			
0004	A2		LDX	#8
0005	08			
0006	0A	SHIFT	ASL	A
0007	26		ROL	$43
0008	43			
0009	06		ASL	$41
000A	41			
000B	90		BCC	CHCNT
000C	07			
000D	18		CLC	
000E	65		ADC	$40
000F	40			
0010	90		BCC	CHCNT
0011	02			
0012	E6		INC	$43
0013	43			
0014	CA	CHCNT	DEX	
0015	D0		BNE	SHIFT
0016	EF			
0017	85		STA	$42
0018	42			
0019	00		BRK	

Besides its obvious use in calculators and point-of-sale terminals, multiplication is a key part of almost all signal processing and control algorithms. The speed at which multiplications can be performed determines the usefulness of a CPU in process control, signal detection, and signal analysis.

This algorithm takes between 170 and 280 clock cycles to multiply on a 6502 microprocessor. The precise time depends on the number of 1 bits in the multiplier. Other algorithms may be able to reduce the average execution time somewhat, but 250 clock cycles will still be a typical execution time for a software multiplication. Some microprocessors (such as the 9900, 8086, and Z8000) have hardware multiplication instructions that are somewhat faster but maximum speed requires the addition of external hardware.

8-Bit Binary Division

Purpose: Divide the 16-bit unsigned number in memory locations 0040 and 0041 (most significant bits in 0041) by the 8-bit unsigned number in memory location 0042. The numbers are normalized so that 1) the most significant bits of both the dividend and the divisor are zero and 2) the number in memory location 0042 is greater than the number in memory location 0041. Thus, the quotient is an 8-bit number. Store the quotient in memory location 0043 and the remainder in location 0044.

Sample Problems:

a.
$$
\begin{aligned}
(0040) &= 40 \ (64 \ \text{decimal}) \\
(0041) &= 00 \\
(0042) &= 08
\end{aligned}
$$

$$
\begin{aligned}
\text{Result} &= (0043) = 08 \\
& (0044) = 00 \\
& \text{i.e., } 64/8 = 8
\end{aligned}
$$

b.
$$
\begin{aligned}
(0040) &= 6D \ (12,909 \ \text{decimal}) \\
(0041) &= 32 \\
(0042) &= 47 \ (71 \ \text{decimal})
\end{aligned}
$$

$$
\begin{aligned}
\text{Result} &= (0043) = B5 \ (181 \ \text{decimal}) \\
& (0044) = 3A \ (58 \ \text{decimal}) \\
& \text{i.e., } 12,909/71 = 181 \ \text{with a remainder of 58}
\end{aligned}
$$

You can perform division on the computer just like you would perform division with pen and paper, i.e., using trial subtractions. Since the numbers are binary, the only question is whether the bit

DIVISION ALGORITHM

in the quotient is 0 or 1, i.e., whether the divisor can be subtracted from what is left of the dividend. Each step in a binary division can be reduced to the following operation:

> If the divisor can be subtracted from the eight most significant bits of the dividend without a borrow, the corresponding bit in the quotient is 1; otherwise it is 0.

The only remaining problem is to line up the dividend and quotient properly. You can do this by shifting the dividend and quotient logically left one bit before each trial subtraction. The dividend and quotient can share a 16-bit register, since the procedure clears one bit of the dividend at the same time as it determines one bit of the quotient.

The complete process for binary division is:

Step 1 - Initialization:
Quotient = 0
Counter = 8

Step 2 - Shift Dividend and Quotient so as to line up properly:
Dividend = 2 × Dividend
Quotient = 2 × Quotient

Step 3 - Perform trial Subtraction. If no Borrow add 1 to Quotient:
If 8 MSBs of Dividend > Divisor then
MSBs of Dividend = MSBs of Dividend - Divisor
Quotient = Quotient + 1

Step 4 - Decrement counter and check for zero:
Counter = Counter − 1
if Counter ≠ 0, go to Step 2
Remainder = 8 MSBs of Dividend

In the case of sample problem b, where the dividend is $326D_{16}$ and the divisor is 47_{16}, the process works as follows:

Initialization:

Dividend	326D
Divisor	47
Quotient	00
Counter	00

After first iteration of Steps 2 - 4:
(Note that the dividend is shifted prior to the trial subtraction)

Dividend	1DDA
Divisor	47
Quotient	01
Counter	07

After second iteration of Steps 2 - 4:

Dividend	3BB4
Divisor	47
Quotient	02
Counter	06

After third iteration:

Dividend	3068
Divisor	47
Quotient	05
Counter	05

After fourth iteration:

Dividend	19D0
Divisor	47
Quotient	0B
Counter	04

After fifth iteration:

Dividend	33A0
Divisor	47
Quotient	16
Counter	03

After sixth iteration:

Dividend	2040
Divisor	47
Quotient	2D
Counter	02

After seventh iteration:

Dividend	4080
Divisor	47
Quotient	5A
Counter	01

After eighth iteration:

Dividend	3A00
Divisor	47
Quotient	B5
Counter	00

So the quotient is B5 and the remainder is 3A.

The MSBs of dividend and divisor are assumed to be zero; this simplifies calculations (the shift prior to the trial subtraction would otherwise place the MSB of the dividend in the Carry). Problems that are not in this form must be simplified by removing parts of the quotient that would overflow an 8-bit word. For example:

$$\frac{1024}{3} = \frac{400 \text{ (Hex)}}{3} = 100 + \frac{100 \text{ (Hex)}}{3}$$

The last problem is now in the proper form. An extra division may be necessary.

Flowchart:

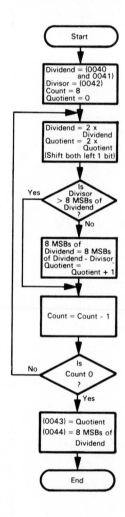

Source Program:

```
            LDX     #8        ;NUMBER OF BITS IN DIVISOR = 8
            LDA     $40       ;START WITH LSB'S OF DIVIDEND
            STA     $43
            LDA     $41       ;GET MSB'S OF DIVIDEND
DIVID       ASL     $43       ;SHIFT DIVIDEND, QUOTIENT LEFT 1 BIT
            ROL     A
            CMP     $42       ;CAN DIVISOR BE SUBTRACTED?
            BCC     CHCNT     ;NO, GO TO NEXT STEP
            SBC     $42       ;YES, SUBTRACT DIVISOR (CARRY = 1)
            INC     $43       ;AND INCREMENT QUOTIENT BY 1
CHCNT       DEX               ;LOOP UNTIL ALL 8 BITS HANDLED
            BNE     DIVID
            STA     $44       ;STORE REMAINDER
            BRK
```

Object Program:

Memory Address (Hex)	Memory Contents (Hex)	Instruction (Mnemonic)	
0000	A2	LDX	#8
0001	08		
0002	A5	LDA	$40
0003	40		
0004	85	STA	$43
0005	43		
0006	A5	LDA	$41
0007	41		
0008	06	DIVID ASL	$43
0009	43		
000A	2A	ROL	A
000B	C5	CMP	$42
000C	42		
000D	90	BCC	CHCNT
000E	04		
000F	E5	SBC	$42
0010	42		
0011	E6	INC	$43
0012	43		
0013	CA	CHCNT DEX	
0014	D0	BNE	DIVID
0015	F2		
0016	85	STA	$44
0017	44		
0018	00	BRK	

Division is used in calculators, terminals, communications error checking, control algorithms, and many other applications.

The algorithm takes between 150 and 230 microseconds to divide on a 6502 with a 1 MHz clock. The precise time depends on the number of 1 bits in the quotient. Other algorithms can reduce the average time somewhat, but 200 microseconds will still be typical for a software division.

The instructions ASL $43 and ROL A together provide a 16-bit arithmetic left shift of the dividend (MSBs in A). The ROL instruction picks up the bit which the ASL instruction left in the Carry.

An 8-bit subtraction is necessary, since there is no simple way to perform a 16-bit subtraction or comparison.

Memory location 0043 and the Accumulator hold both the dividend and the quotient (MSBs in Accumulator). The quotient simply replaces the dividend in memory location 0043 as the dividend is shifted left arithmetically.

We do not have to worry about the Carry in the SBC instruction. It must be '1' since otherwise BCC would have caused a branch. Remember that a Carry value of '1' has no effect on the result of an SBC instruction since the Carry is an inverted borrow.

The following routine offers an improvement in timing over the previous example without increasing memory usage. It also performs error checking.

```
DIV     LDX     #8      ;NUMBER OF BITS IN DIVISOR = 8
        LDA     $40     ;START WITH LSB'S OF DIVIDEND
        STA     $43
        LDA     $41     ;GET MSB'S OF DIVIDEND
        CMP     $42     ;SHOULD BE LESS THAN DIVISOR
        BCS     DONE    ;IF NOT, ERROR EXIT (CARRY = 1)
DIVID   ROL     $43     ;SHIFTDIVIDEND, QUOTIENT LEFT 1 BIT
        ROL     A       ;(AND NEW ANSWER BIT — SEE DEX BELOW)
        CMP     $42     ;CAN DIVISOR BE SUBTRACTED?
        BCC     CHCNT   ;NO, GO TO NEXT STEP (CARRY = 0)
        SBC     $42     ;YES, SUBTRACT DIVISOR (CARRY = 1)
CHCNT   DEX             ;NOTE CARRY ' NEW ANSWER BIT
        BNE     DIVID   ;LOOP UNTIL ALL 8 BITS HANDLED
        ROL     $43     ;SHIFT IN THE LAST ANSWER BIT
        STA     $44     ;STORE REMAINDER (CARRY = 0 HERE)
DONE    RTS             ;QUIT (CARRY 0, NORMAL, CARRY 1, ERROR)
```

Self-Checking Numbers
Double Add Double Mod 10

Purpose: Calculate a checksum digit from a string of BCD digits. The length of the string of digits (number of words) is in memory location 0041; the string of digits (2 BCD digits to a word) starts in memory location 0042. Calculate the checksum digit by the Double Add Double Mod 10 technique[1] and store it in memory location 0040.

The Double Add Double Mod 10 technique works as follows:

```
SELF-CHECKING
NUMBERS
```

1) Clear the checksum to start.
2) Multiply the leading digit by two and add the result to the checksum.
3) Add the next digit to the checksum.
4) Continue the alternating process until you have used all the digits.
5) The least significant digit of the checksum is the self-checking digit.

Self-checking digits are commonly added to identification numbers on credit cards, inventory tags, luggage, parcels, etc., when they are handled by computerized systems. They may also be used in routing messages, identifying files, and other applications. The purpose of the digits is to minimize entry errors such as transposing digits (69 instead of 96), shifting digits (7260 instead of 3726), missing digits by one (65 instead of 64), etc. You can check the self-checking number automatically for correctness upon entry and can eliminate many errors immediately.

The analysis of self-checking methods is quite complex. For example, a plain checksum will not find transposition errors $(4 + 9 = 9 + 4)$. The Double Add Double algorithm will find simple transposition errors $(2 \times 4 + 9 = 17 \neq 2 \times 9 + 4)$; but will miss some errors, such as transpositions across even numbers of digits (367 instead of 763). However, this method will find many common errors! The value of a method depends on what errors it will detect and on the probability of particular errors in an application.

For example, if the string of digits is

$$549321$$

the result will be:

$$\text{Checksum} = 5 \times 2 + 4 + 9 \times 2 + 3 + 2 \times 2 + 1 = 40$$
$$\text{Self-checking digit} = 0 \text{ (least significant digit of a checksum)}$$

Note that an erroneous entry like 543921 would produce a different self-checking digit (4), but erroneous entries like 049321 or 945321 would not be detected.

Sample Problems:

a.
$$
\begin{aligned}
(0041) &= 03 \\
(0042) &= 36 \\
(0043) &= 68 \\
(0044) &= 51
\end{aligned}
$$

Result: $\text{Checksum} = 3 \times 2 + 6 + 6 \times 2 + 8 + 5 \times 2 + 1 = 43$
$$(0040) = 03$$

b.
$$
\begin{aligned}
(0041) &= 04 \\
(0042) &= 50 \\
(0043) &= 29 \\
(0044) &= 16 \\
(0045) &= 83
\end{aligned}
$$

Result: $\text{Checksum} = 5 \times 2 + 0 + 2 \times 2 + 9 + 1 \times 2 + 6 + 8 \times 2 + 3 = 50$
$$(0040) = 00$$

Flowchart:

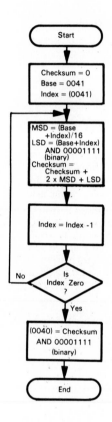

Source Program:

```
            SED                          ;MAKE ALL ARITHIMETIC DECIMAL
            LDX      $41                 ;INDEX = LENGTH OF STRING
            LDY      #0                  ;CHECKSUM = ZERO
CHKDG       LDA      $41,X               ;GET NEXT 2 DIGITS OF DATA
            LSR      A                   ;SHIFT OFF LEAST SIGNIFICANT DIGIT
            LSR      A
            LSR      A
            LSR      A
            STA      $40
            CLC                          ;CLEAR CARRY FROM SHIFTING
            ADC      $40                 ;DOUBLE MOST SIGNIFICANT DIGIT
            STY      $40                 ;DOUBLING A DIGIT NEVER PRODUCES A
                                         ;   CARRY
            ADC      $40                 ;ADD DOUBLED MSD TO CHECKSUM
            STA      $40
            LDA      $41,X               ;GET LEAST SIGNIFICANT DIGIT
            AND      #%00001111          ;(MASK OFF MSD)
            CLC                          ;ADD LSD TO CHECKSUM
            ADC      $40
            TAY
            DEX
            BNE      CHKDG               ;CONTINUE UNTIL ALL DIGITS SUMMED
            AND      #%00001111          ;SAVE LSD OF SELF-CHECKING DIGIT
            STA      $40
            CLD                          ;RETURN TO BINARY MODE
            BRK
```

Object Program:

Memory Address (Hex)	Memory Contents (Hex)	Instruction (Mnemonic)		
0000	F8		SED	
0001	A6		LDX	$41
0002	41			
0003	A0		LDY	#0
0004	00			
0005	B5	CHKDG	LDA	$41,X
0006	41			
0007	4A		LSR	A
0008	4A		LSR	A
0009	4A		LSR	A
000A	4A		LSR	A
000B	85		STA	$40
000C	40			
000D	18		CLC	
000E	65		ADC	$40
000F	40			
0010	84		STY	$40
0011	40			
0012	65		ADC	$40
0013	40			
0014	85		STA	$40
0015	40			
0016	B5		LDA	$41,X
0017	41			
0018	29		AND	#%00001111
0019	0F			
001A	18		CLC	
001B	65		ADC	$40
001C	40			
001D	A8		TAY	
001E	CA		DEX	
001F	D0		BNE	CHKDG
0020	E4			
0021	29		AND	#%00001111
0022	0F			
0023	85		STA	$40
0024	40			
0025	D8		CLD	
0026	00		BRK	

The digits are removed by shifting and masking. Four logical right shifts are needed to separate out the most significant digit.

All arithmetic is performed in the decimal mode. Remember, however, that DEX still produces a binary result.

There is no problem with the Carry from doubling a decimal digit since the result can never be larger than 18. You may be able to eliminate the final CLC instruction if the numbers to be summed are known to be too small to ever produce a Carry.

You can double a decimal number in the Accumulator by adding it to itself in the decimal mode. A typical sequence is as follows (using memory location 0040 for temporary storage):

DOUBLING AND HALVING DECIMAL NUMBERS

```
        SED                 ;MAKE ARITHMETIC DECIMAL
        STA     $40
        CLC                 ;KEEP CARRY FROM AFFECTING ADDITION
        ADC     $40         ;DOUBLE NUMBER
        CLD                 ;RETURN TO BINARY MODE
```

You may not need the SED, CLC, and CLD instructions if other parts of the program set the Carry and Decimal Mode flags appropriately. Note that you cannot use ASL A to double a decimal number because that instruction produces a binary result even if the Decimal Mode flag is set.

You divide a decimal number by 2 simply by shifting it right logically and then subtracting 3 from any digit that is 8 or larger (since 10 BCD is 16 binary). The following program divides a decimal number in memory location 0040 by 2 and places the result in memory location 0041.

```
        LDA     $40         ;GET DECIMAL NUMBER
        LSR     A           ;DIVIDE BY 2 IN BINARY
        TAX
        AND     #%00001111  ;IS LEAST SIGNIFICANT DIGIT 8 OR MORE?
        CMP     #8
        BCC     DONE
        TXA
        SBC     #3          ;YES, SUBTRACT 3 FOR DECIMAL
                            ;   CORRECTION
        TAX
DONE    STX     $41         ;STORE NUMBER DIVIDED BY 2
        BRK
```

There is no problem with the Carry in the SBC instruction since that instruction is only executed if the Carry is set. Remember that SBC subtracts off the complemented Carry (1 - C) so a Carry of 1 does not affect the result.

Try the division method by hand on the decimal numbers 28, 30, and 37. Do you understand why it works? You may also wish to try the program on the same data.

Rounding is simple regardless of whether the numbers are binary or decimal. A binary number can be rounded as follows:

BINARY ROUNDING

> If the most significant bit to be dropped is 1, add 1 to the remaining bits. Otherwise, leave the remaining bits alone.

This rule works because 1 is halfway between 0 and 10 in binary, much as 5 is halfway in decimal (note that 0.5 decimal = 0.1 binary).

So, the following program will round a 16-bit number in memory locations 0040 and 0041 (MSBs in 0041) to an 8-bit number in memory location 0041.

```
        LDA     $40         ;IS MSB OF EXTRA BYTE 1?
        BPL     DONE
        INC     $41         ;YES, ROUND MSB'S UP
DONE    BRK
```

If the number is longer than 16 bits, the rounding must ripple through all the bytes as needed. Note that we could use BIT $40 instead of LDA $40 since the BIT instruction sets the Sign flag according to the most significant bit of the addressed memory location. This approach leaves the Accumulator as it was although it does change the status flags.

Decimal rounding is a bit more difficult because the crossover point is now BCD 50 and the rounding must produce a decimal result. The rule is:

DECIMAL ROUNDING

> If the most significant digit is to be dropped
> is 5 or more, add 1 to the remaining digits.

The following program will round a 4-digit BCD number in memory locations 0040 and 0041 (MSDs in 0041) to a two-digit BCD number in memory location 0041.

```
        LDA     $40     ;IS BYTE TO BE DROPPED 50 OR MORE?
        CMP     #$50
        BCC     DONE
        SED             ;YES, ROUND MSD'S UP BY 1 IN DECIMAL
        LDA     $41
        ADC     #0      ;ADD IN CARRY (KNOWN TO BE SET)
        STA     $41
        CLD             ;RETURN TO BINARY MODE
DONE    BRK
```

Remember that you cannot use the INC instruction to add 1 because that instruction always produces a binary result. The instruction ADC #0 will add 1 to the Accumulator since the Carry must be 1 for the instruction to be executed (otherwise the BCC instruction would have forced a branch). As usual, we must be careful to set and clear the Decimal Mode flag appropriately. For longer numbers, the rounding must ripple through more significant digits as needed.

PROBLEMS

1) Multiple-Precision Binary Subtraction

Purpose: Subtract one multiple-word number from another. The length of the numbers is in memory location 0040, the numbers themselves start (most significant bits first) in memory locations 0041 and 0051, respectively, and the difference replaces the number starting in memory location 0041. Subtract the number starting in 0051 from the one starting in 0041.

Sample Problem:

$$(0040) = 04$$

$$(0041) = 2F$$
$$(0042) = 5B$$
$$(0043) = A7$$
$$(0044) = C3$$

$$(0051) = 14$$
$$(0052) = DF$$
$$(0053) = 35$$
$$(0054) = B8$$

Result:
$$(0041) = 1A$$
$$(0042) = 7C$$
$$(0043) = 72$$
$$(0044) = 0B$$

that is,
$$
\begin{array}{r}
2F5BA7C3 \\
- \ 14DF35B8 \\
\hline
1A7C720B
\end{array}
$$

2) Decimal Subtraction

Purpose: Subtract one multiple-word decimal (BCD) number from another. The length of the numbers is in memory location 0040, the numbers themselves start (most significant digits first) in memory locations 0041 and 0051, respectively, and the difference replaces the number starting in memory location 0041. Subtract the number starting in 0051 from the one starting in 0041.

Sample Problem:

$$(0040) = 04$$

$$(0041) = 36$$
$$(0042) = 70$$
$$(0043) = 19$$
$$(0044) = 85$$

$$(0051) = 12$$
$$(0052) = 66$$
$$(0053) = 34$$
$$(0054) = 59$$

Result:
$$(0041) = 24$$
$$(0042) = 03$$
$$(0043) = 85$$
$$(0044) = 26$$

that is,
$$
\begin{array}{r}
36701985 \\
- \ 12663459 \\
\hline
24038526
\end{array}
$$

3) 8-Bit by 16-Bit Binary Multiplication

Purpose: Multiply the 16-bit unsigned number in memory locations 0040 and 0041 (most significant bits in 0041) by the 8-bit unsigned number in memory location 0042. Store the result in memory locations 0043 through 0045, with the most significant bits in memory location 0045.

Sample Problems:

a.
	(0040)	=	03
	(0041)	=	00
	(0042)	=	05
Result:	(0043)	=	0F
	(0044)	=	00
	(0045)	=	00

that is,   3 x 5 = 15

b.
	(0040)	=	6F
	(0041)	=	72 (29,295 decimal)
	(0042)	=	61 (97 decimal)
Result:	(0043)	=	0F
	(0044)	=	5C
	(0045)	=	2B

that is,   29,295 x 97 = 2,841,615

4) Signed Binary Division

Purpose: Divide the 16-bit signed number in memory locations 0040 and 0041 (most significant bits in 0041) by the 8-bit signed number in memory location 0042. The numbers are normalized so that the magnitude of memory location 0042 is greater than the magnitude of memory location 0041. Store the quotient (signed) in memory location 0043 and the remainder (always positive) in memory location 0044.

Sample Problems:

a.
	(0040)	=	C0
	(0041)	=	FF (-64)
	(0042)	=	08
Result:	(0043)	=	F8 (-8) quotient
	(0044)	=	00 (0) remainder

b.
	(0040)	=	93
	(0041)	=	ED (-4717)
	(0042)	=	47 (71 decimal)
Result:	(0043)	=	BD (-67 decimal)
	(0044)	=	28 (+40 decimal)

Hint: Determine the sign of the result, perform an unsigned division, and adjust the quotient and remainder properly.

5) Self-Checking Numbers Aligned 1, 3, 7 Mod 10

Purpose: Calculate a checksum digit from a string of BCD digits. The length of the string of digits (number of words) is in memory location 0041; the string of digits (2 BCD digits to a word) starts in memory location 0042. Calculate the checksum digit by the Aligned 1, 3, 7 Mod 10 method and store it in memory location 0040.

The Aligned 1, 3, 7 Mod 10 technique works as follows:

1) Clear the checksum to start.
2) Add the leading digit to the checksum.
3) Multiply the next digit by 3 and add the result to the checksum.
4) Multiply the next digit by 7 and add the result to the checksum.
5) Continue the process (Steps 2-4) until you have used all the digits.
6) The self-checking digit is the least significant digit of the checksum.

For example, if the string of digits is:

$$549321$$

the result will be:

$$\text{Checksum} = 5 + 3 \times 4 + 7 \times 9 + 3 + 3 \times 2 + 7 \times 1 = 96$$
$$\text{Self-checking digit} = 6$$

Sample Problems:

a.
$$
\begin{aligned}
(0041) &= 03 \\
(0042) &= 36 \\
(0043) &= 68 \\
(0044) &= 51
\end{aligned}
$$

Result: $\text{Checksum} = 3 + 3 \times 6 + 7 \times 6 + 8 + 3 \times 5 + 7 \times 1 = 93$
$$(0040) = 03$$

b.
$$
\begin{aligned}
(0041) &= 04 \\
(0042) &= 50 \\
(0043) &= 29 \\
(0044) &= 16 \\
(0045) &= 83
\end{aligned}
$$

Result: $\text{Checksum} = 5 + 3 \times 0 + 7 \times 2 + 9 + 3 \times 1 + 7 \times 6 + 8$
$\qquad\qquad + 3 \times 3 = 90$
$$(0040) = 00$$

Hint: Note that $7 = 2 \times 3 + 1$ and $3 = 2 \times 1 + 1$, so the formula $M_i = 2 \times M_{i-1} + 1$ can be used to calculate the next multiplying factor.

REFERENCES

1. J. R. Herr, "Self-Checking Number Systems," Computer Design, June 1974, pp. 85-91.

2. Other methods for implementing multiplication, division, and other arithmetic tasks are discussed in:

   S. Davis, "Digital Processing Gets a Boost from Bipolar LSI Multipliers," EDN, November 5, 1978, pp. 38-43.

   A. Kolodzinski and D. Wainland, "Multiplying with a Microcomputer," Electronic Design, January 18, 1978, pp. 78-83.

   B. Parasuraman "Hardware Multiplication Techniques for Microprocessor Systems," Computer Design, April 1977, pp. 75-82.

   T. F. Tao et al., "Applications of Microprocessors in Control Problems," 1977 Joint Automatic Control Conference Proceedings, San Francisco, CA., June 22-24, 1977.

   S. Waser "State-of-the-art in High-Speed Arithmetic Integrated Circuits," Computer Design, July 1978, pp. 67-75.

   S. Waser "Dedicated Multiplier ICs Speed Up Processing in Fast Computer Systems," Electronic Design, September 13, 1978, pp. 98-103.

   S. Waser and A. Peterson, "Medium-Speed Multipliers Trim Cost, Shrink Bandwidth in Speech Transmission," Electronic Design, February 1, 1979, pp. 58-65.

   A. J. Weissberger and T. Toal, "Tough Mathematical Tasks Are Child's Play for Number Cruncher," Electronics, February 17, 1977, pp. 102-107.

Chapter 9
TABLES AND LISTS

Tables and lists are two of the basic data structures used with all computers. We have already seen tables used to perform code conversions and arithmetic. Tables may also be used to identify or respond to commands and instructions, linearize data, provide access to files or records, define the meaning of keys or switches, and choose among alternate programs. Lists are usually less structured than tables. Lists may record tasks that the processor must perform, messages or data that the processor must record, or conditions that have changed or should be monitored. Tables are a simple way of making decisions or solving problems, since no computations or logical functions are necessary. The task, then, reduces to organizing the table so that the proper entry is easy to find. Lists allow the execution of sequences of tasks, the preparation of sets of results, and the construction of interrelated data files (or data bases). Problems include how to add elements to a list and remove elements from it.

EXAMPLES

Add Entry to List

Purpose: Add the contents of memory location 0040 to a list if it is not already present in the list. The length of the list is in memory location 0041 and the list itself begins in memory location 0042.

Sample Problems:

a.
(0040)	=	6B
(0041)	=	04
(0042)	=	37
(0043)	=	61
(0044)	=	38
(0045)	=	1D

Result:
(0041)	=	05
(0046)	=	6B

The entry (6B) is added to the list, since it is not already present. The length of the list is incremented by 1.

b.
(0040)	=	6B
(0041)	=	04
(0042)	=	37
(0043)	=	6B
(0044)	=	38
(0045)	=	1D

Result: No change, since the entry (6B) is already in the list (in memory location 0043).

Flowchart:

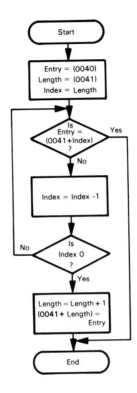

Source Program:

```
        LDA    $40       ;GET ENTRY
        LDX    $41       ;INDEX = LENGTH OF LIST
SRLST   CMP    $41,X     ;IS ENTRY = ELEMENT IN LIST?
        BEQ    DONE      ;YES, DONE
        DEX              ;NO, GO ON TO NEXT ELEMENT
        BNE    SRLST
        INC    $41       ;ADD 1 TO LIST LENGTH
        LDX    $41
        STA    $41,X     ;ADD ENTRY TO LIST
DONE    BRK
```

Object Program:

Memory Address (Hex)	Memory Contents (Hex)	Instruction (Mnemonic)		
0000	A5		LDA	$40
0001	40			
0002	A6		LDX	$41
0003	41			
0004	D5	SRLST	CMP	$41,X
0005	41			
0006	F0		BEQ	DONE
0007	09			
0008	CA		DEX	
0009	D0		BNE	SRLST
000A	F9			
000B	E6		INC	$41
000C	41			
000D	A6		LDX	$41
000E	41			
000F	95		STA	$41,X
0010	41			
0011	00	DONE	BRK	

Clearly, this method of adding elements is very inefficient if the list **HASHING**
is long. We could improve the procedure by limiting the search to
part of the list or by ordering the list. **We could limit the search by using the entry to get a starting point in the list. This method is called "hashing",** and is much like selecting a starting page in a dictionary or directory on the basis of the first letter in an entry. We could order the list by numerical value. The search could then end when the list values went beyond the entry (larger or smaller, depending on the ordering technique used). A new entry would have to be inserted properly, and all the other entries would have to be moved down in the list.

The program could be restructured to use two tables. One table could provide a starting point in the other table; for example, the search point could be based on the most or least significant 4-bit digit in the entry.

The program does not work if the length of the list is zero (what happens?). We could avoid this problem by checking the length initially. The initialization procedure would then be:

```
        LDX     $41         ;INDEX = LENGTH OF LIST
        BEQ     ADELM       ;ADD ENTRY TO LIST IF LENGTH IS ZERO
          •
          •
          •
ADELM   INC     $41         ;ADD 1 TO LIST LENGTH
```

Unlike many other processors, the 6502's Zero flag is affected by Load instructions.

If each entry were longer than one word, a pattern-matching program would be necessary. The program would have to proceed to the next entry if a match failed; that is, skip over the last part of the current entry once a mismatch was found.

Check an Ordered List

Purpose: Check the contents of memory location 0041 to see if that value is in an ordered list. The length of the list is in memory location 0042; the list itself begins in memory location 0043 and consists of unsigned binary numbers in increasing order. If the contents of location 0041 are in the list, clear memory location 0040; otherwise, set memory location 0040 to FF_{16}.

Sample Problems:

a.
$$
\begin{aligned}
(0041) &= 6B \\
(0042) &= 04 \\
(0043) &= 37 \\
(0044) &= 55 \\
(0045) &= 7D \\
(0046) &= A1
\end{aligned}
$$

Result: (0040) = FF, since 6B is not in the list.

b.
$$
\begin{aligned}
(0041) &= 6B \\
(0042) &= 04 \\
(0043) &= 37 \\
(0044) &= 55 \\
(0045) &= 6B \\
(0046) &= A1
\end{aligned}
$$

Result: (0040) = 00, since 6B is in the list.

Flowchart:

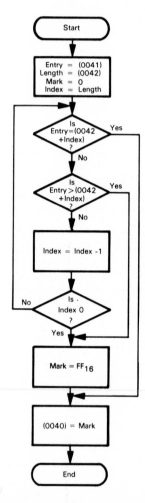

The searching process is a bit different here since the elements are ordered. Once we find an element smaller than the entry (remember that we are moving backward through the list in the usual 6502 fashion), the search is over, since subsequent elements will be even smaller. You may want to try an example to convince yourself that the procedure works. Note that an element smaller than the entry is indicated by a comparison that does not produce a borrow (that is, Carry = 1).

As in the previous problem, a table or other method that could choose a good starting point would speed up the search. **One method would be to start in the middle and determine which half of the list the entry was in, then divide the half into halves, etc. This method is called a binary search, since it divides the remaining part of the list in half each time.**[1]

SEARCHING METHODS

Source Program:

```
        LDA     $41         ;GET ENTRY
        LDX     $42         ;INDEX = LENGTH OF LIST
        LDY     #0          ;MARK = ZERO FOR ELEMENT IN LIST
SRLST   CMP     $42,X       ;IS ENTRY EQUAL TO ELEMENT?
        BEQ     DONE        ;YES, SEARCH COMPLETED
        BCS     NOTIN       ;ENTRY NOT IN LIST IF GREATER THAN ELEMENT
        DEX
        BNE     SRLST
NOTIN   LDY     #$FF        ;MARK = FF FOR NOT IN LIST
DONE    STY     $40         ;SAVE MARK
        BRK
```

Object Program:

Memory Address (Hex)	Memory Contents (Hex)	Instruction (Mnemonic)	
0000	A5	LDA	$41
0001	41		
0002	A6	LDX	$42
0003	42		
0004	A0	LDY	#0
0005	00		
0006	D5	SRLST CMP	$42,X
0007	42		
0008	F0	BEQ	DONE
0009	07		
000A	B0	BCS	NOTIN
000B	03		
000C	CA	DEX	
000D	D0	BNE	SRLST
000E	F7		
000F	A0	NOTIN LDY	#$FF
0010	FF		
0011	84	DONE STY	$40
0012	40		
0013	00	BRK	

This algorithm is a bit slower than the one in the example given under "Add Entry to List" because of the extra conditional jump (BCS NOTIN). The average execution time for this simple search technique increases linearly with the length of the list while the average execution time for a binary search increases logarithmically. For example, if the length of the list is doubled, the simple technique takes twice as long on the average while the binary search method only requires one extra iteration.

Remove Element from Queue

Purpose: Memory locations 0042 and 0043 contain the address of the head of the queue (MSBs in 0043). Place the address of the first element (head) of a queue into memory locations 0040 and 0041 (MSBs in 0041) and update the queue to remove the element. Each element in the queue is two bytes long and contains the address of the next two-byte element in the queue. The last element in the queue contains zero to indicate that there is no next element.

Queues are used to store data in the order in which it will be used, or tasks in the order in which they will be executed. The queue is a first-in, first-out data structure; i.e., elements are removed from the queue in the same order in which they were entered. Operating systems place tasks in queues so that they will be executed in the proper order. I/O drivers transfer data to or from queues so that it will be transmitted or handled in the proper order. Buffers may be queued so that the next available one can easily be found and those that are released can easily be added to the available storage. Queues may also be used to link requests for storage, timing, or I/O so that they can be satisfied in the correct order.

In real applications, each element in the queue will typically contain a large amount of information or storage space besides the address required to link the element to the next one.

Sample Problems:

a.

$$(0042) = 46 \atop (0043) = 00 \} \text{ address of first element in queue}$$

$$(0046) = 4D \atop (0047) = 00 \} \text{ address of second element in queue}$$

$$(004D) = 00 \atop (004E) = 00 \} \text{ end of queue}$$

Result:

$$(0040) = 46 \atop (0041) = 00 \} \text{ address of element removed from queue}$$

$$(0042) = 4D \atop (0043) = 00 \} \text{ address of new first element in queue}$$

b.

$$(0042) = 00 \atop (0043) = 00 \} \text{ empty queue}$$

Result:

$$(0040) = 00 \atop (0041) = 00 \} \text{ no element available from queue}$$

Flowchart:

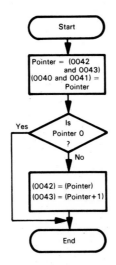

Source Program:

```
        LDA    $42        ;REMOVE HEAD OF QUEUE
        STA    $40
        LDA    $43
        STA    $41
        ORA    $42        ;IS QUEUE EMPTY?
        BEQ    DONE       ;YES, DONE
        LDY    #0         ;NO, MOVE NEXT ELEMENT TO HEAD OF QUEUE
        LDA    ($40),Y
        STA    $42
        INY
        LDA    ($40),Y
        STA    $43
DONE    BRK
```

Object Program:

Memory Address (Hex)	Memory Contents (Hex)	Instruction (Mnemonic)	
0000	A5	LDA	$42
0001	42		
0002	85	STA	$40
0003	40		
0004	A5	LDA	$43
0005	43		
0006	85	STA	$41
0007	41		
0008	05	ORA	$42
0009	42		
000A	F0	BEQ	DONE
000B	0B		
000C	A0	LDY	#0
000D	00		
000E	B1	LDA	($40),Y
000F	40		
0010	85	STA	$42
0011	42		
0012	C8	INY	
0013	B1	LDA	($40),Y
0014	40		
0015	85	STA	$43
0016	43		
0017	00	DONE BRK	

Queuing can handle lists that are not in sequential memory locations. Each element in the queue must contain the address of the next element. Such lists allow you to handle data or tasks in the proper order, change variables, or fill in definitions in a program. Extra storage is required but elements can easily be added to the queue or deleted from it.

Post-indexing, or indirect indexed addressing, is very handy here since it allows us to use the contents of memory locations 0040 and 0041 as a pointer. Those locations contain the address of the head of the queue which, in turn, contains the address of the next element. The memory locations in which the address of the element is stored must be on page zero, since they are used with the post-indexed addressing mode. All other addresses can be anywhere in memory. The post-indexed mode could also be used later to transfer data to or from the element that has just been removed from the queue.

Remember that post-indexing is only available for addresses on page zero. Furthermore, only Index Register Y can be used in this mode.

Note the use of the sequence

```
LDA    $43
ORA    $42
```

to determine if the 16-bit number in memory locations 0042 and 0043 is zero. Try to devise some other sequences that could handle this problem — it obviously occurs whenever you use a 16-bit counter rather than the 8-bit counter that we have used in most of the examples.

One problem with the 6502 instruction set is that there are no instructions that specifically move 16-bit addresses (or data) from one place to another or that perform other 16-bit operations. Of course, such instructions would have to operate eight bits at a time, but some instruction fetch and decode cycles could be saved. Most other microprocessors have such instructions.

It may be useful to maintain pointers to both ends of the queue rather than just to its head.[2,3] The data structure may then be used in either a first-in, first-out manner or in a last-in, first-out manner, depending on whether new elements are added to the head or to the tail. How would you change the example program so that memory locations 0044 and 0045 contain the address of the last element (tail) of the queue?

If there are no elements in the queue, the program clears memory locations 0040 and 0041. A program that requested an element from the queue would have to check those memory locations to see if its request had been satisfied. Can you suggest other ways to provide this information?

8-Bit Sort

Purpose: Sort an array of unsigned binary numbers into descending order. The length of the array is in memory location 0040 and the array itself begins in memory location 0041.

Sample Problem:

$$
\begin{array}{rcl}
(0040) & = & 06 \\
(0041) & = & 2A \\
(0042) & = & B5 \\
(0043) & = & 60 \\
(0044) & = & 3F \\
(0045) & = & D1 \\
(0046) & = & 19
\end{array}
$$

Result:
$$
\begin{array}{rcl}
(0041) & = & D1 \\
(0042) & = & B5 \\
(0043) & = & 60 \\
(0044) & = & 3F \\
(0045) & = & 2A \\
(0046) & = & 19
\end{array}
$$

A simple sorting technique works as follows:

SIMPLE
SORTING
ALGORITHM

Step 1)   Clear a flag INTER.

Step 2)   Examine each consecutive pair of numbers in the array. If any are out of order, exchange them and set INTER.

Step 3)   If INTER = 1 after the entire array has been examined, return to Step 1.

INTER will be set if any consecutive pair of numbers is out of order. Therefore, if INTER = 0 at the end of a pass through the entire array, the array is in proper order.

The technique operates as shown in the following simple case. Let us assume that we want to sort an array into descending order; the array has four elements — 12, 03, 15, 08. We will work backwards through the array in normal 6502 processing style.

1st Iteration:

Step 1)   INTER = 0

Step 2)   Final order of the array is:
15
12
03
08
since the second pair (03,15) is exchanged and so is the third pair (12,15). INTER = 1.

2nd Iteration:

Step 1)   INTER = 0

Step 2)   Final order of the array is:
15
12
08
03
since the first pair (08,03) is exchanged. INTER = 1.

3rd Iteration:

Step 1) INTER = 0

Step 2) The elements are already in order; no exchanges are necessary, and INTER remains zero.

Note that one extra iteration is always performed to ensure that the elements are in the proper order. Clearly, there is a large potential for improvement in this method and new sorting techniques are an important area of current research.[6]

Flowchart:

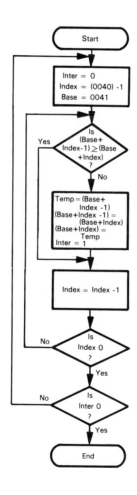

Source Program:

```
SORT    LDY     #0          ;INTERCHANGE FLAG = ZERO
        LDX     $40         ;GET LENGTH OF ARRAY
        DEX                 ;ADJUST ARRAY LENGTH TO NUMBER OF PAIRS
PASS    LDA     $40,X       ;IS PAIR OF ELEMENTS IN ORDER?
        CMP     $41,X
        BCS     COUNT       ;YES, TRY NEXT PAIR
        LDY     #1          ;NO, SET INTERCHANGE FLAG
        PHA                 ;INTERCHANGE ELEMENTS USING THE STACK
        LDA     $41,X
        STA     $40,X
        PLA
        STA     $41,X
COUNT   DEX                 ;CHECK FOR COMPLETED PASS
        BNE     PASS
        DEY                 ;WERE ALL ELEMENTS IN ORDER?
        BEQ     SORT        ;NO, GO THROUGH ARRAY AGAIN
        BRK
```

Object Program:

Memory Address (Hex)	Memory Contents (Hex)	Instruction (Mnemonic)		
0000	A0	SORT	LDY	#0
0001	00			
0002	A6		LDX	$40
0003	40			
0004	CA		DEX	
0005	B5	PASS	LDA	$40,X
0006	40			
0007	D5		CMP	$41,X
0008	41			
0009	B0		BCS	COUNT
000A	0A			
000B	A0		LDY	#1
000C	01			
000D	48		PHA	
000E	B5		LDA	$41,X
000F	41			
0010	95		STA	$40,X
0011	40			
0012	68		PLA	
0013	95		STA	$41,X
0014	41			
0015	CA	COUNT	DEX	
0016	D0		BNE	PASS
0017	ED			
0018	88		DEY	
0019	F0		BEQ	SORT
001A	E5			
001B	00		BRK	

The case where two elements in the array are equal is very important. The program should not perform an interchange in that case since that interchange would be performed in every pass. The result would be that every pass would set the Interchange flag, thus producing an endless loop. The program compares the elements in the specified order so that the Carry flag is set if the elements are already arranged correctly. Remember that comparing two equal values sets the Carry flag since that flag is an inverted borrow after subtractions or comparisons.

The 6502 Conditional Branch instructions can be limiting, and are particularly limiting in this program. Following an instruction like CMP, we have only BCC — branch if $(M) > (A)$ — and BCS — branch if $(M) \leq (A)$. The 6502 has no Branch instructions for the cases where the equality condition is on the other side, that is, $(M) \geq (A)$ and $(M) \leq (A)$. Therefore, we must be careful of the order of operations.

Before starting each sorting pass, we must be careful to reinitialize the Index and the Interchange flag.

The program must reduce the Counter by 1 initially, since the number of consecutive pairs is one less than the number of elements (the last element has no successor).

This program does not work properly if there are fewer than two elements in the array. How could you handle this degenerate case?

There are many sorting algorithms that vary widely in efficiency. References 1, 4, and 5 describe some of these.

OTHER SORTING METHODS

The Stack is easy to use for temporary storage in this program since the PHA (Push Accumulator or Store Accumulator in Stack) and PLA (Pull Accumulator or Load Accumulator from Stack) instructions are each only one byte long. The address is in the Stack Pointer (extended with 01 as its page number). If you wish, you can substitute a fixed memory location, such as 003F. The interchange then is:

```
STA     $3F        ;INTERCHANGE ELEMENTS USING TEMPORARY
                   ;  STORAGE
LDA     $41,X
STA     $40,X
LDA     $3F
STA     $41,X
```

See Chapter 10 for a further discussion of the 6502 RAM Stack.

Using an Ordered Jump Table

Purpose: Use the contents of memory location 0042 as an index to a jump table starting in memory location 0043. Each entry in the jump table contains a 16-bit
address with LSBs in the first byte. The program should transfer control to
the address with the appropriate index; that is, if the index is 6, the program should jump to address entry #6 in the table. Assume that the table
has fewer than 128 entries.

Sample Problem:

$$(0042) = 02 \quad \text{index for jump table}$$

$$\left.\begin{array}{l}(0043) = 4C \\ (0044) = 00\end{array}\right\} \text{zeroth element in jump table}$$

$$\left.\begin{array}{l}(0045) = 50 \\ (0046) = 00\end{array}\right\} \text{first element in jump table}$$

$$\left.\begin{array}{l}(0047) = 54 \\ (0048) = 00\end{array}\right\} \text{second element in jump table}$$

$$\left.\begin{array}{l}(0049) = 58 \\ (004A) = 00\end{array}\right\} \text{third element in jump table}$$

Result: (PC)   =   0054, since that is entry #2 (starting from zero) in the
jump table. The next instruction to be executed will be
the one located at that address.

Flowchart:

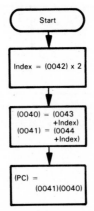

The last box results in a transfer of control to the address obtained from the table.

Source Program:

```
LDA   $42        ;GET INDEX
ASL   A          ;DOUBLE INDEX FOR 2-BYTE TABLE
TAX
LDA   $43,X      ;GET LSB'S OF JUMP ADDRESS
STA   $40
LDA   $44,X      ;GET MSB'S OF JUMP ADDRESS
STA   $41
JMP   ($40)      ;TRANSFER CONTROL TO DESTINATION
```

Object Program:

Memory Address (Hex)	Memory Contents (Hex)	Instruction (Mnemonic)	
0000	A5	LDA	$42
0001	42		
0002	0A	ASL	A
0003	AA	TAX	
0004	B5	LDA	$43,X
0005	43		
0006	85	STA	$40
0007	40		
0008	B5	LDA	$44,X
0009	44		
000A	85	STA	$41
000B	41		
000C	6C	JMP	($40)
000D	40		
000E	00		

Jump tables are very useful in situations where one of several routines must be selected for execution. Such situations arise in decoding commands (entered, for example, from a control keyboard), selecting test programs, choosing alternative methods, or selecting an I/O configuration.

The jump table replaces a series of conditional jump operations. The program that accesses the jump table could be used to access several different tables merely by using the post-indexed, or indirect indexed, addressing mode, in which the starting address of the table is placed in RAM on page zero.

The data must be multiplied by 2 to give the correct index since each entry in the jump table occupies two bytes.

The instruction JMP ($40) uses indirect addressing: the destination is the address stored at the specified location rather than the specified location itself. JMP is the only 6502 instruction that uses indirect addressing. Note that there is no page-zero mode and that the address is stored in the usual 6502 fashion with the least significant bits first.

The terminology used in describing Jump or Branch instructions is often quite confusing. A Jump instruction that is described as using direct addressing actually loads the specified address into the Program Counter; this works more like immediate addressing | **JUMP AND BRANCH TERMINOLOGY** |

than like direct addressing as applied to other instructions such as Load or Store. A Jump instruction using indirect addressing works like other instructions using direct addressing.

No ending operation (such as a BRK instruction) is necessary since JMP ($40) transfers control to the address obtained from the jump table.

References 7 and 8 contain additional examples of the use of jump tables. The program assumes that the jump table contains fewer than 128 entries (why?). How could you change the program to allow longer tables?

PROBLEMS

1) Remove an Entry From a List

Purpose: Remove the contents of memory location 0040 from a list if it is present. The length of the list is in memory location 0041 and the list itself begins in memory location 0042. Move the entries below the one removed up one position and reduce the length of the list by 1.

Sample Problems:

a.
$$(0040) = 6B \quad \text{entry to be removed from list}$$

$$(0041) = 04 \quad \text{length of list}$$

$$(0042) = 37 \quad \text{first element in list}$$
$$(0043) = 61$$
$$(0044) = 28$$
$$(0045) = 1D$$

Result: No change, since the entry is not in the list.

b.
$$(0040) = 6B \quad \text{entry to be removed from list}$$

$$(0041) = 04 \quad \text{length of list}$$

$$(0042) = 37 \quad \text{first element in list}$$
$$(0043) = 6B$$
$$(0044) = 28$$
$$(0045) = 1D$$

Result: $(0041) = 03 \quad \text{length of list reduced by 1}$

$$(0042) = 37$$
$$(0043) = 28 \quad \text{other elements in list moved up one position}$$
$$(0044) = 1D$$

The entry is removed from the list and the ones below it are moved up one position. The length of the list is reduced by 1.

2) Add an Entry to an Ordered List

Purpose: Place the contents of memory location 0040 into an ordered list if they are not already there. The length of the list is in memory location 0041. The list itself begins in memory location 0042 and consists of unsigned binary numbers in increasing order. Place the new entry in the correct position in the list, adjust the elements below it down, and increase the length of the list by 1.

Sample Problems:

a.

(0040)	= 6B	entry to be added to list
(0041)	= 04	length of list
(0042)	= 37	first element in list
(0043)	= 55	
(0044)	= 7D	
(0045)	= A1	

Result:

(0041)	= 05	length of list increased by 1
(0044)	= 6B	entry placed in list
(0045)	= 7D	other elements in the list moved down one position
(0046)	= A1	

b.

(0040)	= 6B	entry to be added to list
(0041)	= 04	length of list
(0042)	= 37	first element in list
(0043)	= 55	
(0044)	= 6B	
(0045)	= A1	

Result: No change, since the entry is already in the list.

3) Add an Element to a Queue

Purpose: Add the address in memory locations 0040 and 0041 (MSBs in 0041) to a queue. The address of the first element of the queue is in memory locations 0042 and 0043 (MSBs in 0043). Each element in the queue contains either the address of the next element in the queue or zero if there is no next element; all addresses are 16 bits long with the least significant bits in the first byte of the element. The new element goes at the end (tail) of the queue; its address will be in the element that was at the end of the queue and it will contain zero to indicate that it is now the end of the queue.

Sample Problem:

(0040)	= 4D	new element to be added to queue
(0041)	= 00	
(0042)	= 46	pointer to head of queue
(0043)	= 00	
(0046)	= 00	last element in queue
(0047)	= 00	

Result:

(0046)	= 4D	old last element points to
(0047)	= 00	new last element
(004D)	= 00	new last element in queue
(004E)	= 00	

How would you add an element to the queue if memory locations 0044 and 0045 contained the address of the tail of the queue (the last element)?

4) 16-Bit Sort

Purpose: Sort an array of unsigned 16-bit binary numbers into descending order. The length of the array is in memory location 0040 and the array itself begins in memory location 0041. Each 16-bit number is stored with the least significant bits in the first byte.

Sample Problem:

(0040)	=	03	length of list
(0041)	=	D1	LSBs of first element in list
(0042)	=	19	MSBs of first element in list
(0043)	=	60	
(0044)	=	3F	
(0045)	=	2A	
(0046)	=	B5	

Result:				
	(0041)	=	2A	LSBs of first element in sorted list
	(0042)	=	B5	MSBs of first element in sorted list
	(0043)	=	60	
	(0044)	=	3F	
	(0045)	=	D1	
	(0046)	=	19	

The numbers are B52A, 3F60, and 19D1.

5) Using a Jump Table with a Key

Purpose: Use the contents of memory location 0040 as the key to a jump table starting in memory location 0041. Each entry in the jump table contains an 8-bit key value followed by a 16-bit address (MSBs in second byte) to which the program should transfer control if the key is equal to that key value.

Sample Problem:

(0040)	=	38	key value for search
(0041)	=	32	key value for first entry
(0042)	=	4A	LSBs of jump address for first entry
(0043)	=	00	MSBs of jump address for first entry
(0044)	=	35	
(0045)	=	4E	
(0046)	=	00	
(0047)	=	38	
(0048)	=	52	
(0049)	=	00	

Result:	(PC)	=	0052, since that address corresponds to key value 38.

REFERENCES

1. D. Knuth, The Art of Computer Programming, Volume III: Sorting and Searching (Reading, Mass.: Addison-Wesley, 1978).

   D. Knuth, "Algorithms," Scientific American, April 1977, pp. 63-80.

2. K. J. Thurber and P. C. Patton, Data Structures and Computer Architecture (Lexington, Mass.: Lexington Books, 1977).

3. J. Hemenway and E. Teja, "Data Structures - Part 1," EDN, March 5, 1979, pp. 89-92.

4. B. W. Kernighan and P. J. Plauger, The Elements of Programming Style (New York: McGraw-Hill, 1978).

5. K. A. Schember and J. R. Rumsey, "Minimal Storage Sorting and Searching Techniques for RAM Applications," Computer, June 1977, pp. 92-100.

6. "Sorting 30 Times Faster with DPS," Datamation, February 1978, pp. 200-203.

7. L. A. Leventhal, "Cut Your Processor's Computation Time," Electronic Design, August 16, 1977, pp. 82-89.

8. J. B. Peatman, Microcomputer-Based Design (New York: McGraw-Hill, 1977), Chapter 7.

Chapter 10
SUBROUTINES

None of the examples that we have shown so far is typically a program all by it-self. Most real programs perform a series of tasks, many of which may be the same or may be common to several different programs. We need a way to formu-late these tasks once and make the formulations conveniently available both in different parts of the current program and in other programs.

The standard method is to write subroutines that perform par-ticular tasks. The resulting sequences of instructions can be written once, tested once, and then used repeatedly. They can
form a subroutine library that provides documented solutions to common prob-lems.

> SUBROUTINE LIBRARY

Most microprocessors have special instructions for transferring control to subroutines and restoring control to the main program. We often refer to the special instruction that transfers control to a subroutine as Call, Jump-to-Subroutine, Jump and Mark Place, or Jump and Link. The special instruction that restores control to the main pro-gram is usually called Return. On the 6502 microprocessor, the Jump-to-Subroutine (JSR) instruction saves the old value of the Program Counter in the RAM Stack before placing the starting address of the subroutine into the Program Counter; the Return-from-Subroutine (RTS) instruction gets the old value from the Stack and puts it back in the Program Counter. The effect is to transfer program control, first to the subroutine and then back to the main program. Clearly the subroutine may itself transfer control to a subroutine, and so on.

> SUBROUTINE INSTRUCTIONS

In order to be really useful, a subroutine must be general. A routine that can perform only a specialized task, such as looking for a particular letter in an input string of fixed length, will not be very useful. If, on the other hand, the subroutine can look for any let-ter in strings of any length, it will be far more helpful. We call the data or addresses that the subroutine allows to vary "parameters." An important part of writing subroutines is deciding which variables should be parameters.

One problem is transferring the parameters to the subroutine; this process is called passing parameters. The simplest method is for the main program to place the parameters into registers. Then the
subroutine can simply assume that the parameters are there. Of course, this technique is limited by the number of registers that are available. The parameters may, however, be addresses as well as data. For example, a sorting routine could begin with Index Register X containing the address on page zero at which the length of the array is lo-cated.

> PASSING PARAMETERS

The 6502 microprocessor is limited by the fact that it has no address-length (16-bit) registers in which to pass address-length parameters. However, such parameters can easily be passed by reserving locations on page zero; these loca-tions effectively act as additional registers. A further advantage of this approach is that addresses on page zero can be accessed using the post-indexed (indirect indexed) and pre-indexed (indexed indirect) addressing modes, as well as the short page-zero forms of direct and indexed addressing.

Another approach is to use the Stack. The main program can place the parameters in the Stack and the subroutine can retrieve them. The advantages of this method are that the Stack is usually fairly large (up to one page) and that data in the Stack is not lost even if the Stack is used again. The disadvantages are that few 6502 instructions use the Stack, and the Jump-to-Subroutine instruction stores the return address at the top of the Stack.

Still another approach is to assign an area of memory for parameters. The main program can place the address of the area on page zero and the subroutine can retrieve the data using the post-indexed addressing mode. However, this approach is awkward if the parameters are themselves addresses.

Sometimes a subroutine must have special characteristics. **A subroutine is relocatable if it can be placed anywhere in memory.** You can use such a subroutine easily, regardless of the placement of other programs or the arrangement of the memory. **A strictly relocatable program can use no absolute addresses; all addresses must be relative to the start of the program.** A relocating loader is necessary to place the program in memory properly; the loader will start the program after other programs and will add the starting address or relocation constant to all addresses in the program.

| RELOCATION |

A subroutine is reentrant if it can be interrupted and called by the interrupting program and still give the correct results for both the interrupting and interrupted programs. Reentrancy is important for standard subroutines in an interrupt-based system. Otherwise the interrupt service routines cannot use the standard subroutines without causing errors. Microprocessor subroutines are easy to make reentrant, since the Call instruction uses the Stack and that procedure is automatically reentrant. The only remaining requirement is that the subroutine use the registers and Stack rather than fixed memory locations for temporary storage. This is a bit awkward, but usually can be done if necessary.

| REENTRANT SUBROUTINE |

A subroutine is recursive if it calls itself. Such a subroutine clearly must also be reentrant. However, recursive subroutines are uncommon in microprocessor applications.

Most programs consist of a main program and several subroutines. This is advantageous because you can use proven routines and debug and test the other subroutines separately. You must, however, be careful to use the subroutines properly and remember their exact effects on registers, memory locations, and flags.

SUBROUTINE DOCUMENTATION

Subroutine listings must provide enough information so that users need not examine the subroutine's internal structure. Among the necessary specifications are:

| DOCUMENTING SUBROUTINES |

• A description of the purpose of the subroutine
• A list of input and output parameters
• Registers and memory locations used
• A sample case

If these guidelines are followed, the subroutine will be easy to use.

EXAMPLES

It is important to note that the following examples all reserve an area of memory for the RAM Stack. If the monitor in your microcomputer establishes such an area, you may use it instead. If you wish to try establishing your own Stack area, remember to save and restore the monitor's Stack Pointer in order to produce a proper return at the end of your main program.

To save the monitor Stack Pointer, use the instruction sequence

```
TSX
STX      TEMP
```

To restore the monitor Stack Pointer, use the sequence

```
LDX      TEMP
TXS
```

Note that the Stack Pointer can only be loaded or stored via Register X. Remember that the 6502 always keeps its Stack on page 1 of memory so that the real Stack address is 01ss, where ss is the contents of the 8-bit Stack Pointer register.

We have used address $01FF_{16}$ as the starting point for the Stack. You may have to consistently replace that address with one more suitable for your configuration. You should consult your microcomputer's User's Manual to determine the required changes.

The basic sequence for initializing the Stack Pointer is thus

```
LDX      #$FF     ;PLACE STACK AT TOP OF PAGE 1
TXS
```

Hex to ASCII

Purpose: Convert the contents of the Accumulator from a hexadecimal digit to an ASCII character. Assume that the original contents of the Accumulator form a valid hex digit.

Sample Problems:

a.   (A) = 0C

    Result: (A) = 43   ASCII C

b.   (A) = 06

    Result: (A) = 36   ASCII 6

Flowchart:

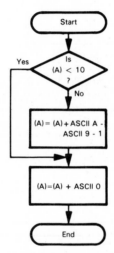

The calling program starts the Stack at memory location 01FF, gets the data from memory location 0040, calls the conversion subroutine, and stores the result in memory location 0041.

```
        *=0
        LDX     #$FF        ;PLACE STACK AT END OF PAGE 1
        TXS
        LDA     $40         ;GET HEXADECIMAL DATA
        JSR     ASDEC       ;CONVERT DATA TO ASCII
        STA     $41         ;STORE RESULT
        BRK
```

The subroutine converts the hexadecimal data to ASCII.

```
        *=$20
ASDEC   CMP     #10         ;IS DATA A DECIMAL DIGIT?
        BCC     ASCZ
        ADC     #'A-'9-2    ;NO, ADD OFFSET FOR LETTERS
ASCZ    ADC     #'0         ;CONVERT TO ASCII BY ADDING ASCII ZERO
        RTS
```

Subroutine Documentation:

```
;
;SUBROUTINE ASDEC
;
;PURPOSE: ASDEC CONVERTS A HEXADECIMAL
;   DIGIT IN THE ACCUMULATOR TO AN
;   ASCII DIGIT IN THE ACCUMULATOR
;
;INITIAL CONDITIONS: HEX DIGIT IN A
;
;FINAL CONDITIONS: ASCII CHARACTER IN A
;
;REGISTERS USED: A
;
;SAMPLE CASE
;   INITIAL CONDITIONS: 6 IN ACCUMULATOR
;   FINAL CONDITIONS: ASCII 6 (HEX 36)
;      IN ACCUMULATOR
;
```

Object Program:

Memory Address (Hex)	Memory Contents (Hex)		Instruction (Mnemonic)	
1) Calling program				
0000	A2		LDX	#$FF
0001	FF			
0002	9A		TXS	
0003	A5		LDA	$40
0004	40			
0005	20		JSR	ASDEC
0006	20			
0007	00			
0008	85		STA	$41
0009	41			
000A	00		BRK	
2) Subroutine				
0020	C9	ASDEC	CMP	#10
0021	0A			
0022	90		BCC	ASCZ
0023	02			
0024	69		ADC	#'A-'9-2
0025	06			
0026	69	ASCZ	ADC	#'0
0027	30			
0028	60		RTS	

The instructions LDX #$FF and TXS start the Stack at memory location 01FF. Remember that the Stack grows downward (toward lower addresses) and that the 6502 Stack Pointer always contains the address on page one of the next empty location (rather than the last filled one as on some other microprocessors).

The Jump-to-Subroutine instruction places the subroutine starting address (0020) in the Program Counter and saves the old Program Counter (the address of the last byte of the JSR instruction) in the Stack. The procedure is:

STEP 1 — Save MSBs of old Program Counter in Stack, decrement Stack Pointer.

STEP 2 — Save LSBs of old Program Counter in Stack, decrement Stack Pointer.

Note that the Stack Pointer is decremented after the data is stored.

The MSBs of the Program Counter are stored first, but those bits end up at the higher address (in the usual 6502 fashion) since the Stack is growing down.

The result in the example is:

$$(01FF) = 00$$
$$(01FE) = 07$$
$$(S) = FD$$

The value which the Jump-to-Subroutine instruction saves is the Program Counter before the last byte of the JSR instruction has been fetched. This value is therefore one less than the proper return address. The Return-from-Subroutine (RTS) instruction retrieves the top two entries from the Stack, adds one (because of the odd 6502 offset just mentioned), and places the result back in the Program Counter. The procedure is:

STEP 1 — Increment Stack Pointer, load eight bits from Stack, place result into LSBs of Program Counter.

STEP 2 — Increment Stack Pointer, load eight bits from Stack, place result into MSBs of Program Counter.

STEP 3 — Increment Program Counter before actually fetching an instruction.

Here the Stack Pointer is incremented before the data is loaded.

The result in the example is:

$$(PC) = (00FF)(00FE) + 1$$
$$= 0008$$
$$(S) = FF$$

This subroutine has a single parameter and produces a single result. The Accumulator is the obvious place to put both.

The calling program consists of three steps: placing the data in the Accumulator, calling the subroutine, and storing the result in memory. The overall initialization must also place the Stack in the appropriate area of memory.

The subroutine is reentrant since it uses no data memory; it is relocatable since the address ASCZ is only used in a Conditional Branch instruction with relative addressing.

Note that the Jump-to-Subroutine instruction results in the execution of four or five instructions taking 13 or 14 clock cycles. A subroutine call can take a long time even though it appears to be a single instruction in the program.

If you plan to use the Stack for passing parameters, remember that Jump-to-Subroutine saves the return address at the top of the Stack. You can move the Stack Pointer to Index Register X to get access to the data, but you must remember to provide the proper offsets. You can also gain access to the data by using two extra PLA instructions to move the Stack Pointer past the return address, but you must then remember to adjust the Stack Pointer back to its original value before returning.

Length of a String of Characters

Purpose: Determine the length of a string of ASCII characters. The starting address of the string is in memory locations 0040 and 0041. The end of the string is marked by a carriage return character (CR, $0D_{16}$). Place the length of the string (excluding carriage return) in the Accumulator.

Sample Problems:

a.
$$(0040) = 43 \quad \text{starting address of string}$$
$$(0041) = 00$$

$$(0043) = 52 \quad \text{'R'}$$
$$(0044) = 41 \quad \text{'A'}$$
$$(0045) = 54 \quad \text{'T'}$$
$$(0046) = 48 \quad \text{'H'}$$
$$(0047) = 45 \quad \text{'E'}$$
$$(0048) = 52 \quad \text{'R'}$$
$$(0049) = 0D \quad \text{CR}$$

Result: $(A) = 06$

b.
$$(0040) = 43 \quad \text{starting address of string}$$
$$(0041) = 00$$

$$(0043) = 0D$$

Result: $(A) = 00$

Flowchart:

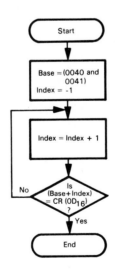

10-7

Source Program:

The calling program starts the Stack at memory location 01FF, stores the starting address of the string in memory locations 0040 and 0041, calls the string length subroutine, and stores the result in memory location 0042. Memory locations 0040 and 0041 are used as if they were extra registers.

```
        *=0
        LDX    #$FF       ;PLACE STACK AT END OF PAGE 1
        TXS
        LDA    #$43       ;SAVE STARTING ADDRESS OF STRING
        STA    $40
        LDA    #0
        STA    $41
        JSR    STLEN      ;DETERMINE LENGTH OF STRING
        STA    $42        ;STORE STRING LENGTH
        BRK
```

The subroutine determines the length of the string of ASCII characters and places the length in the Accumulator.

```
        *=$20
STLEN   LDY    #$FF       ;STRING LENGTH = -1
        LDA    #$0D       ;GET ASCII CARRIAGE RETURN TO COMPARE
CHKCR   INY               ;ADD 1 TO STRING LENGTH
        CMP    ($40),Y    ;IS NEXT CHARACTER A CARRIAGE RETURN?
        BNE    CHKCR      ;NO, KEEP LOOKING
        TYA               ;SAVE STRING LENGTH IN ACCUMULATOR
        RTS
```

Subroutine Documentation:

```
;
;SUBROUTINE STLEN
;
;PURPOSE: STLEN DETERMINES THE LENGTH OF AN ASCII STRING
;   (NUMBER OF CHARACTERS BEFORE A CARRIAGE RETURN)
;
;INITIAL CONDITIONS: STARTING ADDRESS OF STRING IN MEMORY
;   LOCATIONS 0040 AND 0041
;
;FINAL CONDITIONS: NUMBER OF CHARACTERS IN A
;
;REGISTERS USED: A, Y, ALL FLAGS EXCEPT OVERFLOW
;MEMORY LOCATIONS USED: 0040 , 0041
;
;SAMPLE CASE:
;   INITIAL CONDITIONS: 0043 IN MEMORY LOCATIONS 0040 AND 0041
;       (0043) = 35, (0044) = 46, (0045) = 0D
;   FINAL CONDITIONS: (A) = 02
;
```

Object Program:

	Memory Address (Hex)	Memory Contents (Hex)	Instruction (Mnemonic)	
1) Calling program				
	0000	A2	LDX	#$FF
	0001	FF		
	0002	9A	TXS	
	0003	A9	LDA	#$43
	0004	43		
	0005	85	STA	$40
	0006	40		
	0007	A9	LDA	#0
	0008	00		
	0009	85	STA	$41
	000A	41		
	000B	20	JSR	STLEN
	000C	20		
	000D	00		
	000E	85	STA	$42
	000F	42		
	0010	00	BRK	
2) Subroutine				
	0020	A0	STLEN LDY	#$FF
	0021	FF		
	0022	A9	LDA	#$0D
	0023	0D		
	0024	C8	CHKCR INY	
	0025	D1	CMP	($40),Y
	0026	40		
	0027	D0	BNE	CHKCR
	0028	FB		
	0029	98	TYA	
	002A	60	RTS	

The calling program consists of four steps: initializing the Stack Pointer, placing the starting address of the string in memory locations 0040 and 0041, calling the subroutine, and storing the result.

The subroutine is not reentrant, since it uses fixed memory addresses 0040 and 0041. However, if these locations are considered as extra registers and their contents are automatically saved and restored with the user registers, the subroutine can be used in a reentrant manner. Many computers of all sizes use registers that are actually located in memory; this approach makes memory management more complex but does not change the basic procedures.

The subroutine changes Index Register Y as well as the Accumulator. The programmer must be aware that data stored in Index Register Y will be lost; the subroutine documentation must describe what registers are used.

One way to preserve register contents during a subroutine is to save them in the Stack and then restore them before returning. This approach makes life easier for the user of the routine, but costs extra time and memory (in the program and in the Stack). To save and restore Index Register Y, you would have to add the sequence

```
TYA          ;SAVE OLD CONTENTS OF Y
PHA
```

to the beginning of the program and

```
PLA          ;RESTORE OLD CONTENTS OF Y
TAY
```

to the end of the program.

This subroutine has a single input parameter, which is an address. The easiest way to pass this parameter is through two memory locations on page zero. The 6502 has no address-length registers in which this parameter could be passed.

If the terminating character were not always an ASCII carriage return, we could make that character into another parameter. Now the calling program would have to place the terminating character in the Accumulator and the starting address of the string in memory locations 0040 and 0041 before calling the subroutine.

One way to pass parameters that are fixed for a particular call is to place their values in program memory immediately after the Jump-to-Subroutine instruction.[1] You can use the old Program Counter (saved at the top of the Stack) to access the data, but you must adjust the return address (increase it by the number of bytes used for parameters) before transferring control back to the main program. For example, we could pass the value of the terminating character this way. The main program would contain the pseudo-operation .BYTE'. immediately after the JSR instruction. The subroutine could place the return address in memory locations 0050 and 0051 and access the various parameters using post-indexing. The following sequence could save the return address, remembering that the Stack is always on page 1 of memory and that the Stack Pointer always contains the address of the next available location.

```
TSX                    ;GET STACK POINTER
LDA       $0101,X      ;GET MSB'S OF RETURN ADDRESS
STA       $50
LDA       $0102,X      ;GET LSB'S OF RETURN ADDRESS
STA       $51
```

Be careful of the fact that the return address is actually the address of the last (third) byte of the JSR instruction, not the address immediately after the JSR instruction as it is on most other microprocessors. The actual return address must also be offset by 1, since RTS will automatically add 1 to it.

The instructions PHA (Store Accumulator in Stack) and PLA (Load Accumulator from Stack) transfer eight bits of data between the Accumulator and the RAM Stack. Index Registers X and Y can only be saved and restored via the Accumulator. As in the Jump-to-Subroutine instruction, the Stack Pointer is decremented after data is stored in the Stack and incremented before data is loaded from it. Remember that the RAM Stack grows downward (to lower addresses).

Maximum Value

Purpose: Find the largest element in a block of unsigned binary numbers. The length of the block is in Index Register Y and the starting address of the block is in memory locations 0040 and 0041. The maximum value is returned in the Accumulator.

Sample Problem:

$$(Y) = 05 \quad \text{length of block}$$
$$(0040) = 43 \quad \text{starting address of block}$$
$$(0041) = 00$$

$$(0043) = 67$$
$$(0044) = 79$$
$$(0045) = 15$$
$$(0046) = E3$$
$$(0047) = 72$$

Result: (A) = E3, since this is the largest of five unsigned numbers

Flowchart:

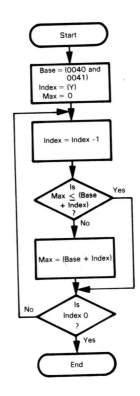

Source Program:

The calling program starts the Stack at memory location 01FF, sets the starting address of the block to 0043, gets the block length from memory location 0030, calls the maximum subroutine, and stores the maximum in memory location 0042.

```
        *=0
        LDX     #$FF        ;PLACE STACK AT END OF PAGE 1
        TXS
        LDA     #$43        ;SAVE STARTING ADDRESS OF BLOCK
        STA     $40
        LDA     #0
        STA     $41
        LDY     $30         ;GET LENGTH OF BLOCK
        JSR     MAXM        ;FIND MAXIMUM VALUE
        STA     $42         ;SAVE MAXIMUM VALUE
        BRK
```

The subroutine determines the maximum value in the block.

```
        *=$20
MAXM    LDA     #0          ;MAXIMUM = ZERO (MINIMUM POSSIBLE VALUE)
CMPE    DEY                 ;DECREMENT INDEX
        PHP                 ;SAVE STATUS
        CMP     ($40),Y     ;IS NEXT ELEMENT ABOVE MAXIMUM?
        BCS     NOCHG       ;NO, KEEP MAXIMUM
        LDA     ($40),Y     ;YES, REPLACE MAXIMUM WITH ELEMENT
NOCHG   PLP                 ;RESTORE STATUS
        BNE     CMPE        ;CONTINUE UNTIL ALL ELEMENTS EXAMINED
        RTS
```

Subroutine Documentation:

```
;
;SUBROUTINE MAXM
;
;PURPOSE: MAXM DETERMINES THE MAXIMUM VALUE IN A BLOCK
;   OF UNSIGNED BINARY NUMBERS
;
;INITIAL CONDITIONS: STARTING ADDRESS OF BLOCK IN MEMORY
;   LOCATIONS 0040 AND 0041, LENGTH OF BLOCK IN Y
;
;FINAL CONDITIONS: MAXIMUM VALUE IN A
;
;REGISTERS USED: A, Y, ALL FLAGS EXCEPT OVERFLOW
;MEMORY LOCATIONS USED: 0040, 0041
;
;SAMPLE CASE:
;   INITIAL CONDITIONS: 0043 IN MEMORY LOCATIONS 0040 AND 0041
;       (Y) = 03, (0043) = 35, (0044) = 46, (0045) = 0D
;   FINAL CONDITIONS: (A) = 46
;
```

This subroutine has two parameters — an address and a number. Memory locations 0040 and 0041 are used to pass the address, and Index Register Y is used to pass the number. The result is a single number that is returned in the Accumulator.

The calling program must place the starting address of the block in memory locations 0040 and 0041 and the length of the block in Index Register Y before transferring control to the subroutine.

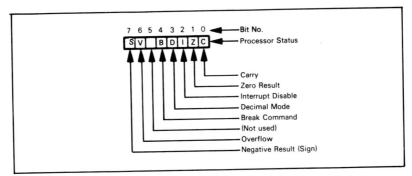

Figure 10-1. The 6502 Status Register

The subroutine returns control with zero in Index Register Y. It is not reentrant unless memory locations 0040 and 0041 are treated as extra registers. It is relocatable since the addresses are relative and the Stack is used for temporary storage.

Note the use of the instructions PHP and PLP which save and restore the Status register. This register is organized as shown in Figure 10-1. We could reorganize the program and change the initial conditions so as to eliminate the need for these instructions (see Chapter 5). The key here would be to provide the address one before the start of the array as a parameter. This is easy to do with most assemblers since they allow simple arithmetic expressions (such as START-1) in the operand field (see Chapter 3). However, the user of the subroutine must be warned that this offset is necessary.

Object Program:

Memory Address (Hex)	Memory Contents (Hex)	Instruction (Mnemonic)	
1) Calling Program			
0000	A2	LDX	#$FF
0001	FF		
0002	9A	TXS	
0003	A9	LDA	#$43
0004	43		
0005	85	STA	$40
0006	40		
0007	A9	LDA	#0
0008	00		
0009	85	STA	$41
000A	41		
000B	A4	LDY	$30
000C	30		
000D	20	JSR	MAXM
000E	20		
000F	00		
0010	85	STA	$42
0011	42		
0012	00	BRK	
2) Subroutine			
0020	A9	MAXM LDA	#0
0021	00		
0022	88	CMPE DEY	
0023	08	PHP	
0024	D1	CMP	($40),Y
0025	40		
0026	B0	BCS	NOCHG
0027	02		
0028	B1	LDA	($40),Y
0029	40		
002A	28	NOCHG PLP	
002B	D0	BNE	CMPE
002C	F5		
002D	60	RTS	

Pattern Match[2]

Purpose: Compare two strings of ASCII characters to see if they are the same. The length of the strings is in Index Register Y. The starting address of one string is in memory locations 0042 and 0043; the starting address of the other is in memory locations 0044 and 0045. If the two strings match, clear the Accumulator; otherwise, set the Accumulator to FF_{16}.

Sample Problems:

a.

$$(Y) = 03 \quad \text{length of strings}$$

$(0042) = 46$
$(0043) = 00$ } starting address of string #1

$(0044) = 50$
$(0045) = 00$ } starting address of string #2

$(0046) = 43$ 'C'
$(0047) = 41$ 'A'
$(0048) = 54$ 'T'

$(0050) = 43$ 'C'
$(0051) = 41$ 'A'
$(0052) = 54$ 'T'

Result: $(A) = 00$, since the strings are the same

b.

$$(Y) = 03 \quad \text{length of strings}$$

$(0042) = 46$
$(0043) = 00$ } starting address of string #1

$(0044) = 50$
$(0045) = 00$ } starting address of string #2

$(0046) = 52$ 'R'
$(0047) = 41$ 'A'
$(0048) = 54$ 'T'

$(0050) = 43$ 'C'
$(0051) = 41$ 'A'
$(0052) = 54$ 'T'

Result: $(A) = FF$, since the first characters differ

Flowchart:

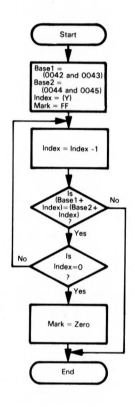

Source Program:

The calling program starts the Stack at memory location 01FF, sets the two starting addresses to 0046 and 0050 respectively, gets the string length from memory location 0041, calls the pattern match subroutine, and places the result in memory location 0040.

```
        *=0
        LDX     #$FF         ;PLACE STACK AT END OF PAGE 1
        TXS
        LDA     #$46         ;SAVE STARTING ADDRESS OF STRING 1
        STA     $42
        LDA     #0
        STA     $43
        LDA     #$50         ;SAVE STARTING ADDRESS OF STRING 2
        STA     $44
        LDA     #0
        STA     $45
        LDY     $41          ;GET LENGTH OF STRINGS
        JSR     PMTCH        ;CHECK FOR MATCH
        STA     $40          ;SAVE MATCH INDICATOR
        BRK
```

The subroutine determines if the two strings are the same.

```
        *=$20
PMTCH   LDX     #$FF         ;MARK = FF (HEX) FOR NO MATCH
CMPE    DEY
        LDA     ($42),Y      ;GET CHARACTER FROM STRING 1
        CMP     ($44),Y      ;IS THERE A MATCH WITH STRING 2?
        BNE     DONE         ;NO, DONE — STRINGS DO NOT MATCH
        TYA                  ;RESTORE STATUS FROM INDEX
        BNE     CMPE
        LDX     #0           ;MARK = ZERO, STRINGS MATCH
DONE    TXA
        RTS
```

Subroutine Documentation:

```
;
;SUBROUTINE PMTCH
;
;PURPOSE:  PMTCH DETERMINES IF TWO STRINGS MATCH
;
;INITIAL CONDITIONS: STARTING ADDRESSES OF STRINGS
;    IN MEMORY LOCATIONS 0042 AND 0043, 0044 AND 0045
;    LENGTH OF STRINGS IN INDEX REGISTER Y
;
;FINAL CONDITIONS: ZERO IN A IF STRINGS MATCH,
;    FF IN A OTHERWISE
;
;REGISTERS USED:  A, X, Y, ALL FLAGS EXCEPT OVERFLOW
;MEMORY LOCATIONS USED:  0042, 0043, 0044, 0045
;
;SAMPLE CASE:
;    INITIAL CONDITIONS:  0046 IN 0042 AND 0043, 0050
;       IN 0044 AND 0045, (Y) = 02
;       (0046) = 36, (0047) = 39
;       (0050) = 36, (0051) = 39
;    FINAL CONDITIONS:  (A) = 0 SINCE THE STRINGS MATCH
;
```

Object Program:

Memory Address (Hex)	Memory Contents (Hex)	Instruction (Mnemonic)	
1) Calling program			
0000	A2	LDX	#$FF
0001	FF		
0002	9A	TXS	
0003	A9	LDA	#$46
0004	46		
0005	85	STA	$42
0006	42		
0007	A9	LDA	#0
0008	00		
0009	85	STA	$43
000A	43		
000B	A9	LDA	#$50
000C	50		
000D	85	STA	$44
000E	44		
000F	A9	LDA	#0
0010	00		
0011	85	STA	$45
0012	45		
0013	A4	LDY	$41
0014	41		
0015	20	JSR	PMTCH
0016	20		
0017	00		
0018	85	STA	$40
0019	40		
001A	00	BRK	
2) Subroutine			
0020	A2	PMTCH LDX	#$FF
0021	FF		
0022	88	CMPE DEY	
0023	B1	LDA	($42),Y
0024	42		
0025	D1	CMP	($44),Y
0026	44		
0027	D0	BNE	DONE
0028	05		
0029	98	TYA	
002A	D0	BNE	CMPE
002B	F6		
002C	A2	LDX	#0
002D	00		
002E	8A	DONE TXA	
002F	60	RTS	

This subroutine, like the preceding ones, changes all the flags except Overflow. You should generally assume that a subroutine call changes the flags unless it is specifically stated otherwise. If the main program needs the old flag values (for later checking), it must save them in the Stack before calling the subroutine. This is accomplished with the PHP instruction.

This subroutine uses all the registers and four memory locations on page zero. There are three parameters — two starting addresses and the length of the strings.

The instruction TYA has no purpose other than to set the Zero flag according to the contents of Index Register Y. We could eliminate the need for that instruction by reorganizing the subroutine. One alternative would be to change the parameters so that the addresses were both offset by 1 (that is, both string addresses would actually refer to the byte immediately preceding the character string). Remember, however, that the user should be able to supply parameters to the subroutine in the simplest and most obvious form possible. The user should not have to offset addresses by one or make other adjustments for the convenience of the subroutine; such practices result in numerous, annoying programming errors. The program should make such rote adjustments unless time or memory constraints are critical.

Another alternative would be to decrement the index by 1 initially to avoid the problem of accessing beyond the end of the string. The end of the loop would then decrement the index and branch back as long as the result was positive, i.e.,

```
        DEY
        BPL     CMPE
```

This approach would work as long as the string was less than 130 bytes long. The limitation occurs because the 6502 Sign flag is set if the result is an unsigned number greater than 127 (decimal).

Multiple-Precision Addition

Purpose: Add two multiple-byte binary numbers. The length of the numbers (in bytes) is in Index Register Y, the starting addresses of the numbers are in memory locations 0042 and 0043 and in 0044 and 0045, and the starting address of the result is in memory locations 0046 and 0047. All the numbers begin with the most significant bits.

Sample Problem:

$$(Y) = 04 \quad \text{length of numbers in bytes}$$

$$\begin{matrix} (0042) &=& 48 \\ (0043) &=& 00 \end{matrix} \Big\} \text{ starting address of first number}$$

$$\begin{matrix} (0044) &=& 4C \\ (0045) &=& 00 \end{matrix} \Big\} \text{ starting address of second number}$$

$$\begin{matrix} (0046) &=& 50 \\ (0047) &=& 00 \end{matrix} \Big\} \text{ starting address of result}$$

(0048)	=	2F	MSBs of first number
(0049)	=	5B	
(004A)	=	A7	
(004B)	=	C3	LSBs of first number
(004C)	=	14	MSBs of second number
(004D)	=	DF	
(004E)	=	35	
(004F)	=	B8	LSBs of second number

Result:

(0050)	=	44	MSBs of result
(0051)	=	3A	
(0052)	=	DD	
(0053)	=	7B	LSBs of result

that is,

```
  2F5BA7C3
+ 14DF35B8
  443ADD7B
```

Flowchart:

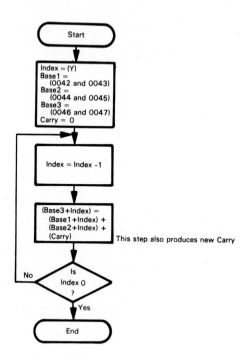

Start

Index = (Y)
Base1 =
   (0042 and 0043)
Base2 =
   (0044 and 0045)
Base3 =
   (0046 and 0047)
Carry = 0

Index = Index -1

(Base3+Index) =
   (Base1+Index) +
   (Base2+Index) +
   (Carry)   This step also produces new Carry

No   Is
   Index 0
   ?

Yes

End

Source Program:

The calling program starts the Stack at memory location 01FF, sets the starting addresses of the various numbers to 0048, 004C, and 0050, respectively, gets the length of the numbers from memory location 0040, and calls the multiple-precision addition subroutine.

```
        *=0
        LDX     #$FF        ;PLACE STACK AT END OF PAGE 1
        TXS
        LDA     #$48        ;SAVE STARTING ADDRESS OF FIRST NUMBER
        STA     $42
        LDA     #$4C        ;SAVE STARTING ADDRESS OF SECOND NUMBER
        STA     $44
        LDA     #$50        ;SAVE STARTING ADDRESS OF RESULT
        STA     $46
        LDA     #0          ;SAVE PAGE NUMBER FOR ALL ADDRESSES
        STA     $43
        STA     $45
        STA     $47
        LDY     $40         ;GET LENGTH OF NUMBERS IN BYTES
        JSR     MPADD       ;MULTIPLE-PRECISION ADDITION
        BRK
```

The subroutine performs multiple-precision binary addition.

```
            *=$20
MPADD   CLC                 ;CLEAR CARRY TO START
ADDB    DEY
        LDA     ($42),Y     ;GET BYTE FROM FIRST NUMBER
        ADC     ($44),Y     ;ADD BYTE FROM SECOND NUMBER
        STA     ($46),Y     ;STORE RESULT
        TYA                 ;ALL BYTES ADDED?
        BNE     ADDB        ;NO, CONTINUE
        RTS
```

Subroutine Documentation:

```
;
;SUBROUTINE MPADD
;
;PURPOSE: MPADD ADDS TWO MULTI-BYTE BINARY NUMBERS
;
;INITIAL CONDITIONS: STARTING ADDRESSES OF NUMBERS (MSB'S)
;   IN MEMORY LOCATIONS 0042 AND 0043, 0044 AND 0045
;   STARTING ADDRESS OF RESULT IN MEMORY LOCATIONS 0046 AND 0047
;   LENGTH OF NUMBERS IN INDEX REGISTER Y
;
;REGISTERS USED: A, Y, ALL FLAGS
;MEMORY LOCATIONS USED: 0042, 0043, 0044, 0045, 0046, 0047
;
;SAMPLE CASE:
;   INITIAL CONDITIONS: 0048 IN 0042 AND 0043,
;     004C IN 0044 AND 0045, 0050 IN 0046 AND 0047,
;     (Y) = 02, (0048) = A7, (0049) = C3, (004C) = 35, (004D) = B8
;   FINAL CONDITIONS: (0050) = DD, (0051) = 7B
;
```

Object Program:

Memory Address (Hex)	Memory Contents (Hex)		Instruction (Mnemonic)	
1) Calling program				
0000	A2		LDX	#$FF
0001	FF			
0002	9A		TXS	
0003	A9		LDA	#$48
0004	48			
0005	85		STA	$42
0006	42			
0007	A9		LDA	#$4C
0008	4C			
0009	85		STA	$44
000A	44			
000B	A9		LDA	#$50
000C	50			
000D	85		STA	$46
000E	46			
000F	A9		LDA	#0
0010	00			
0011	85		STA	$43
0012	43			
0013	85		STA	$45
0014	45			
0015	85		STA	$47
0016	47			
0017	A4		LDY	$40
0018	40			
0019	20		JSR	MPADD
001A	20			
001B	00			
001C	00		BRK	
2) Subroutine				
0020	18	MPADD	CLC	
0021	88	ADDB	DEY	
0022	B1		LDA	($42),Y
0023	42			
0024	71		ADC	($44),Y
0025	44			
0026	91		STA	($46),Y
0027	46			
0028	98		TYA	
0029	D0		BNE	ADDB
002A	F6			
002B	60		RTS	

This subroutine has four parameters — three addresses and the length of the numbers. Six memory locations on page zero and Index Register Y are used for passing parameters.

As with the previous example, we could eliminate the need for the TYA instruction by reorganizing the program or by offsetting the address parameters by 1.

PROBLEMS

Note that you are to write both a calling program for the sample problem and a properly documented subroutine.

1) ASCII to Hex

Purpose: Convert the contents of the Accumulator from the ASCII representation of a hexadecimal digit to the actual digit. Place the result in the Accumulator.

Sample Problems:

a.   (A) = 43 ASCII C

    Result: (A) = 0C

b.   (A) = 36 ASCII 6

    Result: (A) = 06

2) Length of a Teletypewriter Message

Purpose: Determine the length of an ASCII-coded teletypewriter message. The starting address of the string of characters in which the message is embedded is in memory locations 0042 and 0043. The message itself starts with an ASCII STX character (02_{16}) and ends with ASCII ETX (03_{16}). Place the length of the message (the number of characters between the STX and the ETX) in the Accumulator.

Sample Problem:

$$(0042) = 44$$
$$(0043) = 00$$
starting address of string

(0044) = 49

(0045) = 02 STX

(0046) = 47 'G'

(0047) = 4F 'O'

(0048) = 03 ETX

    Result: (A) = 02

3) Minimum Value

Purpose: Find the smallest element in a block of unsigned binary numbers. The length of the block is in Index Register Y and the starting address of the block is in memory locations 0040 and 0041. The minimum value is returned in the Accumulator.

Sample Problem:

(Y) = 05 length of block

$$(0040) = 43$$
$$(0041) = 00$$
starting address of block

(0043) = 67

(0044) = 79

(0045) = 15

(0046) = E3

(0047) = 73

    Result: (A) = 15, since this is the smallest of the five unsigned numbers

4) String Comparison

Purpose: Compare two strings of ASCII characters to see which is larger (i.e., which follows the other in "alphabetical" ordering). The length of the strings is in Index Register Y, the starting address of string 1 is in memory locations 0042 and 0043, and the starting address of string 2 is in memory locations 0044 and 0045. If string 1 is larger than or equal to string 2, clear the Accumulator; otherwise, set the Accumulator to FF_{16}.

Sample Problems:

a.

$$(Y) = 03 \quad \text{length of strings}$$

(0042) = 46 } starting address of string #1
(0043) = 00

(0044) = 4A } starting address of string #2
(0045) = 00

(0046) = 43   'C'
(0047) = 41   'A'
(0048) = 54   'T'

(004A) = 42   'B'
(004B) = 41   'A'
(004C) = 54   'T'

Result: (A) = 00, since 'CAT' is "larger" than 'BAT'

b.

$$(Y) = 03 \quad \text{length of strings}$$

(0042) = 46 } starting address of string #1
(0043) = 00

(0044) = 4A } starting address of string #2
(0045) = 00

(0046) = 43   'C'
(0047) = 41   'A'
(0048) = 54   'T'

(004A) = 43   'C'
(004B) = 41   'A'
(004C) = 54   'T'

Result: (A) = 00, since the two strings are the same

c.

$$(Y) = 03 \quad \text{length of strings}$$

(0042) = 46 } starting address of string #1
(0043) = 00

(0044) = 4A } starting address of string #2
(0045) = 00

(0046) = 43   'C'
(0047) = 41   'A'
(0048) = 54   'T'

(004A) = 43   'C'
(004B) = 55   'U'
(004C) = 54   'T'

Result: (A) = FF, since 'CUT' is "larger" than 'CAT'

5) Decimal Subtraction

Purpose: Subtract one multiple-digit decimal (BCD) number from another. The length of the numbers (in bytes) is in Index Register Y and the starting addresses of the numbers are in memory locations 0042 and 0043 and 0044 and 0045. Subtract the number with the starting address in 0044 and 0045 from the one with the starting address in 0042 and 0043. The starting address of the result is in memory locations 0046 and 0047. All the numbers begin with the most significant digits. The sign of the result is returned in the Accumulator — zero if the result is positive, FF_{16} if it is negative.

Sample Problem:

$$(Y) = 04 \quad \text{length of numbers in bytes}$$

$$\left.\begin{array}{l}(0042) = 48 \\ (0043) = 00\end{array}\right\} \text{starting address of minuend}$$

$$\left.\begin{array}{l}(0044) = 4C \\ (0045) = 00\end{array}\right\} \text{starting address of subtrahend}$$

$$\left.\begin{array}{l}(0046) = 50 \\ (0047) = 00\end{array}\right\} \text{starting address of difference}$$

$$\begin{array}{l}(0048) = 36 \quad \text{most significant digits of minuend} \\ (0049) = 70 \\ (004A) = 19 \\ (004B) = 85 \quad \text{least significant digits of minuend}\end{array}$$

$$\begin{array}{l}(004C) = 12 \quad \text{most significant digits of subtrahend} \\ (004D) = 66 \\ (004E) = 34 \\ (004F) = 59 \quad \text{least significant digits of subtrahend}\end{array}$$

Result: $(A) = 00$ positive result

$$\begin{array}{l}(0050) = 24 \quad \text{most significant digits of difference} \\ (0051) = 03 \\ (0052) = 85 \\ (0053) = 26 \quad \text{least significant digits of difference}\end{array}$$

that is,

$$\begin{array}{r} 36701985 \\ - 12663459 \\ \hline + 24038526 \end{array}$$

REFERENCES

1. Other examples of this technique (for the 8080 microprocessor) are in S. Mazor and C. Pitchford, "Develop Cooperative Microprocessor Subroutines," <u>Electronic Design</u>, June 7, 1978, pp. 116-118.

2. J. T. O'Donnell, "6502 Routine Compares Character Strings," <u>EDN</u>, August 5, 1978, p. 54.

Chapter 11
INPUT/OUTPUT

There are two problems in the design of input/output sections: one is how to interface peripherals to the computer and transfer data, status, and control signals; the other is how to address I/O devices so that the CPU can select a particular one for a data transfer. Clearly, the first problem is both more complex and more interesting. We will therefore discuss the interfacing of peripherals here and leave addressing to a more hardware-oriented book.

In theory, the transfer of data to or from an I/O device is similar to the transfer of data to or from memory. In fact, we can consider the memory as just another I/O device. The memory is, however, special for the following reasons:

I/O AND MEMORY

1) It operates at almost the same speed as the processor.

2) It uses the same type of signals as the CPU. The only circuits usually needed to interface the memory to the CPU are drivers, receivers, and level translators.

3) It requires no special formats or any control signals besides a Read/Write pulse.

4) It automatically latches data sent to it.

5) Its word length is the same as the computer's.

Most I/O devices do not have such convenient features. They may operate at speeds much slower than the processor; for example, a teletypewriter can transfer only 10 characters per second, while a slow processor can transfer 10,000 characters per second. The range of speeds is also very wide — sensors may provide one reading per minute, while video displays or floppy disks may transfer 250,000 bits per second. Furthermore, I/O devices may require continuous signals (motors or thermometers), currents rather than voltages (teletypewriters), or voltages at far different levels than the signals used by the processor (gas-discharge displays). I/O devices may also require special formats, protocols, or control signals. Their word lengths may be much shorter or much longer than the word length of the computer. These variations make the design of I/O sections difficult and mean that each peripheral presents its own special interfacing problem.

We may, however, provide a general description of devices and interfacing methods. We may roughly separate devices into three categories, based on their data rates:

I/O CATEGORIES

1) **Slow devices that change state no more than once per second.** Changing their states typically requires milliseconds or longer. Such devices include lighted displays, switches, relays, and many mechanical sensors and actuators.

2) **Medium-speed devices that transfer data at rates of 1 to 10,000 bits per second.** Such devices include keyboards, printers, card readers, paper tape readers and punches, cassettes, ordinary communications lines, and many analog data acquisition systems.

3) **High-speed devices that transfer data at rates of over 10,000 bits per second.** Such devices include magnetic tapes, magnetic disks, high-speed line printers, high-speed communications lines, and video displays.

The interfacing of slow devices is simple. Few control signals are necessary unless the devices are multiplexed, i.e.,
several are handled from one port, as shown in Figures 11-1 to

11-4. **Input data** from slow devices **need not be latched,** since it remains stable for a
long time interval. **Output data must,** of course, **be latched.** The only problems with
input are transitions that occur while the computer is reading the data. One-shots,
cross-coupled latches, or software delay routines can smooth the transitions.

A single port can handle several slow devices. Figure 11-1 shows a demultiplexer
that automatically directs the next output data to the next device by counting output
operations. Figure 11-2 shows a control port that provides select inputs to a
demultiplexer. The data outputs here can come in any order, but an additional output
instruction is necessary to change the state of the control port. Output demultiplexers
are commonly used to drive several displays from the same output port. Figures 11-3
and 11-4 show the same alternatives for an input multiplexer.

Note the differences between input and output with slow devices:

1) **Input data need not be latched,** since the input device holds the data for an enor-
    mous length of time by computer standards. Output data must be latched, since
    the output device will not respond to data that is present for only a few CPU clock
    cycles.

2) **Input transitions cause problems because of their duration; brief output tran-
    sitions cause no problems because the output devices (or the observers)
    react slowly.**

3) **The major constraints on input are reaction time and responsiveness, the ma-
    jor constraints on output are response time and observability.**

**Medium-speed devices must be synchronized in some way
to the processor clock.** The CPU cannot simply treat these
devices as if they held their data forever or could receive data
at any time. Instead, the CPU must be able to determine when

a device has new input data or is ready to receive output data. It must also have a way
of telling a device that new output data is available or that the previous input data has
been accepted. Note that the peripheral may be or contain another processor.

The standard unclocked procedure is the handshake. Here the
sender indicates the availability of data to the receiver and

transfers the data; the receiver completes the handshake by acknowledging the reception of the data. The receiver may control the situation by initially requesting the data or
by indicating its readiness to accept data; the sender then sends the data and completes the handshake by indicating that data is available. In either case, the sender
knows that the transfer has been completed successfully and the receiver knows when
new data is available.

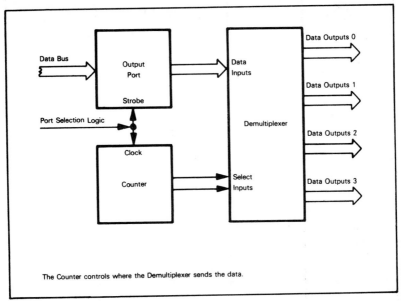

Figure 11-1. An Output Demultiplexer Controlled by a Counter

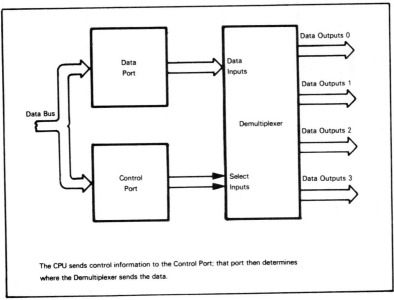

Figure 11-2. An Output Demultiplexer Controlled by a Port

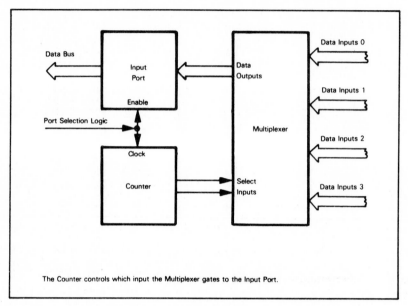

The Counter controls which input the Multiplexer gates to the Input Port.

Figure 11-3. An Input Multiplexer Controlled by a Counter

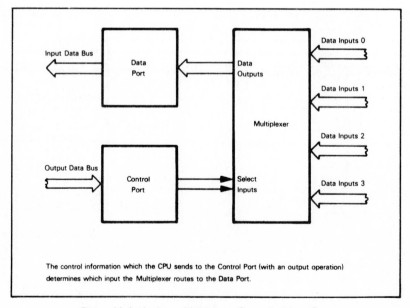

The control information which the CPU sends to the Control Port (with an output operation) determines which input the Multiplexer routes to the Data Port.

Figure 11-4. An Input Multiplexer Controlled by a Port

Figures 11-5 and 11-6 show typical input and output operations using the handshake method. **The procedure whereby the CPU checks the readiness of the peripheral before transferring data is called "polling".** Clearly, polling can occupy a large amount of processor time if there are many I/O devices. **There are several ways of providing the handshake signals.** Among these are:

- **Separate dedicated I/O lines.** The processor may handle these as additional I/O ports or through special lines or interrupts. The 6502 microprocessor does not have special serial I/O lines, but such lines are available on the 6520 Peripheral Interface Adapter (or PIA), the 6522 Versatile Interface Adapter (or VIA), and the 6532 Peripheral Interface/Memory (or Multifunction) device.

- **Special patterns on the I/O lines.** These may be single start and stop bits or entire characters or groups of characters. The patterns must be easy to distinguish from background noise or inactive states.

We often call a separate I/O line that indicates the availability of data or the occurrence of a transfer a "strobe". A strobe may, for example, clock data into a latch or fetch data from a buffer.

STROBE

Many peripherals transfer data at regular intervals; i.e., synchronously. Here the only problem is starting the process by lining up to the first input or marking the first output. In some cases, the peripheral provides a clock input from which the processor can obtain timing information.

Transmission errors are a problem with medium-speed devices. Several methods can lessen the likelihood of such errors; they include:

REDUCING
TRANSMISSION
ERRORS

- **Sampling input data at the center of the transmission interval in order to avoid edge effects;** that is, keep away from the edges where the data is changing.

- **Sampling each input several times and using majority logic such as best three out of five.**[1]

- **Generating and checking parity;** an extra bit is used that makes the number of 1 bits in the correct data even or odd.

- **Using other error detecting and correcting codes** such as checksums, LRC (longitudinal redundancy check), and CRC (cyclic redundancy check).[2]

High-speed devices that transfer more than 10,000 bits per second **require special methods.** The usual technique is to construct a special-purpose controller that transfers data directly between the memory and the I/O device. This process is called direct memory access (DMA). The DMA controller must force the CPU off the busses, provide addresses and control signals to the memory, and transfer the data. Such a controller will be fairly complex, typically consisting of 50 to 100

INTERFACING
HIGH-SPEED
DEVICES

DIRECT
MEMORY
ACCESS

chips, although LSI devices are now available.[3] The CPU must initially load the Address and Data Counters in the controller so that the controller will know where to start and how much to transfer.

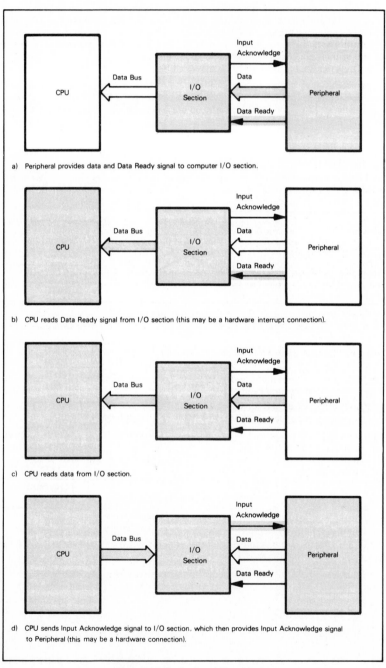

a) Peripheral provides data and Data Ready signal to computer I/O section.

b) CPU reads Data Ready signal from I/O section (this may be a hardware interrupt connection).

c) CPU reads data from I/O section.

d) CPU sends Input Acknowledge signal to I/O section, which then provides Input Acknowledge signal to Peripheral (this may be a hardware connection).

Figure 11-5. An Input Handshake

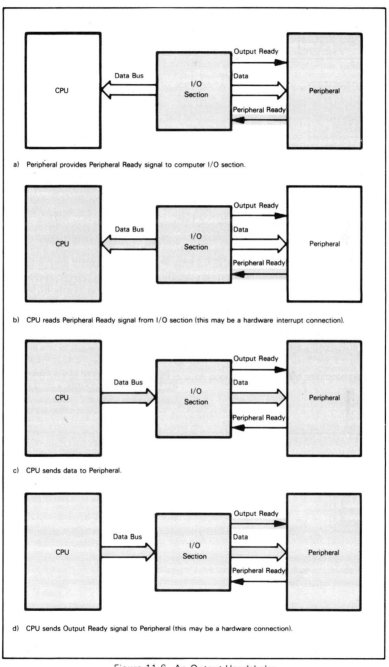

a) Peripheral provides Peripheral Ready signal to computer I/O section.

b) CPU reads Peripheral Ready signal from I/O section (this may be a hardware interrupt connection).

c) CPU sends data to Peripheral.

d) CPU sends Output Ready signal to Peripheral (this may be a hardware connection).

Figure 11-6. An Output Handshake

TIMING INTERVALS (DELAYS)

One problem that we will face throughout the discussion of input/output **is the generation of timing intervals with specific lengths.** Such intervals are necessary to debounce mechanical switches (i.e., to smooth their irregular transitions), to provide pulses with specified lengths and frequencies for displays, and to provide timing for devices that transfer data regularly (e.g., a teletypewriter that sends or receives one bit every 9.1 ms).

We can produce timing intervals in several ways:

1) **In hardware with one-shots or monostable multivibrators.** These devices produce a single pulse of fixed duration in response to a pulse input.

2) **In a combination of hardware and software with a flexible programmable timer** such as those that are included in the 6522 Versatile Interface Adapter (to be described later in this chapter). The 6522 timers can provide timing intervals of various lengths with a variety of starting and ending conditions.

3) **In software with delay routines.** These routines use the processor as a counter. This use is possible since the processor has a stable clock reference, but it clearly underutilizes the processor. However, delay routines require no additional hardware and often use processor time that would otherwise be wasted.

The choice among these three methods depends on your application. The software method is inexpensive but may overburden the processor. The programmable timers are relatively expensive but are easy to interface and may be able to handle many complex timing tasks. The timers that are included in the 6522 Versatile Interface Adapter and in the 6530 and 6532 Multifunction Devices are available at no additional cost as long as those parts are being used. These parts may be somewhat more expensive than simpler devices, but may be justifiable as complete packages. Such parts with integral timers are used in many board-level microcomputers, including the KIM, SYM, VIM, and AIM-65. The use of one-shots should be avoided whenever possible.

DELAY ROUTINES

A simple delay routine works as follows:

BASIC
SOFTWARE
DELAY

Step 1 - Load a register with a specified value.

Step 2 - Decrement the register.

Step 3 - If the result of Step 2 is not zero, repeat Step 2.

This routine does nothing except use time. The amount of time used depends upon the execution time of the various instructions. **The maximum length of the delay is limited by the size of the register;** however, the entire routine can be placed inside a similar routine that uses another register, and so on.

Be careful — the actual time used depends on the clock rate at which the processor is running, the speed of memory accesses, and operating conditions such as temperature, power supply voltage, and circuit loading which may affect the speed at which the processor executes instructions.

The following example uses Index Registers X and Y to provide delays as long as 255 ms. The choice of registers is

TRANSPARENT
DELAY
ROUTINE

arbitrary. You may find the use of the Accumulator or of memory locations more convenient. Remember, however, that the 6502 has no explicit Decrement Accumulator instruction. We could produce a routine that does not change the contents of any user registers. The sequence

```
PHP        ;SAVE STATUS REGISTER
PHA        ;SAVE ACCUMULATOR
TXA        ;SAVE INDEX REGISTER X
PHA
TYA        ;SAVE INDEX REGISTER Y
PHA
```

would save the contents of all the registers initially and the sequence

```
PLA        ;RESTORE INDEX REGISTER Y
TAY
PLA        ;RESTORE INDEX REGISTER X
TAX
PLA        ;RESTORE ACCUMULATOR
PLP        ;RESTORE STATUS REGISTER
```

would restore the registers at the end of the routine. **A subroutine that does not affect any registers or flags is said to be "transparent" to the calling program.** The instruction sequences that save and restore the registers must, of course, be included in the time budget.

DELAY PROGRAM

Purpose: The program provides a delay of 1 ms times the contents of Index Register Y.

Flowchart:

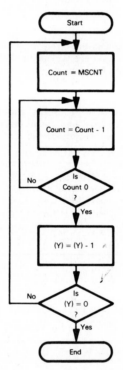

The value of MSCNT depends on the speed of the CPU and the memory cycle

Source Program:

```
DELAY   LDX     #MSCNT    ;GET COUNT FOR 1 MS DELAY
DLY1    DEX               ;COUNT = COUNT - 1
        BNE     DLY1      ;CONTINUE UNTIL COUNT = ZERO
        DEY               ;DECREMENT NUMBER OF REMAINING MS
        BNE     DELAY     ;CONTINUE UNTIL NUMBER OF MS = ZERO
        RTS
```

Object Program: (starting in location 0030)

Memory Location (Hex)	Memory Contents (Hex)	Instruction (Mnemonic)		
0030	A2	DELAY	LDX	#MSCNT
0031	MSCNT			
0032	CA	DLY1	DEX	
0033	D0		BNE	DLY1
0034	FD			
0035	88		DEY	
0036	D0		BNE	DELAY
0037	F8			
0038	60		RTS	

Time Budget:

Instruction		Number of Times Executed
LDX	#MSCNT	(Y)
DEX		(Y) x MSCNT
BNE	DLY1	(Y) x MSCNT
DEY		(Y)
BNE	DELAY	(Y)
RTS		1

The total time used should be (Y) x 1 ms. If the memory is operating at full speed, the instructions require the following numbers of clock cycles.

		Ignoring Page Boundaries
LDX #MSCNT	2 or 3	2
DEX or DEY	2	2
BNE	2, 3, or 4	2 or 3
RTS	6	6

The alternative times for LDX #MSCNT depend on whether a page boundary is crossed. The alternative times for BNE depend on whether the branch does not occur (2), occurs to an address on the same page (3), or occurs to an address on a different page (4). A page is a set of 256 contiguous memory locations which have the same eight most significant bits (or page number) in their addresses. We will assume that the routine is located so that no page boundaries are crossed, and we can use the rightmost column of the last table for timing purposes.

Ignoring the Jump-to-Subroutine (JSR) and Return from Subroutine (RTS) instructions (which occur only once), the program takes:

$$(Y) \times (2 + 5 \times MSCNT - 1 + 5) - 1 \quad \text{clock cycles}$$

The -1's are caused by the fact that the BNE instruction requires less time during the final iteration when the Counter has reached zero and no branch occurs.

So, to make the delay 1 ms,

$$5 + 5 \times MSCNT = N_C$$

where N_C is the number of clock cycles per millisecond. At the standard 1 MHz 6502 clock rate, $N_C = 1000$ so

$$5 \times MSCNT = 995$$

$$MSCNT = 199 \ (C7_{16}) \text{ at a 6502 clock rate of 1 MHz}$$

6502 DELAY LOOP CONSTANT

6502 INPUT/OUTPUT CHIPS

Most 6502 input/output sections are based on LSI interface chips. These devices combine latches, buffers, flip-flops, and other logic circuits needed for handshaking and other simple interfacing techniques. They contain many logic connections, certain sets of which can be selected according to the contents of programmable registers. Thus the designer has the equivalent of a Circuit Designer's Casebook under his or her control. The initialization phase of the program places the appropriate values in registers to select the required logic connections. An input/output section based on programmable LSI interface chips can handle many different applications and changes or corrections can be made in software rather than by rewiring.

We will discuss the following LSI interface chips that can be used with the 6502 microprocessor:

1) **The 6520 Peripheral Interface Adapter.** This device contains two 8-bit I/O ports and four individual control lines; it is exactly the same as the 6820 device used with 6800-based microcomputers.[4]

2) **The 6522 Versatile Interface Adapter.** This device contains two 8-bit I/O ports, four individual control lines, two 16-bit counter/timers, and an 8-bit shift register.

3) **The 6530 Peripheral Interface/Memory or Multifunction (Support) Device.** This device contains two 8-bit I/O ports, an 8-bit counter/timer with a prescaler, 1024 bytes of ROM, and 64 bytes of RAM.

4) **The 6532 Peripheral Interface/Memory or Multifunction (Support) Device.** This device contains two 8-bit I/O ports, an 8-bit counter/timer with a prescaler, and 128 bytes of RAM.

The following acronyms are often used in describing these devices: the 6520 PIA, the 6522 VIA, and the 6530 or 6532 RIOT (for ROM or RAM, I/O, and Timer combination). Our I/O examples later in this chapter will all use the 6522 Versatile Interface Adapter. Examples of the use of the 6520 device can be found in 6800 Assembly Language Programming;[5] those examples can easily be adapted to the 6502 microprocessor (remember the comparisons of the instruction sets in Tables 3-6 and 3-7).

THE 6520 PERIPHERAL INTERFACE ADAPTER

Figure 11-7 is the block diagram of **a PIA**. The device **contains two nearly identical 8-bit ports** — A, which is usually an input port, and B, which is usually an output port. **Each port contains:**

- **A Data or Peripheral register that holds either input or output data.** This register is latched when used for output but unlatched when used for input.

- **A Data Direction register.** The bits in this register determine whether the corresponding data register bits (and pins) are inputs (0) or outputs (1).

> **PIA REGISTERS AND CONTROL LINES**

- **A Control register that holds the status signals required for handshaking, and other bits that select logic connections within the PIA.**

- **Two control lines that are configured by the control registers.** These lines can be used for the handshaking signals shown in Figures 11-5 and 11-6.

The meanings of the bits in the Data Direction and Control registers are related to the underlying hardware and are entirely arbitrary as far as the assembly language programmer is concerned. You must either memorize them or look them up in the appropriate tables (Tables 11-2 through 11-6).

Each PIA occupies four memory addresses. The RS (register select) lines choose one of the four registers, as described in Table 11-1. Since there are six registers (two peripheral, two data direction, and two control) in each PIA, one further bit is needed for addressing. Bit 2 of each control register determines whether the other address on that side refers to the Data Direction register (0) or to the Peripheral register (1). This sharing of an external address means that:

> **PIA ADDRESSES**

1) A program must change the bit in the Control register in order to use the register that is not currently being addressed.

2) The programmer must know the contents of the Control register in order to know which register is being addressed. RESET clears the Control register and thus addresses the Data Direction register.

Table 11-1. Addressing 6520 PIA Internal Registers

Address Lines		Control Register Bit		Register Select
RS1	RS0	CRA-2	CRB-2	
0	0	1	X	Peripheral Register A
0	0	0	X	Data Direction Register A
0	1	X	X	Control Register A
1	0	X	1	Peripheral Register B
1	0	X	0	Data Direction Register B
1	1	X	X	Control Register B
X = Either 0 or 1				

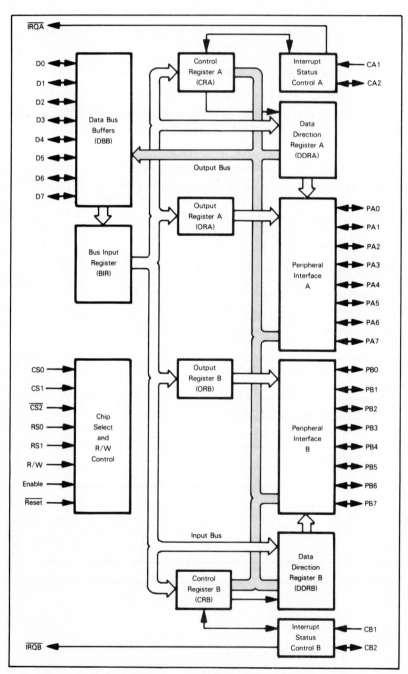

Figure 11-7. Block Diagram of the 6520 Peripheral Interface Adapter

PIA CONTROL REGISTER

Table 11-2 shows the organization of the PIA Control registers. We may describe the general purpose of each bit as follows:

Bit 7: status bit set by transitions on control line 1 and cleared by reading the Peripheral (Data) register

Bit 6: same as bit 7 except set by transitions on control line 2

Bit 5: determines whether control line 2 is an input (0) or output (1)

Bit 4: Control line 2 input: determines whether bit 6 is set by high-to-low transitions (0) or low-to-high transitions (1) on control line 2
Control line 2 output: determines whether control line 2 is a pulse (0) or a level (1)

Bit 3: Control line 2 input: if 1, enables interrupt output from bit 6
Control line 2 output: determines ending condition for pulse (0 = handshake acknowledgement lasting until next transition on control line 1, 1 = brief strobe lasting one clock cycle) or value of level

Bit 2: selects Data Direction register (0) or Data register (1)

Bit 1: determines whether bit 7 is set by high-to-low transitions (0) or low-to-high transitions (1) on control line 1

Bit 0: if 1, enables interrupt output from bit 7 of Control register.

Tables 11-3 through 11-6 describe the bits in more detail. Since E is normally tied to the $\Phi2$ clock, you can interpret "E" pulse as "clock pulse."

Table 11-2. Organization of the PIA Control Registers

	7	6	5	4	3	2	1	0
CRA	IRQA1	IRQA2	CA2 Control			DDRA Access	CA1 Control	
	7	6	5	4	3	2	1	0
CRB	IRQB1	IRQB2	CB2 Control			DDRB Access	CB1 Control	

Table 11-3. Control of 6520 PIA Interrupt Inputs CA1 and CB1

CRA-1 (CRB-1)	CRA-0 (CRB-0)	Interrupt Input CA1 (CB1)	Interrupt Flag CRA-7 (CRB-7)	MPU Interrupt Request IRQA (IRQB)
0	0	↓ Active	Set high on ↓ of CA1 (CB1)	Disabled — IRQ remains high
0	1	↓ Active	Set high on ↓ of CA1 (CB1)	Goes low when the interrupt flag bit CRA-7 (CRB-7) goes high
1	0	↑ Active	Set high on ↑ of CA1 (CB1)	Disabled — IRQ remains high
1	1	↑ Active	Set high on ↑ of CA1 (CB1)	Goes low when the interrupt flag bit CRA-7 (CRB-7) goes high

Notes:
1. ↑ indicates positive transition (low to high)
2. ↓ indicates negative transition (high to low)
3. The Interrupt flag bit CRA-7 is cleared by an MPU Read of the A Data Register. and CRB-7 is cleared by an MPU Read of the B Data Register
4. If CRA-0 (CRB-0) is low when an interrupt occurs (Interrupt disabled) and is later brought high. IRQA (IRQB) occurs after CRA-0 (CRB-0) is written to a "one"

Table 11-4. Control of 6520 PIA Interrupt Inputs CA2 and CB2

CRA-5 (CRB-5)	CRA-4 (CRB-4)	CRA-3 (CRB-3)	Interrupt Input CA2 (CB2)	Interrupt Flag CRA-6 (CRB-6)	MPU Interrupt Request IRQA (IRQB)
0	0	0	↓ Active	Set high on ↓ of CA2 (CB2)	Disabled — IRQ remains high
0	0	1	↓ Active	Set high on ↓ of CA2 (CB2)	Goes low when the interrupt flag bit CRA-6 (CRB-6) goes high
0	1	0	↑ Active	Set high on ↑ of CA2 (CB2)	Disabled — IRQ remains high
0	1	1	↑ Active	Set high on ↑ of CA2 (CB2)	Goes low when the interrupt flag bit CRA-6 (CRB-6) goes high

Notes:
1. ↑ indicates positive transition (low to high)
2. ↓ indicates negative transition (high to low)
3. The Interrupt flag bit CRA-6 is cleared by an MPU Read of the A Data Register and CRB-6 is cleared by an MPU Read of the B Data Register.
4. If CRA-3 (CRB-3) is low when an interrupt occurs (Interrupt disabled) and is later brought high. IRQA (IRQB) occurs after CRA-3 (CRB-3) is written to a "one"

Table 11-5. Control of 6520 PIA CB2 Output Line

CRB-5	CRB-4	CRB-3	CB2	
			Cleared	Set
1	0	0	Low on the positive transition of the first E pulse following an MPU Write "B" Data Register operation.	High when the interrupt flag bit CRB-7 is set by an active transition of the CB1 signal.
1	0	1	Low on the positive transition of the first E pulse after an MPU Write "B" Data Register operation.	High on the positive edge of the first "E" pulse following an "E" pulse which occurred while the part was deselected.
1	1	0	Low when CRB-3 goes low as a result of an MPU Write in Control Register "B"	Always low as long as CRB-3 is low. Will go high on an MPU Write in Control Register "B" that changes CRB-3 to "one"
1	1	1	Always high as long as CRB-3 is high. Will be cleared when an MPU Write Control Register "B" results in clearing CRB-3 to "zero"	High when CRB-3 goes high as a result of an MPU Write into Control Register "B"

Table 11-6. Control of 6520 PIA CA2 Output Line

CRA-5	CRA-4	CRA-3	CA2	
			Cleared	Set
1	0	0	Low on negative transition of E after an MPU Read "A" Data operation.	High when the interrupt flag bit CRA-7 is set by an active transition of the CA1 signal.
1	0	1	Low on negative transition of E after an MPU Read "A" Data operation.	High on the negative edge of the first "E" pulse which occurs during a deselect.
1	1	0	Low when CRA-3 goes low as a result of an MPU Write to Control Register "A"	Always low as long as CRA-3 is low. Will go high on an MPU Write to Control Register "A" that changes CRA-3 to "one".
1	1	1	Always high as long as CRA-3 is high. Will be cleared on an MPU Write to Control Register "A" that clears CRA-3 to a "zero"	High when CRA-3 goes high as a result of an MPU Write to Control Register "A".

CONFIGURING THE PIA

The program must select the logic connections in the PIA before using it. This selection (or configuration) is usually part of the startup routine. The steps in the configuration are:

1) Address the Data Direction register by clearing bit 2 of the Control register. Since the Reset signal clears all the internal registers, this step is unnecessary in the overall startup routine.

2) Establish the directions of the I/O pins by loading the Data Direction register.

3) Select the required logic connections in the PIA by loading the Control register. Set bit 2 of the Control register so as to address the Data register.

Step 1 can be performed as follows:

```
        LDA     #0              ;CLEAR PIA CONTROL REGISTER
        STA     PIACR
```

or

```
        LDA     PIACR
        AND     #%11111011      ;SELECT DATA DIRECTION REGISTER
        STA     PIACR
```

Once the program has performed Step 1, Step 2 is simply a matter of clearing each input bit position and setting each output bit position in the Data Direction Register. Some simple examples are:

```
1)      LDA     #0              ;ALL LINES INPUTS
        STA     PIADDR

2)      LDA     #$FF            ;ALL LINES OUTPUTS
        STA     PIADDR

3)      LDA     #$F0            ;MAKE LINES 4-7 OUTPUTS, 0-3 INPUTS
        STA     PIADDR
```

Step 3 is clearly the difficult part of the configuration, since it involves selecting the logic connections in the PIA. Some points to remember are:

1) Bits 6 and 7 of the Control register are set by transitions on the control lines and are cleared by reading the Data register. You <u>cannot</u> change these bits by writing data into the Control register.

2) Bit 2 of the Control register must be set to address the Data register.

3) Bit 1 determines which pulse edge will set bit 7. Bit 1 is 0 for a high-to-low transition; bit 1 is 1 for a low-to-high transition.

4) Bit 0 is the interrupt enable for control line 1. Remember that it must be set to enable interrupts, unlike the 6502 interrupt bit, which must be cleared to enable interrupts. Chapter 12 describes interrupts in more detail.

5) Bit 5 must be set if control line 2 is to be output. Bits 3 and 4 then determine how control line 2 works. Remember that sides A and B differ, since side A can only produce a read strobe while side B can only produce a write strobe. Once the strobe option has been selected, the strobes automatically follow each reading of Data Register A or writing of Data Register B. You must configure each side of each PIA in the startup program.

EXAMPLES OF PIA CONFIGURATION

1) A simple input port with no control lines (as needed for a set of switches):

```
        LDA     #0              ;CLEAR OUT CONTROL REGISTER
        STA     PIACR
        STA     PIADDR          ;MAKE ALL LINES INPUTS
        LDA     #%00000100      ;SELECT DATA REGISTER
        STA     PIACR
```

Bit 2 of the Control register must be set to address the Data register. The same sequence can be used if a high-to-low transition (negative transition) on control line 1 indicates Data Ready or Peripheral Ready.

2) A simple output port with no control lines (as needed for a set of single LED displays):

```
        LDA     #0              ;CLEAR OUT CONTROL REGISTER
        STA     PIACR
        LDA     #$FF            ;MAKE ALL LINES OUTPUTS
        STA     PIADDR
        LDA     #%00000100      ;SELECT DATA REGISTER
        STA     PIACR
```

3) An input port with a control input that indicates DATA READY with a low-to-high transition (positive transition):

```
        LDA     #0              ;CLEAR OUT CONTROL REGISTER
        STA     PIACR
        STA     PIADDR          ;MAKE ALL LINES INPUTS
        LDA     #%00000110      ;MAKE DATA READY ACTIVE LOW-TO-HIGH
        STA     PIACR
```

The DATA READY or DATA AVAILABLE line is tied to control line CA1 or CB1. Bit 1 of the Control register is set so as to recognize low-to-high transitions on control line 1. This configuration is suitable for most encoded keyboards.

4) An output port that produces a brief strobe to indicate DATA READY or OUTPUT READY (this could be used for multiplexing displays or for providing a DATA AVAILABLE signal to a printer):

```
        LDA     #0              ;CLEAR OUT CONTROL REGISTER
        STA     PIACR
        LDA     #$FF            ;MAKE ALL LINES OUTPUTS
        STA     PIADDR
        LDA     #%00101100      ;MAKE CONTROL LINE 2 A BRIEF STROBE
        STA     PIACR
```

Bit 5 = 1 to make control line 2 an output, bit 4 = 0 to make it a pulse, and bit 3 = 1 to make it a brief active-low strobe (one clock period in duration). The strobe will automatically follow each instruction that writes data into the B side of the PIA; for example, the instruction

```
        STA     PIADRB
```

will both transfer data and cause a strobe. However, the A side will produce a strobe only after a read operation. The sequence

```
        STA     PIADRA          ;WRITE DATA
        LDA     PIADRA          ;PRODUCE AN OUTPUT STROBE
```

will both transfer data and cause a strobe. The LDA instruction is a "dummy read"; it has no effect other than to cause the strobe (and waste some time). Other instructions besides LDA could also be used — you should try to name some of them.

5) An input port with a handshake Input Acknowledge strobe that can be used to tell a peripheral that the previous data has been accepted (and the computer is ready for more):

```
LDA     #0              ;CLEAR OUT CONTROL REGISTER
STA     PIACR
STA     PIADDR          ;MAKE ALL LINES INPUTS
LDA     #%00100100      ;CONTROL LINE 2 = HANDSHAKE
                        ;  ACKNOWLEDGE
STA     PIACR
```

Bit 5 = 1 to make control line 2 an output, bit 4 = 0 to make it a pulse, and bit 3 = 0 to make it an active-low acknowledgment that remains low until the next active transition on control line 1. The acknowledgment will automatically follow a read operation on the A side of the PIA; for example, the instruction

```
LDA     PIADRA
```

will both read data and cause the acknowledgment. However, the B side will produce an acknowledgment only after a write operation. The sequence

```
LDA     PIADRB          ;READ DATA
STA     PIADRB          ;PRODUCE ACKNOWLEDGMENT
```

will both read data and produce an acknowledgment. The STA instruction is a "dummy write"; it has no other effect than to cause the acknowledgment (and waste some time). Note that the order of the sequence is reversed from the previous example. This configuration is suitable for many CRT terminals that require a complete handshake.

6) An output port with a latched zero control bit (latched individual output or level output). Such an output can be used to turn the peripheral on or off or to control its mode of operation.

```
LDA     #0              ;CLEAR OUT CONTROL REGISTER
STA     PIACR
LDA     #$FF            ;MAKE ALL LINES OUTPUTS
STA     PIADDR
LDA     #%00110100      ;CONTROL LINE 2 = LATCHED ZERO LEVEL
STA     PIACR
```

Bit 5 = 1 to make control line 2 an output, bit 4 = 1 to make it a level or latched bit, and bit 3 = 0 to make the level zero. This output is not affected by operations on the Data register; its value can be changed by changing the value of bit 3 of the PIA Control register, i.e.,

```
LDA     PIACR
ORA     #%00001000      ;MAKE LEVEL ONE
STA     PIACR

LDA     PIACR
AND     #%11110111      ;MAKE LEVEL ZERO
STA     PIACR
```

You can use this configuration to produce active-high strobes or to provide pulses with software-controlled lengths.

USING THE PIA TO TRANSFER DATA

Once the PIA has been configured, you may use its data registers like any other memory locations. The simplest instructions for data transfer are:

PIA INPUT/
OUTPUT

Load Accumulator, which transfers eight bits of data from the specified input pins to the Accumulator, and

Store Accumulator, which transfers eight bits of data from the Accumulator to the specified output pins.

You must be careful in situations where input and output ports do not behave like memory locations. For example, it often makes no sense to write data into input ports or read data from output ports. Be particularly careful if the input port is not latched or if the output port is not buffered.

Other instructions that transfer data to or from memory can also serve as I/O instructions. Typical examples are:

Bit Test, which sets the Zero flag as if the values of a set of input pins had been logically ANDed with the contents of the Accumulator. The Sign (Negative) flag is set to the value of bit 7 of the input port and the Overflow flag is set to the value of bit 6 of the input port. **This instruction provides a simple way to test the PIA status flags;** that is, the instruction

        BIT   PIACR

sets the Sign flag to the value of Control register bit 7 (the status latch for control line 1) and the Overflow flag to the value of Control register bit 6 (the status latch for control line 2).

Compare, which sets the flags as if the values of a set of input pins had been subtracted from the contents of the Accumulator.

Here also you must be aware of the physical limitations of the I/O ports. Be particularly careful of instructions like shifts, Increment, and Decrement, which involve both read and write cycles.

We cannot overemphasize the importance of careful documentation. Often, complex I/O transfers can be concealed in instructions with no obvious functions. You must describe the purposes of such instructions carefully. For example, one could easily be tempted to remove the dummy read and write operations mentioned earlier since they do not appear to accomplish anything.

Bit 7 of the PIA Control register often serves as a status bit, such as Data Ready or Peripheral Ready. You can check its value with either of the following sequences:

PIA STATUS
BITS

```
        LDA     PIACR   ;IS READY FLAG 1?
        BMI     DEVRDY  ;YES, DEVICE READY

        BIT     PIACR   ;IS READY FLAG 1?
        BMI     DEVRDY  ;YES, DEVICE READY
```

Note that you should not use the shift instructions, since they will change the contents of the Control register (why?). The following program will wait for the Ready flag to go high:

```
WAITR   BIT     PIACR   ;IS READY FLAG 1?
        BPL     WAITR   ;NO, WAIT
```

How would you change these programs so that they examine bit 6 instead of bit 7?

The only way to clear bit 7 (or bit 6) is to read the Data register. A dummy read will be necessary if a read operation is not normally part of the response to the bit being set. If the port is used for output, the sequence

```
STA     PIADR       ;SEND DATA
LDA     PIADR       ;CLEAR READ FLAG
```

will do the job. Note that here the dummy read is necessary on either side of the PIA. The Bit Test instruction can also clear the strobe without changing anything except the flags. Be particularly careful in cases where the CPU is not ready for input data or has no output data to send.

THE 6522 VERSATILE INTERFACE ADAPTER (VIA)

The 6522 Versatile Interface Adapter is an enhanced version of the 6520 Peripheral Interface Adapter.[6,7,8]

The 6522 VIA contains the following (see the block diagram in Figure 11-8):

1) **Two 8-bit I/O ports (A and B).** Each pin can be individually selected to be either an input or an output.

2) **Four status and control lines** (two associated with each port).

3) **Two 16-bit counter/timers** which can be used to generate or count pulses. These timers can produce single pulses or a continuous series of pulses.

4) **An 8-bit Shift register** which can convert data between serial and parallel forms.

5) **Interrupt logic** (to be described in Chapter 12) so that I/O can proceed on an interrupt-driven basis.

Thus the Versatile Interface Adapter provides the functions of the PIA plus two 16-bit counter/timers and an 8-bit Shift register. We will describe the use of the counter/timers later in this chapter. The Shift register provides a simple serial I/O capability that is only occasionally useful; we will not discuss it any further.

Each VIA occupies sixteen memory addresses. The RS (register select) lines choose the various internal registers, as described in Table 11-7 **The way that a VIA operates is determined by the contents of four registers.**

1) **Data Direction Register A (DDRA)** determines whether the pins on Port A are inputs (0s) or outputs (1s).

2) **Data Direction Register B (DDRB)** determines whether the pins on Port B are inputs (0s) or outputs (1s).

3) **The Peripheral Control register (PCR)** determines which polarity of transition (rising edge or falling edge) is recognized on the input status lines (CA1 and CB1) and how the other status lines (CA2 and CB2) operate. Figure 11-9 describes the bit assignments in the Peripheral Control register; as usual, the functions and bit positions are arbitrarily selected by the manufacturer. Note that the 6522 Peripheral Control register does not contain status bits (latches) like the 6520 Control register; these bits are located in the separate Interrupt Flag register (see Figure 11-11).

4) **The Auxiliary Control register (ACR)** determines whether the data ports are latched and how the timers and Shift register operate. These functions are not present in the 6520 PIA. Figure 11-10 describes the bit assignments in Auxiliary Control register.

Note that there is a data direction register for each side but only one control register (unlike the 6520, which has a separate control register for each side). Ports A and B are virtually identical. One important difference is that Port B can handle Darlington transistors, which are used to drive solenoids and relays. We will use Port A for input and Port B for output in our examples later in this chapter.

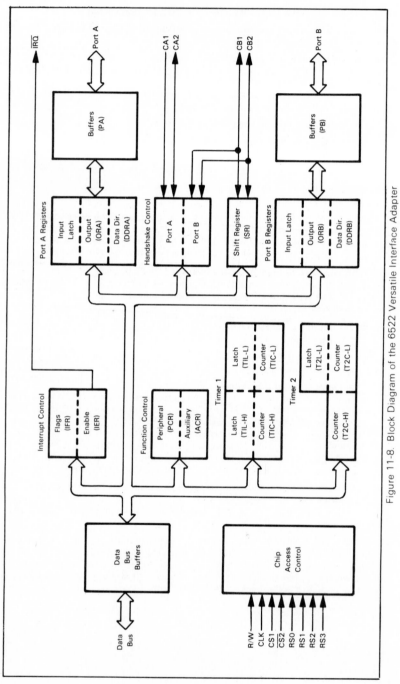

Figure 11-8. Block Diagram of the 6522 Versatile Interface Adapter

Table 11-7. Addressing 6522 VIA Internal Registers

Label	Select Lines				Addressed Location
	RS3	RS2	RS1	RS0	
DEV	0	0	0	0	Output register for I/O Port B
DEV+1	0	0	0	1	Output register for I/O Port A. with handshaking
DEV+2	0	0	1	0	I/O Port B Data Direction register
DEV+3	0	0	1	1	I/O Port A Data Direction register
DEV+4	0	1	0	0	Read Timer 1 Counter low-order byte Write to Timer 1 Latch low-order byte
DEV+5	0	1	0	1	Read Timer 1 Counter high-order byte Write to Timer 1 Latch high-order byte and initiate count
DEV+6	0	1	1	0	Access Timer 1 Latch low-order byte
DEV+7	0	1	1	1	Access Timer 1 Latch high-order byte
DEV+8	1	0	0	0	Read low-order byte of Timer 2 and reset Counter interrupt Write to low-order byte of Timer 2 but do not reset interrupt
DEV+9	1	0	0	1	Access high-order byte of Timer 2; reset Counter interrupt on write
DEV+A	1	0	1	0	Serial I/O Shift register
DEV+B	1	0	1	1	Auxiliary Control register
DEV+C	1	1	0	0	Peripheral Control register
DEV+D	1	1	0	1	Interrupt Flag register
DEV+E	1	1	1	0	Interrupt Enable register
DEV+F	1	1	1	1	Output register for I/O Port A. without handshaking

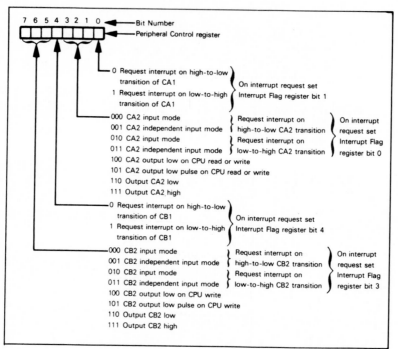

Figure 11-9. 6522 VIA Peripheral Control Register Bit Assignments

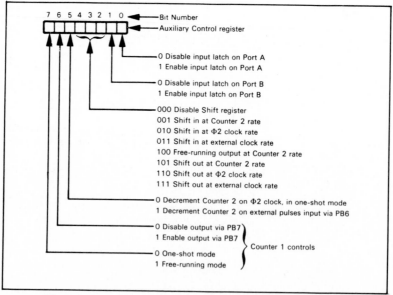

Figure 11-10. 6522 VIA Auxiliary Control Register Bit Assignments

CONFIGURING THE VIA

The program must select the logic connections in the VIA before using it. This selection (or configuration) is usually part of the startup routine. The steps are to establish the directions of the I/O pins by loading the Data Direction register and to select the required logic connections in the VIA by loading the Peripheral Control register and, if necessary, the Auxiliary Control register.

You can establish the directions of the I/O pins as follows:

1) **A '0' in a bit in the Data Direction register makes the corresponding pin an input.** For example, a '0' in bit 5 of Data Direction Register A makes pin PA5 an input.

2) **A '1' in a bit in the Data Direction register makes the corresponding pin an output.** For example, a '1' in bit 3 of Data Direction Register B makes pin PB3 an output.

The directions of almost all I/O pins are fixed after the initialization since most input and output lines transfer data in only one direction (i.e., the microprocessor will never fetch data from a printer or send data to a keyboard).

Some simple examples of setting directions are:

```
1)      LDA     #0        ;ALL LINES INPUTS
        STA     VIADDRA

2)      LDA     #$FF      ;ALL LINES OUTPUTS
        STA     VIADDRB

3)      LDA     #$F0      ;MAKE LINES 4-7 OUTPUTS, 0-3 INPUTS
        STA     VIADDRB
```

You can mix inputs and outputs on a single port by establishing the directions of individual pins appropriately. Port B is buffered so that its contents can be read correctly even when it is being used for output; Port A is not buffered so that its contents can be read correctly only if it is lightly loaded (or designated as inputs).

Configuring the VIA is difficult because of its many functions. Most of the I/O port functions are controlled by the Peripheral Control register, and we shall discuss these first. **Some points to remember are:**

1) **Reset clears all the VIA registers,** making all lines inputs and disabling all interrupts. All edge detection facilities are set to trigger on falling edges (high-to-low transitions).

2) **Bits 0-3 of the Peripheral Control register are used to establish the logic connections for control lines CA1 and CA2; bits 4-7 have the same purposes for control lines CB1 and CB2.**

3) **Control lines CA1 and CB1 are always inputs.** The only choice is whether the corresponding status latches (Interrupt Flag register bits 1 and 4 — see Figure 11-11) are set on falling edges (high-to-low, or negative, transitions) or on rising edges (low-to-high, or positive, transitions). For CA1, bit 0 = 0 for falling edges and 1 for rising edges; for CB1, bit 4 = 0 for falling edges and 1 for rising edges.

4) **Control lines CA2 and CB2 can be either inputs or outputs** (see Tables 11-8 and 11-9). For CA2, bit 3 = 1 to make it an output and 0 to make it an input.

Table 11-8. Configurations for 6522 VIA Control Line CB2

PCR7	PCR6	PCR5	Mode
0	0	0	Interrupt Input Mode — Set CB2 Interrupt flag (IFR3) on a negative transition of the CB2 input signal. Clear IFR3 on a read or write of the Peripheral B Output register.
0	0	1	Independent Interrupt Input Mode — Set IFR3 on a negative transition of the CB2 input signal. Reading or writing ORB does not clear the Interrupt flag.
0	1	0	Input Mode — Set CB2 Interrupt flag on a positive transition of the CB2 input signal. Clear the CB2 Interrupt flag on a read or write of ORB.
0	1	1	Independent Input Mode — Set IFR3 on a positive transition of the CB2 input signal. Reading or writing ORB does not clear the CB2 Interrupt flag.
1	0	0	Handshake Output Mode — Set CB2 low on a write ORB operation. Reset CB2 high with an active transition of the CB1 input signal.
1	0	1	Pulse Output Mode — Set CB2 low for one cycle following a write ORB operation.
1	1	0	Manual Output Mode — The CB2 output is held low in this mode.
1	1	1	Manual Output Mode — The CB2 output is held high in this mode.

Table 11-9. Configurations for 6522 VIA Control Line CA2

PCR3	PCR2	PCR1	Mode
0	0	0	Input Mode — Set CA2 Interrupt flag (IFR0) on a negative transition of the input signal. Clear IFR0 on a read or write of the Peripheral A Output register.
0	0	1	Independent Interrupt Input Mode — Set IFR0 on a negative transition of the CA2 input signal. Reading or writing ORA does not clear the CA2 Interrupt flag.
0	1	0	Input Mode — Set CA2 Interrupt flag on a positive transition of the CA2 input signal. Clear IFR0 with a read or write of the Peripheral A Output register.
0	1	1	Independent Interrupt Input Mode — Set IFR0 on a positive transition of the CA2 input signal. Reading or writing ORA does not clear the CA2 Interrupt flag.
1	0	0	Handshake Output Mode — Set CA2 output low on a read or write of the Peripheral A Output register. Reset CA2 high with an active transition on CA1.
1	0	1	Pulse Output Mode — CA2 goes low for one cycle following a read or write of the Peripheral A Output register.
1	1	0	Manual Output Mode — The CA2 output is held low in this mode.
1	1	1	Manual Output Mode — The CA2 output is held high in this mode.

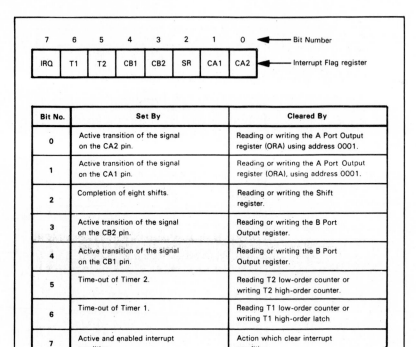

Bit No.	Set By	Cleared By
0	Active transition of the signal on the CA2 pin.	Reading or writing the A Port Output register (ORA) using address 0001.
1	Active transition of the signal on the CA1 pin.	Reading or writing the A Port Output register (ORA), using address 0001.
2	Completion of eight shifts.	Reading or writing the Shift register.
3	Active transition of the signal on the CB2 pin.	Reading or writing the B Port Output register.
4	Active transition of the signal on the CB1 pin.	Reading or writing the B Port Output register.
5	Time-out of Timer 2.	Reading T2 low-order counter or writing T2 high-order counter.
6	Time-out of Timer 1.	Reading T1 low-order counter or writing T1 high-order latch
7	Active and enabled interrupt condition.	Action which clear interrupt condition.

Bits 0, 1, 3, and 4 are the I/O handshake signals. Bit 7 (IRQ) is 1 if any of the interrupts is both active and enabled (see Chapter 12).

Figure 11-11 The 6522 VIA Interrupt Flag Register

Further functions are as follows:

CA2 Input

Bit 2 = 1 to trigger on a rising edge, 0 to trigger on a falling edge.

Bit 1 = 1 to make Interrupt Flag register bit 0 (the CA2 input status latch) independent of operations on I/O Port A, 0 to have that bit cleared by operations on I/O Port A.

The independent mode is useful when CA2 is being used for purposes (such as a real-time clock) that are completely unrelated to the data transfers through the I/O port. The regular mode is useful when CA2 is being used as a handshaking signal which must be cleared to prepare for the next I/O operation (see Figures 11-5 and 11-6).

CA2 Output

Bit 2 = 1 to make CA2 a level, 0 to make it a pulse

If CA2 is a level, bit 1 is its value

If CA2 is a pulse, bit 1 is 0 to have CA2 go low when the CPU transfers data to or from Port A and remain low until an active transition occurs on CA1; bit 1 is 1 to have CA2 go low for one clock cycle after the CPU transfers data to or from Port A.

CB2 is handled exactly the same (using bits 7, 6, and 5 of the Peripheral Control register and bit 3 of the Interrupt Flag register) except that pulses are produced on CB2 only after data is written into Port B. To produce a pulse after reading data, you must use a "dummy write", that is:

```
         LDA      VIAORB     ;GET DATA FROM PORT B
         STA      VIAORB     ;PRODUCE STROBE FROM PORT B
```

The only I/O port function governed by the Auxiliary Control register (Figure 11-10) is input latching. Bit 0 (for Port A) or bit 1 (for port B) must be set to latch the input data on the active transition on control line 1 (as determined by the Peripheral Control register). **Note the following features of the latching function:**

VIA INPUT LATCHES

1) RESET disables the input latches. The 6522 VIA then operates like the 6520 PIA, which has no input latches.

2) For Port A, the data that is latched will always be the data on the peripheral pins. Since Port A is not buffered, that data may not be the same as the data in the Output register when the port is being used for output.

3) For Port B, the data that is latched is either the data on the peripheral pins (for those pins defined as inputs) or the contents of the Output register (for those pins defined as outputs).

Some simple examples of activating the input latches are:

```
         LDA      #%00000001
         STA      VIAACR     ;ACTIVATE LATCH ON PORT A

         LDA      #%00000010
         STA      VIAACR     ;ACTIVATE LATCH ON PORT B

         LDA      #%00000011
         STA      VIAACR     ;ACTIVATE LATCHES ON PORTS A AND B
```

Note that 6522 output ports are automatically latched, just like 6520 output ports.

EXAMPLES OF VIA CONFIGURATION

1) **A simple input port with no control lines** (as needed for a set of switches):

```
        LDA     #0
        STA     VIAPCR          ;MAKE ALL CONTROL LINES INPUTS
        STA     VIADDRA         ;MAKE PORT A LINES INPUTS
```

Remember that Reset clears all the internal registers so that this sequence may not even be necessary. The same sequence can be used if a high-to-low edge (falling edge) on control line CA1 indicates Data Ready or Peripheral Ready.

2) **A simple output port with no control lines** (as needed for a set of single LED displays):

```
        LDA     #0
        STA     VIAPCR          ;MAKE ALL CONTROL LINES INPUTS
        LDA     #$FF
        STA     VIADDRB         ;MAKE PORT B LINES OUTPUTS
```

3) **An input port with an active low-to-high DATA READY signal attached to CA1** (as needed for an encoded keyboard):

```
        LDA     #0
        STA     VIADDRA         ;MAKE PORT A LINES INPUTS
        LDA     #1              ;MAKE RISING EDGE ACTIVE
        STA     VIAPCR
```

Bit 1 of the Peripheral Control register is set so as to recognize low-to-high transitions on control line CA1. Such a transition will set bit 1 of the Interrupt Flag register (see Figure 11-10); reading the data from the port will clear that bit (see the table associated with Figure 11-11). Input latching can be provided by setting bit 0 of the Auxiliary Control register.

4) **An output port that produces a brief strobe to indicate DATA READY or OUTPUT READY** (this could be used for multiplexing displays or for providing a DATA AVAILABLE signal to a printer):

```
        LDA     #$FF
        STA     VIADDRB         ;MAKE PORT B LINES OUTPUTS
        LDA     #%10100000
        STA     VIAPCR
```

The brief strobe on control line CB2 will occur after every output operation. Bit 7 of the Peripheral Control register is 1 to make CB2 an output. bit 6 is 0 to make CB2 a pulse, and bit 5 is 1 to make CB2 a brief (one clock cycle) pulse following each output.

5) **An input port with a handshake Input Acknowledge strobe that can be used to tell a peripheral that the previous data has been accepted** (and that the computer is ready for more):

```
        LDA     #0
        STA     VIADDRA         ;MAKE PORT A LINES INPUTS
        LDA     #%00001000      ;CONTROL LINE 2 = HANDSHAKE
                                ;  ACKNOWLEDGE
```

The strobe on control line CA2 will occur after every input or output operation. It will remain low until the next active transition on control line CA1. Bit 3 of the Peripheral Control register is 1 to make CA2 an output, bit 2 is 0 to make CA2 a pulse, and bit 1 is 0 to make CA2 an active-low acknowledgment that lasts until the next active transition on CA1. Note that the active transition on CA1 is a falling edge since bit 0 of the Peripheral Control register is 0. This configuration is suitable for many CRT terminals that require a complete handshake.

6) **An output port with a latched active-low control bit** (latched output or level output). Such an output bit can be used to turn a peripheral on or off or to control its mode of operation.

```
        LDA     #$FF                ;MAKE PORT B LINES OUTPUTS
        STA     VIADDRB
        LDA     #%11000000          ;CONTROL LINE 2 = LATCHED ZERO LEVEL
        STA     VIAPCR
```

Bit 7 = 1 to make control line CB2 an output, bit 6 = 1 to make it a level or latched bit, and bit 5 = 0 to make the active level zero. This bit is not affected by operations on the I/O port or Output register; its value can be changed by changing bit 5 of the Peripheral Control register, i.e.,

```
        LDA     VIAPCR
        ORA     #%00100000          ;MAKE LEVEL ONE
        STA     VIAPCR
        LDA     VIAPCR
        AND     #%11011111          ;MAKE LEVEL ZERO
        STA     VIAPCR
```

You can use this configuration to produce an active-high or active-low strobe or to provide pulses with software-controlled lengths.

USING THE VIA TO TRANSFER DATA

Once the VIA has been configured, you may use its data registers like any other memory location (just as with the PIA). The common ways to transfer data, status, and control are with the instructions

Load Accumulator, Store Accumulator, Bit Test, and Compare. Note that Output Register A can be addressed in two ways — one with handshaking (address 1) and one without handshaking (address F). The address without handshaking allows you to use CA1 independently of the peripheral attached to I/O Port A. That control line could be used for an alarm, clock input, control panel interface, or extra control input from another peripheral. The Interrupt flag for that input can be cleared directly by clearing the appropriate bits in the Interrupt Flag register (see Figure 11-11). The alternate address for Output Register A and the independent modes for control lines CA2 and CB2 allow use of control lines without having to worry about the automatic handshaking features of the VIA.

11-34

VIA INTERRUPT FLAG REGISTER

We have mentioned the VIA Interrupt Flag register (see Figure 11-11) on several occasions. **The table in Figure 11-11 explains the meanings of the various bits** (bit 7 is a general interrupt request bit that is 1 if any interrupt is both active and enabled).

VIA INTERRUPT FLAG REGISTER

Any of the flags in the Interrupt Flag register may be explicitly cleared by writing a logic 1 into the corresponding bit position. This procedure is useful when the control lines are being used independently of the data ports (as in the independent input mode described in Tables 11-8 and 11-9) or when no data transfers are actually required in response to the flag being set. Some examples of explicitly clearing the flags are:

```
        LDA     #%00000010
        STA     VIAIFR          ;CLEAR CA1 INTERRUPT FLAG

        LDA     #%00001000
        STA     VIAIFR          ;CLEAR CB2 INTERRUPT FLAG

        LDA     #%11111111
        STA     VIAIFR          ;CLEAR ALL INTERRUPT FLAGS
```

The value written into bit 7 does not matter, since that flag cannot be explicitly set or cleared from the CPU.

Bits 0, 1, 3, and 4 of the VIA Interrupt Flag register often serve as handshake status bits such as Data Ready or Peripheral Ready. You can check their values with appropriate masking or shifting operations.

```
        LDA     VIAIFR
        AND     #%00000010      ;IS CA1 FLAG SET?
        BNE     DEVRDY          ;YES, DEVICE READY

        LDA     VIAIFR
        AND     #%00010000      ;IS CB1 FLAG SET?
        BNE     DEVRDY          ;YES, DEVICE READY
```

The flag is then automatically cleared by reading or writing the appropriate port or by explicitly clearing the bit in the Interrupt Flag register. The following program will wait for a Ready flag attached to input CA1 to go high:

```
WAITR   LDA     VIAIFR
        AND     #%00000010      ;IS CA1 FLAG SET?
        BEQ     WAITR           ;NO, WAIT
```

How would you change these programs to handle Ready lines attached to CA2, CB1, or CB2?

Note that the flag will remain set unless some operation clears it. If no operation is actually required, some dummy operation (such as reading the port and discarding the data) will be necessary simply to clear the flag. Be particularly careful in cases where the CPU is not ready for data or has no output data to send. Obviously, careful documentation is essential in cases where the purposes of operations may be far from obvious.

VIA TIMERS[9, 10]

As we noted earlier, the VIA contains two 16-bit counter/timers. These timers are handled as follows:

| VIA TIMERS |

1) **They may be read or written as six memory locations, four for timer 1 and two for timer 2** (see Table 11-7).

2) **Their modes of operation are controlled by bits 5, 6, and 7 of the Auxiliary Control register** (see Figure 11-10).

3) **Their status may be determined by examining bits 5 and 6 of the Interrupt Flag register** (see Figure 11-11).

The timers can be used as follows:

1) **To generate a single time interval.** The timer must be loaded with the number of clock pulses that are required.

2) **To count pulses on pin PB6** (timer 2 only). The timer must be loaded with the number of pulses to be counted. This use of PB6 takes precedence over its normal use as an I/O pin.

3) **To generate continuous time intervals** (timer 1 only) **for use in real-time applications.** The timer must be loaded with the number of clock pulses per interval.

4) **To produce a single pulse or a continuous series of pulses on pin PB7** (timer 1 only). The timer must be loaded with the number of clock pulses per interval. This use of PB7 takes precedence over its normal use as an I/O pin.

OPERATION OF 6522 VIA TIMER 2

Timer 2 is simpler than timer 1 and can be used only to generate a single time interval (the one-shot mode) **or to count pulses on pin PB6.** Bit 5 of the Auxiliary Control register selects the mode:

Bit 5 = 0 for one-shot mode, 1 for pulse-counting mode.

The 16-bit timer occupies two memory locations (see Table 11-7). The first address is used to read or write the 8 least significant bits; reading this address also clears the timer 2 interrupt flag (Figure 11-11). The second address is used to read or write the 8 most significant bits; writing into this address loads the counters, clears the timer 2 interrupt flag, and starts the timing operation. The completion of the operation sets the timer 2 interrupt flag (bit 5 of the Interrupt Flag register as shown in Figure 11-11).

Examples of timer 2 operation are as follows:

1) Wait for 1024 (0400_{16}) clock pulses to elapse.

```
        LDA     #0              ;PUT TIMER 2 IN ONE-SHOT MODE (BIT
                                ;   5 = 0)
        STA     VIAACR
        STA     VIAT2L          ;MAKE PULSE LENGTH 0400 HEX
        LDA     #4
        STA     VIAT2H          ;START TIMING INTERVAL
        LDA     #%00100000      ;GET MASK FOR TIMER 2 INTERRUPT FLAG
WAITD   BIT     VIAIFR          ;IS TIMER 2 FLAG SET?
        BEQ     WAITD           ;NO, INTERVAL NOT COMPLETED
        LDA     VIAT2L          ;YES, CLEAR INTERRUPT FLAG
        BRK
```

Note the following steps in the program:

a) Putting the timer in the one-shot mode by clearing bit 5 of the Auxiliary Control register.

b) Loading the timer with the initial count (0400_{16}) required to give the correct interval. Loading the MSBs of the timer also starts the timing operation.

c) Waiting for the interval to be completed. A timeout sets bit 5 of the Interrupt Flag register.

d) Clearing the interrupt flag so that it does not interfere with other operations. The instruction LDA VIAT2L performs this function.

2) Generate a delay of length given by 10 pulses on pin PB6.

```
        LDA     #0
        STA     VIADDRB         ;MAKE PORT B INPUTS
        LDA     #%00100000      ;PUT TIMER 2 IN PULSE-COUNTING MODE
                                ;   (BIT 5 = 1)
        STA     VIAACR
        LDA     #10             ;MAKE PULSE COUNT 10
        STA     VIAT2L
        LDA     #0
        STA     VIAT2H          ;START PULSE COUNTING
        LDA     #%00100000      ;GET MASK FOR TIMER 2 INTERRUPT FLAG
WAITC   BIT     VIAIFR          ;IS TIMER 2 FLAG SET?
        BEQ     WAITC           ;NO, COUNT NOT COMPLETE
        LDA     VIAT2L          ;YES, CLEAR INTERRUPT FLAG
        BRK
```

This program is the same as the previous example, except that the mode of timer 2 is different. Here the input on pin PB6 could be a periodic clock line or a line that is simply pulsed with each occurrence of some external operation.

OPERATION OF 6522 VIA TIMER 1

Timer 1 has four operating modes (see Figure 11-10) **which allow it to generate a single time-interval** (one-shot mode) **or a continuous series of intervals** (free-running mode). Furthermore, each loading operation can generate an output pulse on PB7 which can be used to control external hardware. Bits 6 and 7 of the Auxiliary Control register determine the mode of timer 2 as follows:

Bit 7 = 1 to generate output pulses on pin PB7, 0 to disable such pulses (in the free-running mode, PB7 is inverted each time the counter reaches zero).

Bit 6 = 1 for free-running mode, 0 for one-shot mode.

Timer 1 occupies four memory addresses (see Table 11-7). The first two addresses are used to read or write the counters. Writing into the second address loads the counters, clears the timer 1 Interrupt flag, and starts the timing operation. The next two addresses are used to read from or write into the latches without affecting the counters. This allows the generation of complex waveforms in the free-running mode. Writing into the most significant bits of the latches also clears the timer 1 interrupt flag.

Examples of timer 1 operation are as follows:

1) Wait for 4096 (1000_{16}) clock pulses to elapse before producing an output on pin PB7.

LDA	#0	;PUT TIMER 1 IN SINGLE PULSE, NO OUTPUT
		; MODE
STA	VIAACR	
STA	VIAT1L	;PULSE LENGTH = 1000 HEX
LDA	#$10	
STA	VIAT1CH	;START TIMING INTERVAL
LDA	#%01000000	;GET MASK FOR TIMER 1 INTERRUPT FLAG
WAITD BIT	VIAIFR	;IS TIMER 1 FLAG SET?
BEQ	WAITD	;NO, INTERVAL NOT COMPLETED
LDA	VIAT1L	;YES, CLEAR TIMER 1 INTERRUPT FLAG
BRK		

The only changes from the program for timer 2 are the different addresses used to load the pulse length and the different bit position (bit 6 instead of bit 5) that is examined for the interrupt flag.

2) Produce an interrupt every 2048 (0800_{16}) clock pulses and produce a continuous series of cycles on pin PB7 with a half-width of 2048 clock pulses.

LDA	#$FF	;MAKE PORT B LINES OUTPUTS
STA	VIADDRB	
LDA	#%11000000	;PUT TIMER 1 IN CONTINUOUS MODE WITH
		; OUTPUT TO PB7
STA	VIAACR	
LDA	#0	;MAKE PULSE LENGTH 0800 HEX
STA	VIAT1L	
LDA	#8	
STA	VIAT1CH	;START TIMING INTERVALS
BRK		

This routine will produce a continuous series of intervals that will be marked by the setting of the timer 1 Interrupt flag (bit 6 of the Interrupt Flag register). The main program can look for the occurrence of each interval (with the waiting routine from Example 1), or (more sensibly) the end of each interval can produce an interrupt (see Chapter 12). The level on PB7 will be inverted at the end of each timer interval (it will go low when the first interval starts). Timer 1 will run continuously with the values in the latches automatically being reloaded into the counters each time the counters reach zero.

THE 6530 AND 6532 MULTIFUNCTION SUPPORT DEVICES

The 6530 and 6532 devices contain memory as well as I/O ports. They are sometimes referred to as combination chips, multifunction support devices, or ROM (RAM)/IO/TIMER chips (RIOTs). The 6530 device has:

- 1024 bytes of ROM
- 64 bytes of RAM
- Two 8-bit I/O ports (A and B), although pins 5 through 7 of Port B are often used for chip selects and an interrupt output
- One 8-bit timer

Figure 11-12 is a block diagram of the 6530 device and Table 11-10 describes its internal addressing. The 6532 device has:

- 128 bytes of RAM
- Two 8-bit I/O ports (A and B), although pin 7 of Port A is often used as a strobe input comparable to pins CA1 or CB1 of a 6520 or 6522 device.
- One 8-bit timer

Figure 11-13 is a block diagram of the 6532 device and Table 11-11 describes its internal addressing. Note that 6532 devices contain no ROM.

The following features of 6530 and 6532 devices should be noted:

1) Neither contains any dedicated I/O control lines, although pin 7 of Port A on a 6532 device can be used for this purpose.

2) Both contain a single 8-bit timer with a prescaler that allows timing intervals with multiplying factors of 1, 8, 64, or 1024 clock pulses. The timer can thus be used to provide intervals far longer than the basic 256 clock counts.

3) The end of the timing interval either causes an interrupt or sets a flag which can be read.

The 6530 and 6532 devices are used in such popular single-board microcomputers as the KIM, VIM, SYM, and AIM-65.[11-14]

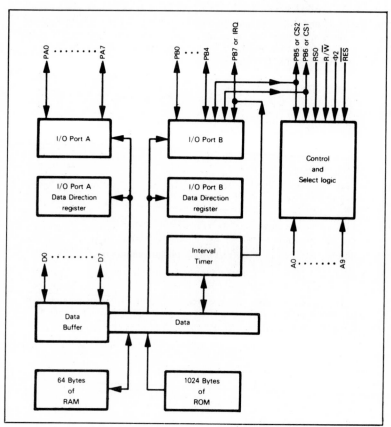

Figure 11-12. Block Diagram of the 6530 Multifunction Device

Table 11-10. Internal Addressing for the 6530 Multifunction Device

Pimary Select			Accessed Locations					
RSO	RAM Select*	I/O Timer Select*						
1	X	X	A0 - A9 directly address one of 1024 ROM bytes					
0	1	0	A0 - A5 directly address one of 64 RAM bytes					
			Secondary Select				Interpretation	
			A3	A2	A1	A0		
0	0	1	X	0	0	0	Access I/O Port A	
0	0	1	X	0	0	1	Access I/O Port A Data Direction register	
0	0	1	X	0	1	0	Access I/O Port B	
0	0	1	X	0	1	1	Access I/O Port B Data Direction register	
0	0	1W	0	1	X	X	Disable $\overline{IRQ}$	
0	0	1W	1	1	X	X	Enable $\overline{IRQ}$	
0	0	1W	X	1	0	0	Write to timer, then decrement every $\Phi2$ pulse	
0	0	1W	X	1	0	1	Write to timer, then decrement every 8 $\Phi2$ pulses	
0	0	1W	X	1	1	0	Write to timer, then decrement every 64 $\Phi2$ pulses	
0	0	1W	X	1	1	1	Write to timer, then decrement every 1024 $\Phi2$ pulses	
0	0	1R	X	1	X	0	Read timer	
0	0	1R	X	1	X	1	Read interrupt flag	

* RAM select and I/O select are "true" if 1, or "false" if 0; true and false are functions of your specification. You specify the combination of address lines that create a "true" line condition.

X   represents "don't care". Bits may be 0 or 1.
1R represents Select during a read.
1W represents Select during a write.

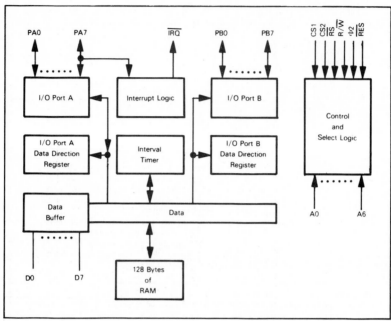

Figure 11-13. Block Diagram of the 6532 Multifunction Device

Table 11-11. Internal Addressing for the 6532 Multifunction Device

Primary Select		Secondary Select					
RAM Select	I/O Timer Select	A4	A3	A2	A1	A0	Interpretation
1	0	X	X	X	X	X	A0 - A6 directly addresses one of 128 RAM bytes
0	1	X	X	0	0	0	Access I/O Port A
0	1	X	X	0	0	1	Access I/O Port A Data Direction register
0	1	X	X	0	1	0	Access I/O Port B
0	1	X	X	0	1	1	Access I/O Port B Data Direction register
0	1W	1	0	1	X	X	Disable $\overline{IRQ}$
0	1W	1	1	1	X	X	Enable $\overline{IRQ}$
0	1W	1	X	1	0	0	Write to timer, then decrement every Φ2 pulse
0	1W	1	X	1	0	1	Write to timer, then decrement every 8 Φ2 pulses
0	1W	1	X	1	1	0	Write to timer, then decrement every 64 Φ2 pulses
0	1W	1	X	1	1	1	Write to timer, then decrement every 1024 Φ2 pulses
0	1R	X	X	1	X	0	Read timer
0	1R	X	X	1	X	1	Read interrupt flags
0	1W	0	X	1	X	0	Request interrupt on high-to-low PA7 transition
0	1W	0	X	1	X	1	Request interrupt on low-to-high PA7 transition
0	1W	0	X	1	0	X	Enable PA7 interrupt request
0	1W	0	X	1	1	X	Disable PA7 interrupt request

X represents "don't care" Bits may be 0 or 1.
1R represents Read access. 1W represents Write access.

EXAMPLES

A Pushbutton Switch

Purpose: To interface a single pushbutton switch to a 6502 microprocessor by means of a 6522 Versatile Interface Adapter. The pushbutton is a single mechanical switch that provides a contact closure (logic level '0') while pressed.

Figure 11-14 shows the circuitry required to interface the pushbutton. It uses one bit of a 6522 VIA, which acts as a buffer; no latch is needed since the pushbutton remains closed for many CPU clock cycles. Pressing the button grounds the VIA input bit. The pullup resistor ensures that the input bit is '1' if the button is not being pressed.

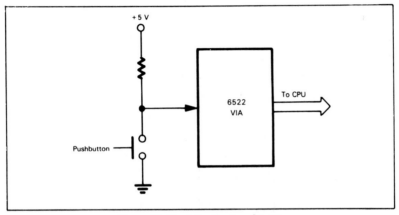

Figure 11-14. A Pushbutton Circuit

Programming Examples:

We will perform two tasks with this circuit. They are:

a) Set a memory location based on the state of the button.

b) Count the number of times that the button is pressed.

Task 1: Determine Switch Closure

Purpose: Set memory location 0040 to one if the button is not being pressed, and to zero if it is being pressed.

Sample Cases:

1) Button open (i.e., not pressed)
   Result = (0040) = 01

2) Button closed (i.e., pressed)
   Result = (0040) = 00

Flowchart:

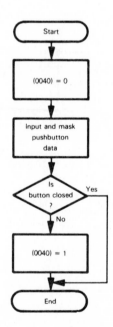

Source Program:

```
        LDA     #0
        STA     VIAPCR          ;MAKE ALL CONTROL LINES INPUTS
        STA     VIADDRA         ;MAKE PORT A LINES INPUTS
        STA     $40             ;MARKER = ZERO
        LDA     VIAORA          ;READ BUTTON POSITION
        AND     #MASK           ;IS BUTTON CLOSED (LOGIC ZERO)?
        BEQ     DONE            ;YES, DONE
        INC     $40             ;NO, MARKER =1
DONE    BRK
```

Object Program:

Memory Location (Hex)	Memory Contents (Hex)		Instruction (Mnemonic)	
0000	A9		LDA	#0
0001	00			
0002	8D		STA	VIAPCR
0003 ⎱ 0004 ⎰	VIAPCR			
0005	8D		STA	VIADDRA
0006 ⎱ 0007 ⎰	VIADDRA			
0008	85		STA	$40
0009	40			
000A	AD		LDA	VIAORA
000B ⎱ 000C ⎰	VIAORA			
000D	29		AND	#MASK
000E	MASK			
000F	F0		BEQ	DONE
0010	02			
0011	E6		INC	$40
0012	40			
0013	00	DONE	BRK	

The addresses VIAPCR (Peripheral Control register), VIADDRA (Data Direction Register A), and VIAORA (Output Register A) depend on how the VIA is connected in your microcomputer. The VIA control lines are not used in this example; the contents of the Peripheral Control register are thus irrelevant but we have cleared that register as a precaution against spurious operations. We have assumed (as is usually the case) that the VIA addresses are not on page zero.

MASK depends on the bit to which the pushbutton is connected; it has a one in the button position and zeros elsewhere.

Button Position (Bit Number)	Mask	
	Binary	Hex
0	00000001	01
1	00000010	02
2	00000100	04
3	00001000	08
4	00010000	10
5	00100000	20
6	01000000	40
7	10000000	80

If the button is attached to bit 6 or bit 7 of the VIA input port, the program can use a Bit Test instruction to set the Overflow or Sign bits and thereby determine the button's state. For example,

Bit 7

```
BIT     VIAORA      ;IS BUTTON CLOSED (LOGIC ZERO)?
BPL     DONE        ;YES, DONE
```

Bit 6

```
BIT     VIAORA      ;IS BUTTON CLOSED (LOGIC ZERO)?
BVC     DONE        ;YES, DONE
```

Note the use of BVC or BVS to check the value of bit 6.

We could also use shift instructions if the button is attached to bits 0, 6, or 7. The sequence for bit 0 is:

```
LSR     VIAORA      ;IS BUTTON CLOSED (LOGIC ZERO)?
BCC     DONE        ;YES, DONE
```

The instructions ASL or ROL can be used with bits 6 or 7. Do the contents of the VIA Data register actually change? Explain your answer.

Task 2: Count Switch Closures

Purpose: Count the number of button closures by incrementing memory location 0040 after each closure.

Sample Case:

Pressing the button ten times after the start of the program should give

(0040) = 0A

Note: In order to count the number of times that the button has been pressed, we must be sure that each closure causes a single transition. However, a mechanical pushbutton does not produce a single transition for each closure, because the mechanical contacts bounce back and forth before settling into their final positions. We can use hardware to eliminate the bounce or we can handle it in software.

The program can debounce the pushbutton by waiting after it finds a closure. The required delay is called the debouncing time and is part of the specifications of the pushbutton. It is typically a few milliseconds long. The program should not examine the pushbutton during this period because it might mistake the bounces for new closures. The program may either enter a delay routine like the one described previously or may simply perform other tasks for the specified amount of time.

Even after debouncing, the program must still wait for the present closure to end before looking for a new closure. This procedure avoids double counting. The following program uses a software delay of 10 ms to debounce the pushbutton. You may want to try varying the delay or eliminating it entirely to see what happens. To run this program, you must also enter the delay subroutine into memory starting at location 0030.

Flowchart:

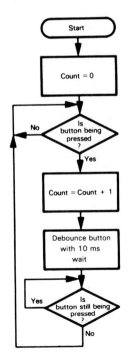

11-47

Source Program:

```
          LDA     #0
          STA     VIAPCR      ;MAKE ALL CONTROL LINES INPUTS
          STA     VIADDRA     ;MAKE PORT A LINES INPUTS
          STA     $40         ;COUNT = ZERO INITIALLY
CHKCL     LDA     VIAORA
          AND     #MASK       ;IS BUTTON BEING PRESSED?
          BNE     CHKCL       ;NO, WAIT UNTIL IT IS
          INC     $40         ;YES, ADD 1 TO CLOSURE COUNT
          LDY     #10         ;WAIT 10 MS TO DEBOUNCE BUTTON
          JSR     DELAY
CHKOP     LDA     VIAORA
          AND     #MASK       ;IS BUTTON STILL BEING PRESSED?
          BEQ     CHKOP       ;YES, WAIT FOR RELEASE
          BNE     CHKCL       ;NO, LOOK FOR NEXT CLOSURE
```

Object Program:

Memory Location (Hex)	Memory Contents (Hex)	Instruction (Mnemonic)		
0000	A9		LDA	#0
0001	00			
0002	8D		STA	VIAPCR
0003⎱ 0004⎰	VIAPCR			
0005	8D		STA	VIADDRA
0006⎱ 0007⎰	VIADDRA			
0008	85		STA	$40
0009	40			
000A	AD	CHKCL	LDA	VIAORA
000B⎱ 000C⎰	VIAORA			
000D	29		AND	#MASK
000E	MASK			
000F	D0		BNE	CHKCL
0010	F9			
0011	E6		INC	$40
0012	40			
0013	A0		LDY	#10
0014	0A			
0015	20		JSR	DELAY
0016	30			
0017	00			
0018	AD	CHKOP	LDA	VIAORA
0019⎱ 001A⎰	VIAORA			
001B	29		AND	#MASK
001C	MASK			
001D	F0		BEQ	CHKOP
001E	F9			
001F	D0		BNE	CHKCL
0020	E9			

The three instructions beginning with the label CHKOP are used to determine when the switch reopens.

Clearly we do not really need a VIA for this simple interface. An addressable tri-state buffer would do the job at far lower cost.

A Toggle Switch

Purpose: To interface a single-pole, double-throw (SPDT) toggle switch to a 6502 microprocessor. The toggle is a mechanical device that is either in the normally closed (NC) position or the normally open (NO) position.

Circuit Diagram:

Figure 11-15 shows the circuitry required to interface the switch. Like the pushbutton, the switch uses one bit of a 6522 VIA that serves as an addressable buffer. Unlike the button, the switch may be left in either position. Typical program tasks are to determine the switch position and to see if the position has changed. Either a one-shot with a pulse length of a few milliseconds or a pair of cross-coupled NAND gates (see Figure 11-16) can debounce a mechanical switch.

> **DEBOUNCING WITH CROSS-COUPLED NAND GATES**

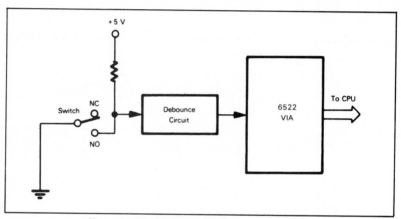

Figure 11-15. An Interface for a Toggle Switch

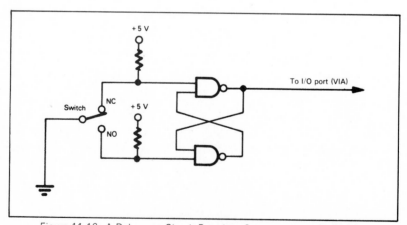

Figure 11-16. A Debounce Circuit Based on Cross-coupled NAND Gates

11-50

The circuits will produce a single step or pulse in response to a change in switch position even if the switch bounces before settling into its new position.

Programming Examples:

We will perform two tasks involving this circuit. They are:

1)   Set a memory location to one when the switch is closed.

2)   Set a memory location to one when the state of the switch changes.

Task 1: Wait for Switch to Close

Purpose: Memory location 0040 is zero until the switch is closed and then is set to one; that is, the processor clears memory location 0040, waits for the switch to be closed, and then sets memory location 0040 to one.

The switch could be marked Run/$\overline{\text{Halt}}$, since the processor will not proceed until the switch is closed.

Flowchart:

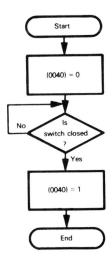

Source Program:

```
        LDA     #0
        STA     VIAPCR          ;MAKE ALL CONTROL LINES INPUTS
        STA     VIADDRA         ;MAKE PORT A LINES INPUTS
        STA     $40             ;MARKER = ZERO
WAITC   LDA     VIAORA          ;READ SWITCH POSITION
        AND     #MASK           ;IS SWITCH CLOSED ('0')?
        BNE     WAITC           ;NO, WAIT
        INC     $40             ;YES, MARKER = ONE
        BRK
```

Object Program:

Memory Location (Hex)	Memory Contents (Hex)	Instruction (Mnemonic)		
0000	A9		LDA	#0
0001	00			
0002	8D		STA	VIAPCR
0003 0004	VIAPCR			
0005	8D		STA	VIADDRA
0006 0007	VIADDRA			
0008	85		STA	$40
0009	40			
000A	AD	WAITC	LDA	VIAORA
000B 000C	VIAORA			
000D	29		AND	#MASK
000E	MASK			
000F	D0		BNE	WAITC
0010	F9			
0011	E6		INC	$40
0012	40			
0013	00		BRK	

Task 2: Wait for Switch to Change

Purpose: Memory location 0040 remains zero until the switch position changes and is then set to 1; i.e., the processor waits until the switch changes position, then sets memory location 0040 to 1.

Flowchart:

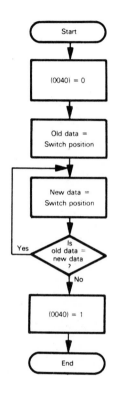

Source Program:

```
        LDA     #0
        STA     VIAPCR      ;MAKE ALL CONTROL LINES INPUTS
        STA     VIADDRA     ;MAKE PORT A LINES INPUTS
        STA     $40         ;MARKER = ZERO
        LDA     VIAORA      ;GET OLD SWITCH POSITION
        AND     #MASK
        STA     $41
WAITCH  LDA     VIAORA      ;GET NEW SWITCH POSITION
        AND     #MASK
        CMP     $41         ;ARE NEW AND OLD POSITIONS THE SAME?
        BEQ     WAITCH      ;YES, WAIT
        INC     $40         ;NO, MARKER = ONE
        BRK
```

Object Program:

Memory Location (Hex)	Memory Contents (Hex)	Instruction (Mnemonic)	
0000	A9	LDA	#0
0001	00		
0002	8D	STA	VIAPCR
0003⎱ 0004⎰	VIAPCR		
0005	8D	STA	VIADDRA
0006⎱ 0007⎰	VIADDRA		
0008	85	STA	$40
0009	40		
000A	AD	LDA	VIAORA
000B⎱ 000C⎰	VIAORA		
000D	29	AND	#MASK
000E	MASK		
000F	85	STA	$41
0010	41		
0011	AD	WAITCH LDA	VIAORA
0012⎱ 0013⎰	VIAORA		
0014	29	AND	#MASK
0015	MASK		
0016	C5	CMP	$41
0017	41		
0018	F0	BEQ	WAITCH
0019	F7		
001A	E6	INC	$40
001B	40		
001C	00	BRK	

A Subtract or Exclusive OR could replace the Compare instruction in the program. Either of these instructions would, however, change the contents of the Accumulator. The Exclusive OR would be useful if several switches were attached to the same VIA, since it would produce a one bit for each switch that changed state. How would you rewrite this program so that it debounces the switch in software?

A Multiple-Position (Rotary, Selector, or Thumbwheel) Switch

Purpose: To interface a multiple-position switch to a 6502 microprocessor. The lead corresponding to the switch position is grounded, while the other leads are high (logic ones).

Circuit Diagram:

Figure 11-17 shows the circuitry required to interface an 8-position switch. The switch uses all eight data bits of one port of a VIA. Typical tasks are to determine the position of the switch and to check whether or not that position has changed. Two special situations must be handled:

1) The switch is temporarily between positions so that no leads are grounded.

2) The switch has not yet reached its final position.

The first of these situations can be handled by waiting until the input is not all '1's, i.e., until a switch lead is grounded. We can handle the second situation by examining the switch again after a delay (such as 1 or 2 seconds) and only accepting the input when it remains the same. This delay will not affect the responsiveness of the system to the switch. We can also use another switch (i.e., a Load switch) to tell the processor when the selector switch should be read.

Programming Examples:

We will perform two tasks involving the circuit of Figure 11-17. These are:

a) Monitor the switch until it is in a definite position, then determine the position and store its binary value in a memory location.

b) Wait for the position of the switch to change, then store the new position in a memory location.

If the switch is in a position, the lead from that position is grounded through the common line. Pullup resistors on the input lines avoid problems caused by noise.

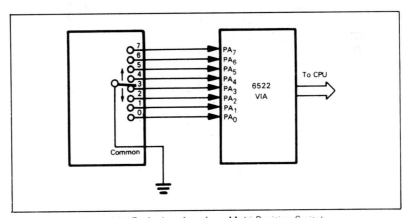

Figure 11-17. An Interface for a Multi-Position Switch

Task 1: Determine Switch Position

Purpose: The program waits for the switch to be in a specific position and then stores the position number in memory location 0040.

Table 11-12 contains the data inputs corresponding to the various switch positions.

Table 11-12. Data Input vs. Switch Position

Switch Position	Data Input	
	Binary	**Hex**
0	11111110	FE
1	11111101	FD
2	11111011	FB
3	11110111	F7
4	11101111	EF
5	11011111	DF
6	10111111	BF
7	01111111	7F

This scheme is inefficient, since it requires eight bits to distinguish among eight different positions.

USING A TTL ENCODER

A TTL or MOS encoder could reduce the number of input bits needed. Figure 11-18 shows a circuit using the 74LS148 TTL 8-to-3 encoder.[15] We attach the switch outputs in inverse order, since the 74LS148 device has active-low inputs and outputs. The output of the encoder circuit is a 3-bit representation of the switch position. Many switches include encoders so that their outputs are coded, usually as a BCD digit (in negative logic).

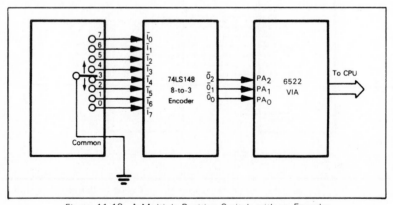

Figure 11-18. A Multiple-Position Switch with an Encoder

The encoder produces active-low outputs, so, for example, switch position 5, which is attached to input 2, produces an output of 2 in negative logic (or 5 in positive logic). You may want to verify the double negative for yourself.

Flowchart:

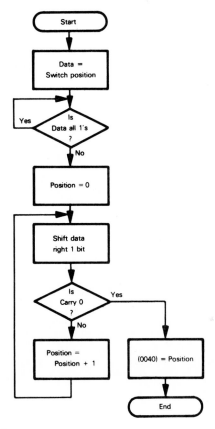

Source Program:

```
        LDA     #0
        STA     VIAPCR      ;MAKE ALL CONTROL LINES INPUTS
        STA     VIADDRA     ;MAKE PORT A LINES INPUTS
CHKSW   LDA     VIAORA
        CMP     #$FF        ;IS SWITCH IN A POSITION?
        BEQ     CHKSW       ;NO, WAIT UNTIL IT IS
        LDX     #0          ;SWITCH POSITION = ZERO
CHKPOS  ROR     A           ;IS NEXT BIT GROUNDED POSITION?
        BCC     DONE        ;YES, SWITCH POSITION FOUND
        INX                 ;NO, INCREMENT SWITCH POSITION
        JMP     CHKPOS
DONE    STX     $40         ;SAVE SWITCH POSITION
        BRK
```

Object Program:

Memory Address (Hex)	Memory Contents (Hex)		Instruction (Mnemonic)	
0000	A9		LDA	#0
0001	00			
0002	8D		STA	VIAPCR
0003 } 0004 }	VIAPCR			
0005	8D		STA	VIADDRA
0006 } 0007 }	VIADDRA			
0008	AD	CHKSW	LDA	VIAORA
0009 } 000A }	VIAORA			
000B	C9		CMP	#$FF
000C	FF			
000D	F0		BEQ	CHKSW
000E	F9			
000F	A2		LDX	#0
0010	00			
0011	6A	CHKPOS	ROR	A
0012	90		BCC	DONE
0013	04			
0014	E8		INX	
0015	4C		JMP	CHKPOS
0016	11			
0017	00			
0018	86	DONE	STX	$40
0019	40			
001A	00		BRK	

Suppose that a faulty switch or defective VIA results in the input always being FF_{16}. How could you change the program so that it would detect this error?

This program could easily be restructured to make it shorter and faster — and relocatable as well. One option would be to replace JMP CHKPOS with BCS CHKPOS; why is this possible and what improvements result? Another option would be to change the initial conditions so that only one jump instruction was required. How would you accomplish that? Hint: start with FF_{16} in Index Register X and increment X before shifting the Accumulator.

This example assumes that the switch is debounced in hardware. How would you change the program to debounce the switch in software?

Task 2: Wait For Switch Position To Change

Purpose: The program waits for the switch position to change and places the new position (decoded) into memory location 0040. The program waits until the switch reaches its new position.

Flowchart:

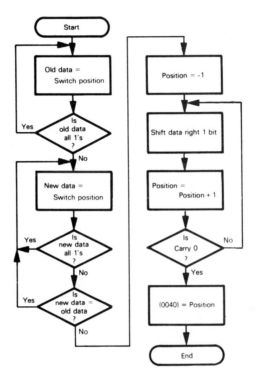

Source Program:

```
        LDA     #0
        STA     VIAPCR      ;MAKE ALL CONTROL LINES INPUTS
        STA     VIADDRA     ;MAKE PORT A LINES INPUTS
CHKFST  LDA     VIAORA
        CMP     #$FF        ;IS SWITCH IN A POSITION?
        BEQ     CHKFST      ;NO, WAIT UNTIL IT IS
        TAX                 ;SAVE OLD POSITION
CHKSEC  LDA     VIAORA
        CMP     #$FF        ;IS SWITCH IN A POSITION?
        BEQ     CHKSEC      ;NO, WAIT UNTIL IT IS
        CPX     VIAORA      ;IS POSITION SAME AS BEFORE?
        BEQ     CHKSEC      ;YES, WAIT FOR IT TO CHANGE
        LDX     #$FF        ;NO, START SWITCH POSITION AT -1
CHKPOS  INX                 ;SWITCH POSITION = SWITCH POSITION + 1
        ROR     A           ;IS NEXT BIT GROUNDED?
        BCS     CHKPOS      ;NO, KEEP LOOKING
        STX     $40         ;STORE SWITCH POSITION
        BRK
```

Object Program:

Memory Address (Hex)	Memory Contents (Hex)		Instruction (Mnemonic)	
0000	A9		LDA	#0
0001	00			
0002	8D		STA	VIAPCR
0003 ⎱ 0004 ⎰	VIAPCR			
0005	8D		STA	VIADDRA
0006 ⎱ 0007 ⎰	VIADDRA			
0008	AD	CHKFST	LDA	VIAORA
0009 ⎱ 000A ⎰	VIAORA			
000B	C9		CMP	#$FF
000C	FF			
000D	F0		BEQ	CHKFST
000E	F9			
000F	AA		TAX	
0010	AD	CHKSEC	LDA	VIAORA
0011 ⎱ 0012 ⎰	VIAORA			
0013	C9		CMP	#$FF
0014	FF			
0015	F0		BEQ	CHKSEC
0016	F9			
0017	EC		CPX	VIAORA
0018 ⎱ 0019 ⎰	VIAORA			
001A	F0		BEQ	CHKSEC
001B	F4			
001C	A2		LDX	#$FF
001D	FF			
001E	E8	CHKPOS	INX	
001F	6A		ROR	A
0020	B0		BCS	CHKPOS
0021	FC			
0022	86		STX	$40
0023	40			
0024	00		BRK	

An alternative method for determining if the switch is in a position is:

```
CHKSW   INC     VIAORA
        BEQ     CHKSW
```

Why does this work? What happens to the input data? Rewrite the program to use the alternative method; how much less memory is required?

A Single LED

Purpose: To interface a single light-emitting diode to a 6502 microprocessor. The LED can be attached so that either a logic zero or a logic one turns it on.

Circuit Diagram:

Figure 11-19 shows the circuitry required to interface an LED. The LED lights when its anode is positive with respect to its cathode (Figure 11-19a). Therefore, you can either light the LED by ground-

```
LED
CONTROL
```

ing the cathode and having the computer supply a one to the anode (Figure 11-19b) or by connecting the anode to +5 volts and having the computer supply a zero to the cathode (Figure 11-19c). Controlling the cathode is the most common approach. The LED is brightest when it operates from pulsed currents of about 10 or 50 mA applied a few hundred times per second. LEDs have a very short turn-on time (in the microsecond range) so they are well suited to multiplexing (operating several from a single port). LED circuits usually need peripheral or transistor drivers and current-limiting resistors. MOS devices normally cannot drive LEDs directly and make them bright enough for easy viewing.

Note: The VIA has an output latch on each port. However, the B port is normally used for output, since it has somewhat more drive capability. In particular, the B port outputs are capable of driving Darlington transistors (providing 3.0 mA minimum at 1.5 V). Darlington transistors are high-gain transistors capable of switching large amounts of current at high speed; they are useful in driving solenoids, relays, and other devices.

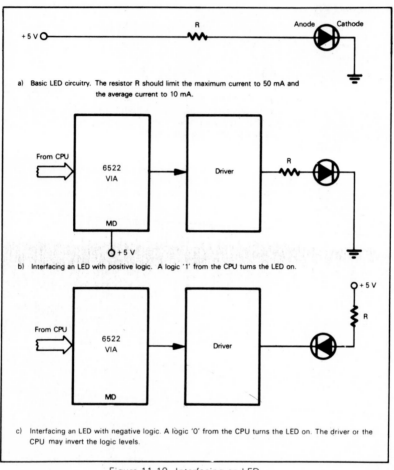

a) Basic LED circuitry. The resistor R should limit the maximum current to 50 mA and the average current to 10 mA.

b) Interfacing an LED with positive logic. A logic '1' from the CPU turns the LED on.

c) Interfacing an LED with negative logic. A logic '0' from the CPU turns the LED on. The driver or the CPU may invert the logic levels.

Figure 11-19. Interfacing an LED

Task: Turn the Light On or Off

Purpose: The program turns a single LED either on or off.

A. Send a Logic One to the LED (turn a positive display on or a negative display off).

Source Program:

(form data initially)

```
        LDA     #0
        STA     VIAPCR      ;MAKE ALL CONTROL LINES INPUTS
        LDA     #$FF
        STA     VIADDRB     ;MAKE PORT B LINES OUTPUTS
        LDA     #MASKP      ;GET DATA FOR LED
        STA     VIAORB      ;SEND DATA TO LED
        BRK
```

The B side of the VIA is used because of the buffering. The CPU can therefore read the data from the output port.

(update data)

```
        LDA     VIAORB      ;GET OLD DATA
        ORA     #MASKP      ;TURN ON LED BIT
        STA     VIAORB      ;SEND DATA TO LED
        BRK
```

MASKP has a one bit in the LED position and zeros elsewhere. Logically ORing with MASKP does not affect the other bit positions, which may contain values for other LEDs. Note that we can read the VIA Output (Data) Register even when the pins are assigned as outputs.

Object Program:

Memory Address (Hex)	Memory Contents (Hex)	Instruction (Mnemonic)	
(form data initially)			
0000	A9	LDA	#0
0001	00		
0002	8D	STA	VIAPCR
0003 0004	VIAPCR		
0005	A9	LDA	#$FF
0006	FF		
0007	8D	STA	VIADDRB
0008 0009	VIADDRB		
000A	A9	LDA	#MASKP
000B	MASKP		
000C	8D	STA	VIAORB
000D 000E	VIAORB		
000F	00	BRK	
(update data)			
0010	AD	LDA	VIAORB
0011 0012	VIAORB		
0013	09	ORA	#MASKP
0014	MASKP		
0015	8D	STA	VIAORB
0016 0017	VIAORB		
0018	00	BRK	

B.   Send a Logic Zero to the LED (turn a positive display off or a negative display on).

The differences are that MASKP must be replaced by its logical complement MASKN and ORA #MASKP must be replaced by AND #MASKN. MASKN has a zero bit in the LED position and ones elsewhere. Logically ANDing with MASKN does not affect the other bit positions.

Seven-Segment LED Display

Purpose: To interface a seven-segment LED display to a 6502 microprocessor. The display may be either common-anode (negative logic) or common-cathode (positive logic).

Circuit Diagram:

Figure 11-20 shows the circuitry required to interface a seven-segment display. Each segment may have one, two, or more LEDs attached in the same way. There are two ways of connecting the displays. One is tying all the cathodes together to ground (see Figure 11-21a); this is a

```
COMMON-ANODE
OR
COMMON-CATHODE
DISPLAYS
```

"common-cathode" display, and a logic one at an anode lights a segment. The other is tying all the anodes together to a positive voltage supply (see Figure 11-21b); this is a "common-anode" display, and a logic zero at a cathode lights a segment. So the common-cathode display uses positive logic and the common-anode display negative logic. Either display requires appropriate drivers and resistors.

The Common line from the display is tied either to ground or to +5 volts. The display segments are customarily labelled:

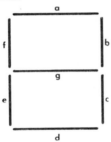

Note: The seven-segment display is widely used because it contains the smallest number of separately controlled segments that can provide recognizable representations of all the decimal digits (see Figure 11-22 and Table 11-13). Seven-segment displays can also produce some letters and other characters (see Table 11-14). Better representations require a substantially larger number of segments and more circuitry.[16] Since seven-segment displays are so popular, low-cost seven-segment decoder/drivers have become widely available. The most popular devices are the 7447 common-anode driver and the 7448 common-cathode driver;[17] these devices have Lamp Test inputs (that turn all the segments on) and blanking inputs and outputs (for blanking leading or trailing zeros).

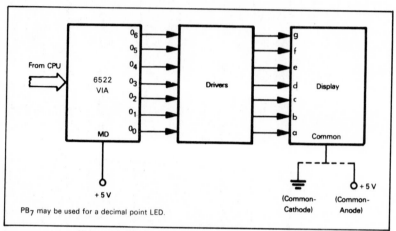

Figure 11-20. Interfacing a Seven-Segment Display

Table 11-13. Seven-Segment Representations of Decimal Numbers

Number	Hexadecimal Representation	
	Common-cathode	Common-anode
0	3F	40
1	06	79
2	5B	24
3	4F	30
4	66	19
5	6D	12
6	7D	02
7	07	78
8	7F	00
9	67	18

Bit 7 is always zero and the others are g, f, e, d, c, b, and a in decreasing order of significance.

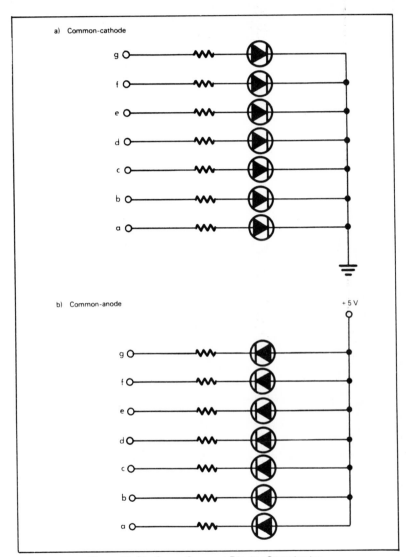

Figure 11-21. Seven-Segment Display Organization

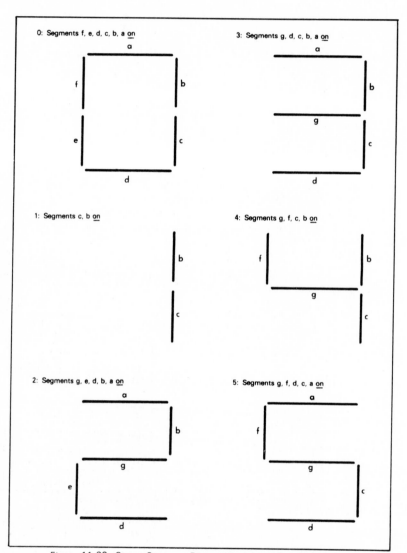

Figure 11-22. Seven-Segment Representations of Decimal Digits

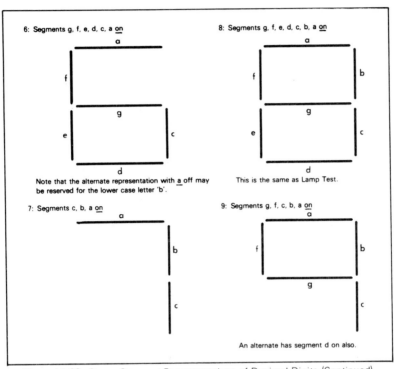

Figure 11-22. Seven-Segment Representations of Decimal Digits (Continued)

Table 11-14. Seven-Segment Representations of Letters and Symbols

Upper-case Letters			Lower-case Letters and Special Characters		
Letter	Hexadecimal Representation		Character	Hexadecimal Representation	
	Common-cathode	Common-anode		Common-cathode	Common-anode
A	77	08	b	7C	03
C	39	46	c	58	27
E	79	06	d	5E	21
F	71	0E	h	74	0B
H	76	09	n	54	2B
I	06	79	o	5C	23
J	1E	61	r	50	2F
L	38	47	u	1C	63
O	3F	40	-	40	3F
P	73	0C	?	53	2C
U	3E	41			
Y	66	19			

Task 1: Display a Decimal Digit

Purpose: Display the contents of memory location 0040 on a seven-segment display if it contains a decimal digit. Otherwise, blank the display.

Sample Problems:

a.   (0040) = 05

  Result is 5 on display

b.   (0040) = 66

  Result is a blank display

Flowchart:

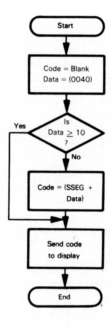

Source Program:

```
          LDA    #0
          STA    VIAPCR        ;MAKE ALL CONTROL LINES INPUTS
          LDA    #$FF
          STA    VIADDRB       ;MAKE PORT B LINES OUTPUTS
          LDA    #BLANK        ;GET BLANK CODE
          LDX    $40           ;GET DATA
          CPX    #10           ;IS DATA 10 OR MORE?
          BCS    DSPLY         ;YES, DISPLAY BLANKS
          LDA    SSEG,X        ;NO, CONVERT DATA TO SEVEN-SEGMENT
                               ;  CODE
DISPLY    STA    VIAORB        ;SEND CODE TO DISPLAY
          BRK
```

BLANK is 00 for a common-cathode display, FF for a common-anode display. An alternative procedure would be to put the blank code at the end of the table and replace all improper data values with 10, i.e., the instructions after STA VIADDRB are:

```
          LDX    $40           ;GET DATA
          CPX    #10           ;IS DATA 10 OR MORE?
          BCC    CNVRT
          LDX    #10           ;YES, REPLACE IT WITH 10
CNVRT     LDA    SSEG,X        ;CONVERT DATA TO SEVEN-SEGMENT CODE
```

Table SSEG is either the common-cathode or common-anode representation of the decimal digits from Table 11-13.

Object Program:

Memory Address (Hex)	Memory Contents (Hex)		Instruction (Mnemonic)	
0000	A9		LDA	#0
0001	00			
0002	8D		STA	VIAPCR
0003 0004 }	VIAPCR			
0005	A9		LDA	#$FF
0006	FF			
0007	8D		STA	VIADDRB
0008 0009 }	VIADDRB			
000A	A9		LDA	#BLANK
000B	BLANK			
000C	A6		LDX	$40
000D	40			
000E	E0		CPX	#10
000F	0A			
0010	B0		BCS	DSPLY
0011	02			
0012	B5		LDA	SSEG,X
0013	20			
0014	8D	DSPLY	STA	VIAORB
0015 0016 }	VIAORB			
0017	00		BRK	
0020-0029		SSEG	(seven-segment code table)	

Several displays may be multiplexed, as shown in Figure 11-23. A brief strobe on control line CB2 clocks the counter and directs data to the next display. RESET starts the decimal counter at 9 so that the first output operation clears the counter and directs data to the first display.

The following program uses the delay routine to pulse each of ten common-cathode displays for 1 ms.

Task 2: Display Ten Decimal Digits

Purpose: Display the contents of memory locations 0040 through 0049 on ten 7-segment displays that are multiplexed with a counter and a decoder. The most significant digit is in 0049.

Sample Problem:

```
(0040)  =  66
(0041)  =  3F
(0042)  =  7F
(0043)  =  7F
(0044)  =  06
(0045)  =  5B
(0046)  =  07
(0047)  =  4F
(0048)  =  6D
(0049)  =  7D
```

The displays read 6537218804

The circuit in Figure 11-23 uses the VIA handshake signal CB2 as a brief output strobe to indicate the occurrence of a data transfer.

Source Program:

```
        LDA    #$FF
        STA    VIADDRB       ;MAKE PORT B LINES OUTPUTS
        LDA    #%10100000
        STA    VIAPCR        ;PROVIDE DATA READY STROBE
SCAN    LDX    #10           ;NUMBER OF DISPLAYS = 10
DSPLY   LDA    $3F,X         ;GET DATA FOR DISPLAY
        STA    VIAORB        ;SEND DATA TO DISPLAY
        JSR    DELAY         ;WAIT 1 MS
        DEX
        BNE    DSPLY         ;COUNT DISPLAYS
        BEQ    SCAN          ;START ANOTHER SCAN
```

Peripheral Control register bit 7 = 1 to make CB2 an output, bit 6 = 1 to make it a pulse, and bit 3 = 1 to make it a brief strobe. We have assumed here that subroutine DELAY has been modified to provide a transparent 1 ms wait.

Object Program:

Memory Address (Hex)	Memory Contents (Hex)		Instruction (Mnemonic)	
0000	A9		LDA	#$FF
0001	FF			
0002	8D		STA	VIADDRB
0003 0004 }	VIADDRB			
0005	A9		LDA	#%10100000
0006	A0			
0007	8D		STA	VIAPCR
0008 0009 }	VIAPCR			
000A	A2	SCAN	LDX	#10
000B	0A			
000C	B5	DSPLY	LDA	$3F,X
000D	3F			
000E	·8D		STA	VIAORB
000F 0010 }	VIAORB			
0011	20		JSR	DELAY
0012	30			
0013	00			
0014	CA		DEX	
0015	D0		BNE	DSPLY
0016	F5			
0017	F0		BEQ	SCAN
0018	F1			

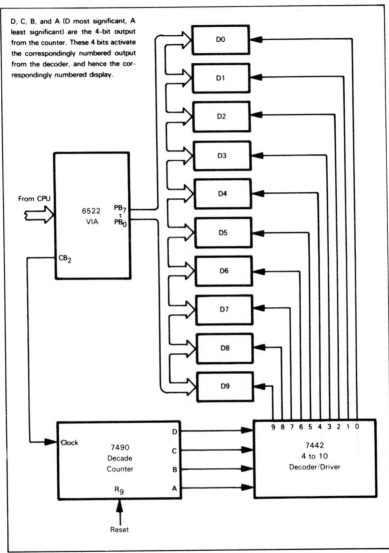

D, C, B, and A (D most significant, A least significant) are the 4-bit output from the counter. These 4 bits activate the correspondingly numbered output from the decoder, and hence the correspondingly numbered display.

Figure 11-23. Interfacing Multiplexed Seven-Segment Displays

11-75

PROBLEMS

1) An On-Off Pushbutton

Purpose: Each closure of the pushbutton complements (inverts) all the bits in memory location 0040. The location initially contains zero. The program should continuously examine the pushbutton and complement location 0040 with each closure. You may wish to complement a display output port instead, thus making the results easier to see.

Sample Case:

Location 0040 initially contains zero.

The first pushbutton closure changes location 0040 to FF_{16}, the second changes it back to zero, the third back to FF_{16}, etc. Assume that the pushbutton is debounced in hardware. How would you include debouncing in your program?

2) Debouncing a Switch in Software

Purpose: Debounce a mechanical switch by waiting until two readings, taken a debounce time apart, give the same result. Assume that the debounce time (in ms) is in memory location 0040 and store the switch position in memory location 0041.

Sample Problem:

(0040) = 03 causes the program to wait 3 ms between readings.

3) Control for a Rotary Switch

Purpose: Another switch serves as a Load switch for a four-position unencoded rotary switch. The CPU waits for the Load switch to close (be zero), and then reads the position of the rotary switch. This procedure allows the operator to move the rotary switch to its final position before the CPU tries to read it. The program should place the position of the rotary switch into memory location 0040. Debounce the Load switch in software.

Sample Problem:

Place rotary switch in position 2. Close Load switch.

Result: (0040) = 02

4) Record Switch Positions on Lights

Purpose: A set of eight switches should have their positions reflected on eight LEDs. That is to say, if the switch is closed (zero), the LED should be on, otherwise the LED should be off. Assume that the CPU output port is connected to the cathodes of the LEDs.

Sample Problem:

```
SWITCH  0  CLOSED
SWITCH  1  OPEN
SWITCH  2  CLOSED
SWITCH  3  OPEN
SWITCH  4  OPEN
SWITCH  5  CLOSED
SWITCH  6  CLOSED
SWITCH  7  OPEN
```

Result:

```
LED  0  ON
LED  1  OFF
LED  2  ON
LED  3  OFF
LED  4  OFF
LED  5  ON
LED  6  ON
LED  7  OFF
```

How would you change the program so that a switch attached to bit 7 of Port A of VIA #2 determines whether the displays are active (i.e., if the control switch is closed, the displays attached to Port B reflect the switches attached to Port A; if the control switch is open, the displays are always off)? A control switch is useful when the displays may distract the operator, as in an airplane.

How would you change the program so that it makes the control switch an on-off pushbutton; that is, each closure inverts the previous state of the displays? Assume that the displays start in the active state and that the program examines and debounces the pushbutton before sending data to the displays.

5) Count on a Seven-Segment Display

Purpose: The program should count from 0 to 9 continuously on a seven-segment display, starting with zero.

Hint: Try different timing lengths for the displays and see what happens. When does the count become visible? What happens if the display is blanked part of the time?

MORE COMPLEX I/O DEVICES

More complex I/O devices differ from simple keyboards, switches, and displays in that:

1) They transfer data at higher rates.
2) They may have their own internal clocks and timing.
3) They produce status information and require control information, as well as transferring data.

Because of their high data rates, you cannot handle these I/O devices casually. If the processor does not provide the appropriate service, the system may miss input data or produce erroneous output data. You are therefore working under much more exacting constraints than in dealing with simpler devices. Interrupts are a convenient method for handling complex I/O devices, as we shall see in Chapter 12.

Peripherals such as keyboards, teletypewriters, cassettes, and floppy disks produce their own internal timing. These devices provide streams of data, separated by specific timing intervals. The computer must synchronize the initial input or output operation with the peripheral clock and then provide the proper interval between subsequent operations. A simple delay loop like the one shown previously can produce the timing interval. The synchronization may require one or more of the following procedures:

<table><tr><td>SYNCHRONIZING
WITH I/O
DEVICES</td></tr></table>

1) Looking for a transition on a clock or strobe line provided by the peripheral for timing purposes. The simplest method is to tie the strobe to a VIA control line and wait until the appropriate bit of the VIA Interrupt Flag register is set.
2) Finding the center of the time interval during which the data is stable. We would prefer to determine the value of the data at the center of the pulse rather than at the edges, where the data may be changing. Finding the center requires a delay of one-half of a transmission interval (bit time) after the edge. Sampling the data at the center also means that small timing errors have little effect on the accuracy of the reception.
3) Recognizing a special starting code. This is easy if the code is a single bit or if we have some timing information. The procedure is more complex if the code is long and could start at any time. Shifting will be necessary to determine where the transmitter is starting its bits, characters, or messages (this is often called a search for the correct "framing").
4) Sampling the data several times. This reduces the probability of receiving data incorrectly from noisy lines. Majority logic (such as best 3 out of 5 or 5 out of 8) can be used to decide on the actual data value.

Reception is, of course, much more difficult than transmission, since the peripheral controls the reception and the computer must interpret timing information generated by the peripheral. In transmission, the computer provides the proper timing and formatting for a specific peripheral.

Peripherals may require or provide other information besides data and timing. We refer to other information transmitted by the computer as "control information"; it may select modes of operation, start or stop processes, clock registers, enable buffers, choose formats or protocols, provide operator displays, count operations, or identify the type and priority of the operation. We refer to other information transmitted by the peripheral as "status information"; it may indicate the mode of operation, the readiness of devices, the presence of error conditions, the format of protocol in use, and other states or conditions.

<table><tr><td>CONTROL
AND STATUS
INFORMATION</td></tr></table>

The computer handles control and status information just like data. This information seldom changes, even though actual data may be transferred at a high rate. The control or status information may be single bits, digits, words, or multiple words. Often single bits or short fields are combined and handled by a single input or output port.

Combining status and control information into bytes reduces the total number of I/O port addresses required by the peripherals. However, the combination does mean that individual status input bits must be separately interpreted and control output bits must be separately determined. The procedures for isolating status bits and setting or resetting control bits are as follows:

Separating Out Status Bits

Step 1)   Read status data from the peripheral

Step 2)   Logical AND with a mask (the mask has ones in bit positions that must be examined and zeros elsewhere)

Step 3)   Shift the separated bits to the least significant bit positions.

SEPARATING STATUS INFORMATION

Step 3 is unnecessary if the field is a single bit, since the Zero flag will contain the complement of that bit after Step 2 (try it!). A Shift or Load instruction can replace Step 2 if the field is a single bit and occupies the least significant, most significant, or next to most significant bit position (positions 0, 7, or 6). These positions are often reserved for the most frequently used status information. You should try to write the required instruction sequences for the 6502 processor. Note, in particular, the use of the Bit Test instruction. This instruction performs a logical AND between the contents of the Accumulator and the contents of a memory location but does not save the result; the flags are set as follows:

BIT TEST INSTRUCTION

Zero flag = 1 if the logical AND produces a zero result, 0 if it does not.

Sign flag = bit 7 of the contents of the memory location (independent of the value in the Accumulator).

Overflow flag = bit 6 of the contents of the memory location (independent of the value in the Accumulator).

Setting and Clearing Control Bits

Step 1)   Read prior control information

Step 2)   Logical AND with mask to clear bits (mask has zeros in bit positions to be cleared, ones elsewhere)

Step 3)   Logical OR with mask to set bits (mask has ones in bit positions to be set, zeros elsewhere)

Step 4)   Send new control information to peripheral

COMBINING CONTROL INFORMATION

Here again the procedure is simpler if the field is a single bit and occupies a position at either end of the byte.

Some examples of separating and combining status bits are:

1) A 3-bit field in bit positions 2 through 4 of a VIA Ouput (Data) register is a scaling factor. Place that factor into the Accumulator.

```
;
; READ STATUS DATA FROM INPUT PORT
;
        LDA     VIAOR       ;READ STATUS DATA
;
; MASK OFF UNWANTED BITS AND SHIFT RESULT
;
        AND     #%00011100  ;MASK SCALING FACTOR
        LSR     A           ;SHIFT TWICE TO NORMALIZE
        LSR     A
```

2) The Accumulator contains a 2-bit field that must be placed in bit positions 3 and 4 of a VIA Output (Data) register.
   TEMP = $0040
   MASK = %11100111

```
;
; MOVE DATA TO FIELD POSITIONS
;
        ASL     A           ;SHIFT DATA TO BIT POSITIONS 3 AND 4
        ASL     A
        ASL     A
        AND     #%00011000  ;CLEAR OUT OTHER BITS
        STA     TEMP
;
COMBINE NEW FIELD VALUE WITH OTHER DATA
;
        LDA     VIOADR
        AND     HMASK       ;CLEAR FIELD TO BE CHANGED
        ORA     TEMP        ;COMBINED NEW DATA WITH OLD
        STA     VIOAR       ;OUTPUT COMBINED DATA
```

Documentation is a serious problem in handling control and status information. The meanings of status inputs or control outputs are seldom obvious. The programmer should clearly indicate the purposes of input and output operations in the comments, e.g., "CHECK IF READER IS ON," "CHOOSE EVEN PARITY OPTION," or "ACTIVATE BIT RATE COUNTER." The Logical and Shift instructions will otherwise be very difficult to remember, understand, or debug.

DOCUMENTING STATUS AND CONTROL TRANSFERS

EXAMPLES

An Unencoded Keyboard

Purpose: Recognize a key closure from an unencoded 3 x 3 keyboard and place the number of the key that was pressed into the Accumulator.

Keyboards are just collections of switches (see Figure 11-24). Small numbers of keys are easiest to handle if each key is attached separately to a bit of an input port. Interfacing the keyboard is then the same as interfacing a set of switches.

Keyboards with more than eight keys require more than one input port and therefore multibyte operations. This is particularly wasteful if the keys are logically separate, as in a calculator or terminal keyboard where the user will only strike one at a time. The number of input lines required may be reduced by connecting the keys into a matrix, as shown in Figure 11-25. Now each key represents a potential connection between a row and a column. The keyboard matrix requires n + m external lines, where n is the number of rows and m is the number of columns. This compares to n x m external lines if each key is separate. Table 11-15 compares the number of keys required by typical configurations.

MATRIX KEYBOARD

A program can determine which key has been pressed by using the external lines from the matrix. The usual procedure is a "keyboard scan." We ground Row 0 and examine the column lines. If any lines are grounded, a key in that row has been pressed, causing a row-to-column connection. We can determine which key was pressed by determining which column line is grounded; that is, which bit of the input port is zero. If no column line is grounded, we proceed to Row 1 and repeat the scan. Note that we can check to see if any keys at all have been pressed by grounding all the rows at once and examining the columns.

KEYBOARD SCAN

The keyboard scan requires that the row lines be tied to an output port and the column lines to an input port. Figure 11-26 shows the arrangement. The CPU can ground a particular row by placing a zero in the appropriate bit of the output port and ones in the other bits.

The CPU can determine the state of a particular column by examining the appropriate bit of the input port.

Table 11-15. Comparison Between Independent Connections and Matrix Connections for Keyboards

Keyboard Size	Number of Lines with Independent Connections	Number of Lines with Matrix Connections
3 x 3	9	6
4 x 4	16	8
4 x 6	24	10
5 x 5	25	10
6 x 6	36	12
6 x 8	48	14
8 x 8	64	16

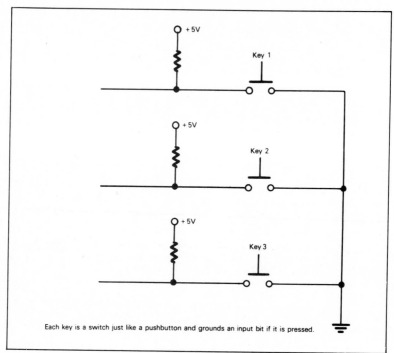

Each key is a switch just like a pushbutton and grounds an input bit if it is pressed.

Figure 11-24. A Small Keyboard

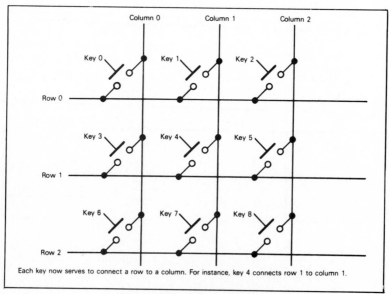

Each key now serves to connect a row to a column. For instance, key 4 connects row 1 to column 1.

Figure 11-25. A Keyboard Matrix

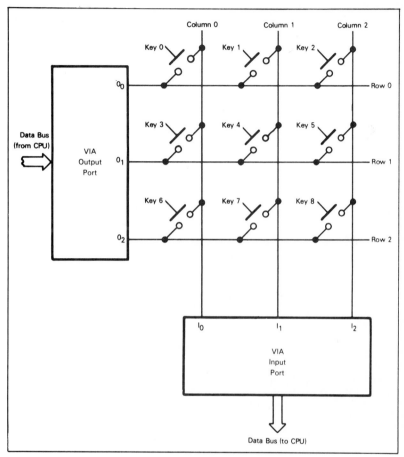

Figure 11-26. I/O Arrangement for a Keyboard Scan

Task 1: Determine Key Closure

Purpose: Wait for a Key to be Pressed.

The procedure is as follows:

1) Ground all the rows by clearing all the output bits.
2) Fetch the column inputs by reading the input port.
3) Return to Step 1 if all the column inputs are ones.

WAITING FOR A KEY CLOSURE

Flowchart:

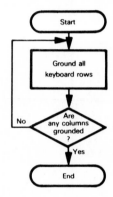

Source Program:

```
        LDA     #$FF
        STA     VIADDRB     ;MAKE PORT B LINES OUTPUTS
        LDA     #0
        STA     VIAPCR      ;MAKE ALL CONTROL LINES INPUTS
        STA     VIADDRA     ;MAKE PORT A LINES INPUTS
        STA     VIAORB      ;GROUND ALL KEYBOARD ROWS
WAITK   LDA     VIAORA      ;GET KEYBOARD COLUMN DATA
        AND     #%00000111  ;MASK COLUMN BITS
        CMP     #%00000111  ;ARE ANY COLUMNS GROUNDED?
        BEQ     WAITK       ;NO, WAIT UNTIL ONE IS
        BRK
```

Object Program:

Memory Address (Hex)	Memory Contents (Hex)		Instruction (Mnemonic)	
0000	A9		LDA	#$FF
0001	FF			
0002	8D		STA	VIADDRB
0003 0004	VIADDRB			
0005	A9		LDA	#0
0006	00			
0007	8D		STA	VIAPCR
0008 0009	VIAPCR			
000A	8D		STA	VIADDRA
000B 000C	VIADDRA			
000D	8D		STA	VIAORB
000E 000F	VIAORB			
0010	AD	WAITK	LDA	VIAORA
0011 0012	VIAORA			
0013	29		AND	#%00000111
0014	07			
0015	C9		CMP	#%00000111
0016	07			
0017	F0		BEQ	WAITK
0018	F7			
0019	00		BRK	

VIA Port B is the keyboard output port and Port A is the input port.

Masking off all but the column bits eliminates any problems that could be caused by the states of the unused input lines.

We could generalize the routine by naming the output and masking patterns:

    ALLG   =%11111000
    OPEN   =%00000111

These names could then be used in the actual program; a different keyboard would require only a change in the definitions and a re-assembly.

Of course, one port of a VIA is all that is really necessary for a 3 x 3 or 4 x 4 keyboard. Try rewriting the program so that it uses only Port A.

Task 2: Identify Key

Purpose: Identify a key closure by placing the number of the key into the Accumulator.

The procedure is as follows:

1) Set key number to -1, keyboard output port to all ones except for a zero in bit 0, and row counter to number of rows.
2) Fetch the column inputs by reading the input port.
3) If any column inputs are zero, proceed to Step 7.
4) Add the number of columns to the key number to reach next row.
5) Update the contents of the output port by shifting the zero bit left one position.
6) Decrement row counter. Go to Step 2 if any rows have not been scanned, otherwise go to Step 9.
7) Add 1 to key number. Shift column inputs right one bit.
8) If Carry = 1, return to Step 7.
9) End of program.

Flowchart:

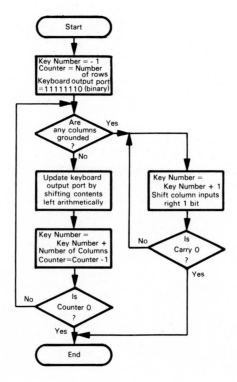

Source Program:

```
          LDA     #0
          STA     VIAPCR        ;MAKE ALL CONTROL LINES INPUTS
          STA     VIADDRA       ;MAKE PORT A LINES INPUTS
          LDA     #$FF
          STA     VIADDRB       ;MAKE PORT B LINES OUTPUTS
          TAX                   ;KEY NUMBER = -1
          LDA     #%11111110    ;START BY GROUNDING ROW ZERO
          STA     VIAORB
          LDY     #3            ;COUNTER = NUMBER OF ROWS
FROW      LDA     VIAORA        ;GET COLUMN INPUTS
          AND     #%00000111    ;ISOLATE COLUMN BITS
          CMP     #%00000111    ;ARE ANY COLUMNS GROUNDED?
          BNE     FCOL          ;YES, GO DETERMINE WHICH ONE
          TXA                   ;NO, MOVE KEY NUMBER TO NEXT ROW
          CLC
          ADC     #3            ;BY ADDING NUMBER OF COLUMNS
          TAX
          ASL     VIAORB        ;UPDATE SCAN PATTEN FOR NEXT ROW
          DEY                   ;HAVE ALL ROWS BEEN SCANNED?
          BNE     FROW          ;NO, SCAN NEXT ONE
          BRK
FCOL      INX                   ;KEY NUMBER = KEY NUMBER + 1
          LSR     A             ;IS THIS THE COLUMN GROUNDED?
          BCS     FCOL          ;NO, EXAMINE NEXT ONE
          BRK
```

Object Program:

Memory Address (Hex)	Memory Contents (Hex)		Instruction (Mnemonic)	
0000	A9		LDA	#0
0001	00			
0002	8D		STA	VIAPCR
0003 ⎫ 0004 ⎬	VIAPCR		LD	A,00001111B
0005	8D		STA	VIADDRA
0006 ⎫ 0007 ⎬	VIADDRA			
0008	A9		LDA	#$FF
0009	FF			
000A	8D		STA	VIADDRB
000B ⎫ 000C ⎬	VIADDRB			
000D	AA		TAX	
000E	A9		LDA	#%11111110
000F	FE			
0010	8D		STA	VIAORB
0011 ⎫ 0012 ⎬	VIAORB			
0013	A0		LDY	#3
0014	03			
0015	AD	FROW	LDA	VIAORA
0016 ⎫ 0017 ⎬	VIAORA			
0018	29		AND	#%00000111
0019	07			
001A	C9		CMP	#%00000111
001B	07			
001C	D0		BNE	FCOL
001D	0C			
001E	8A		TXA	
001F	18		CLC	
0020	69		ADC	#3
0021	03			
0022	AA		TAX	
0023	0E		ASL	VIAORB
0024 ⎫ 0025 ⎬	VIAORB			
0026	88		DEY	
0027	D0		BNE	FROW
0028	EC			
0029	00		BRK	
002A	E8	FCOL	INX	
002B	4A		LSR	A
002C	B0		BCS	FCOL
002D	FC			
002E	00		BRK	

We have included a CLC instruction for clarity, but it is not actually necessary. The only case in which the BNE instruction does not cause a branch is the one in which the two operands used in CMP are equal. In that case, the Carry flag is always set to indicate that no borrow has been generated. So we could replace the sequence

```
        CLC
        ADC    #3        ;BY ADDING NUMBER OF COLUMNS
```

with the single instruction

```
        ADC    #2        ;BY ADDING NUMBER OF COLUMNS (NOTE
                         ;  CARRY = 1)
```

Each time a row scan fails, we must add the number of columns to the key number to move past the current row (try the procedure on the keyboard in Figure 11-26).

What is the result of the program if no keys are being pressed? Change the program so that it starts the scan over again in that case. We could insert an extra INX instruction before the first BRK. What would the final value be in Index Register X if no keys were being pressed? Would it be different from the case in which the highest numbered key was being pressed? Note that the Zero flag could also be used to distinguish the case where no keys were pressed. Can you explain how?

An alternative is to use the bidirectional capability of the VIA. The procedure would be:

1) Ground all the columns and save the row inputs.

2) Ground all the rows and save the column inputs.

3) Use the row and column inputs together to determine the key number from a table.

Try to write a program to implement this procedure.

This program can be generalized by making the number of rows, the number of columns, and the masking pattern into named parameters with EQUATE (=) pseudo-operations.

An Encoded Keyboard[18]

Purpose: Fetch data, when it is available, from an encoded keyboard that provides a strobe along with each data transfer.

An encoded keyboard provides a unique code for each key. It has internal electronics that perform the scanning and identification procedure of the previous example. The tradeoff is between the simpler software required by the encoded keyboard and the lower cost of the unencoded keyboard.

Encoded keyboards may use diode matrices, TTL encoders, or MOS encoders. The codes may be ASCII, EBCDIC, or a custom code. PROMs are often part of the encoding circuitry.

The encoding circuitry may do more than just encode key closures. It may also debounce the keys and handle "rollover," the | **ROLLOVER** |
problem of more than one key being struck at the same time. Common ways of handling rollover are: "2-key rollover," whereby two keys (but not more) struck at the same time are resolved into separate closures, and "n-key rollover," whereby any number of keys struck at the same time are resolved into separate closures.

The encoded keyboard also provides a strobe with each data transfer. The strobe signals that a new closure has occurred. Figure 11-27 shows the interface between an encoded keyboard and the 6502 microprocessor. The 6522 Versatile Interface Adapter provides input latching on both Ports A and B; these latches are enabled by setting bit 1 (for Port B) or bit 0 (for Port A) of the Auxiliary Control register (see Figure 11-10). In this mode, the data on the input pins is latched when the Interrupt flag is set and wil not change until the Interrupt flag is cleared. Note that the latching works somewhat differently on the B side, where the contents of the Output register are latched if the pin is programmed as an output.

The keyboard strobe is tied to input CA1. A transition on the strobe line causes Interrupt Flag Register bit 1 to go high. Bit 0 of the Peripheral Control register (see Figure 11-9) determines whether the VIA recognizes high-to-low transitions on CA1 (bit 0 = 0) or low-to-high transitions (bit 0 = 1). Thus the VIA contains an edge-sensitive latched status port as well as a data port. It also contains an inverter that can be used to handle strobes of either polarity. A VIA can replace many simple circuit elements; you can make corrections in circuit logic by changing the contents of the Control registers (in software) rather than by rewiring a breadboard. For example, changing the active edge requires the changing of a single program bit, whereas it might require additional parts and rewiring on a breadboard.

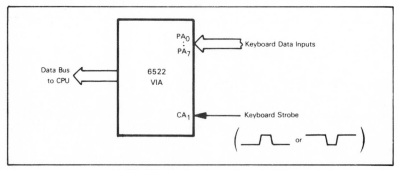

Figure 11-27. I/O Interface for an Encoded Keyboard

Task: Input from Keyboard

Purpose: Wait for an active-low strobe on VIA control line CA1 and then place the data from Port A into the Accumulator. Note that reading the data from the Output (Data) register clears the status bit in the Interrupt Flag register (this circuitry is part of the 6522 VIA).

Flowchart:

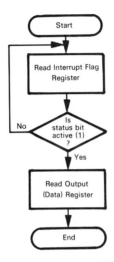

The hardware must hold the control lines in a logic '1' state during reset to prevent the accidental setting of status flags. An initial read of the Data (Output) registers in the startup routine may be used to clear the status flags. As noted earlier, you can also clear bits in the 6522 Interrupt Flag register by writing logic '1's into them.

Source Program:

```
        LDA     #0
        STA     VIAPCR          ;MAKE ALL CONTROL LINES INPUTS
        STA     VIADDRA         ;MAKE PORT A LINES INPUTS
        LDA     #%00000001
        STA     VIAACR          ;ENABLE LATCHING ON PORT A
        LDA     #%00000010      ;GET PATTERN FOR EXAMINING CA1 FLAG
KBWAIT  BIT     VIAIFR          ;IS THERE NEW KEYBOARD DATA?
        BEQ     KBWAIT          ;NO, WAIT UNTIL THERE IS
        LDA     VIAORA          ;YES, FETCH DATA
        BRK
```

Object Program:

Memory Address (Hex)	Memory Contents (Hex)	Instruction (Mnemonic)		
0000	A9		LDA	#0
0001	00			
0002	8D		STA	VIAPCR
0003⎱ 0004⎰	VIAPCR			
0005	8D		STA	VIADDRA
0006⎱ 0007⎰	VIADDRA			
0008	A9		LDA	#%00000001
0009	01			
000A	8D		STA	VIAACR
000B⎱ 000C⎰	VIAACR			
000D	A9		LDA	#%00000010
000E	02			
000F	2C	KBWAIT	BIT	VIAIFR
0010⎱ 0011⎰	VIAIFR			
0012	F0		BEQ	KBWAIT
0013	FB			
0014	AD		LDA	VIAORA
0015⎱ 0016⎰	VIAORA			
0017	00		BRK	

To make the status bit respond to low-to-high transitions on CA1, you must set bit 0 of the Peripheral Control register.

The other handshake status flags are bits 0 (for CA2), 3 (for CB2), and 4 (for CB1) of the Interrupt Flag register.

Show that reading the Output (Data) register clears the status flag. Hint: save the contents of the Interrupt Flag register in memory before the instruction LDA VIAORA is executed. What happens if you replace LDA with STA? How about CMP, INC, ROL? Note that either reading or writing the Output (Data) register clears the status bit. What happens if you read Port A from the non-handshaking address (see Table 11-7)? What happens if you replace LDA VIAORA with LDA VIAORB?

A Digital-to-Analog Converter[19-22]

Purpose: Send data to an 8-bit digital-to-analog converter, which has an active-low latch enable.

Digital-to-analog converters produce the continuous signals required by motors, heaters, actuators, and other electrical and mechanical output devices. Typical converters consist of switches and resistor ladders with the appropriate resistance values. You must generally provide a reference voltage and some other digital and analog circuitry, although complete units are becoming available at low cost.

Figure 11-28 describes the 8-bit Signetics NE5018 D/A converter, which contains an on-chip 8-bit parallel data input latch. A low level on the $\overline{LE}$ (Latch Enable) input gates the input data into the latches, where it remains after $\overline{LE}$ goes high.

Figure 11-29 illustrates the interfacing of the device to a 6502 system. Note that the B side of the VIA automatically produces the active-low strobe required to latch the data

> **D/A CONVERTER INTERFACE**

into the converter; CB2 acts as an Output Ready signal. Remember that CB2 automatically goes low for one cycle following a write operation on the B port Output (Data) register if CB2 is in the pulse output mode (see Table 11-9). The Peripheral Control register bits are:

> Bit 7 = 1 to make CB2 an output
> Bit 6 = 0 to make CB2 a pulse
> Bit 5 = 1 to make CB2 a brief Output Ready strobe (one clock cycle in duration).

Note that the VIA contains an output latch. The data therefore remains stable during and after the conversion. The converter typically requires only a few microseconds to produce an analog output. Thus, the converter latch could be left enabled if the port were not used for any other purpose.

In applications where eight bits of resolution are not enough, 10- to 16-bit converters can be used. Additional port logic is required to pass all the data bits; some converters provide part of this logic.

The VIA here serves both as a parallel data port and as a control port. CB2 is a pulse that lasts one clock cycle after the data is latched into the VIA. This pulse is long enough to meet the requirements (typically 400 ns) of the NE5018 converter.

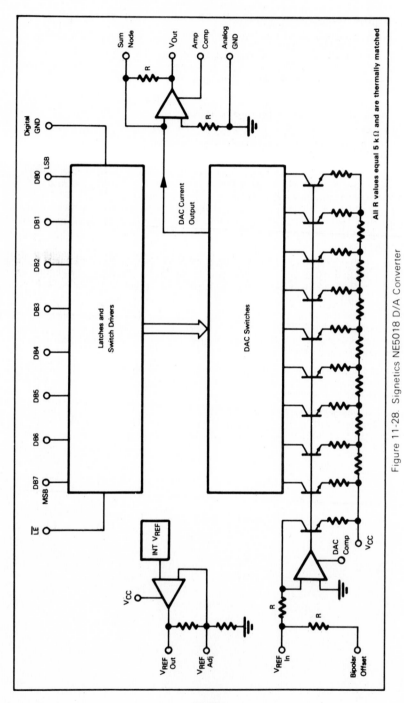

Figure 11-28 Signetics NE5018 D/A Converter

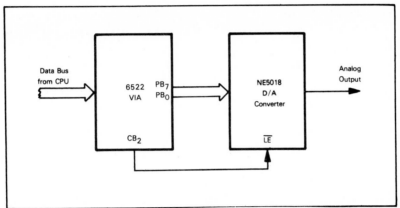

Figure 11-29 Interface for an 8-bit Digital-to-Analog Converter

Task: Output to Converter

Purpose: Send data from memory location 0040 to the converter.

Flowchart:

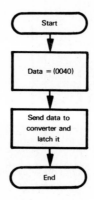

Source Program:

```
LDA    #$FF
STA    VIADDRB      ;MAKE PORT B LINES OUTPUTS
LDA    #%10100000
STA    VIAPCR       ;PROVIDE BRIEF LATCH ENABLE STROBE
LDA    $40          ;GET DATA
STA    VIAORB       ;SEND DATA TO DAC AND LATCH
BRK
```

Object Program:

Memory Address (Hex)	Memory Contents (Hex)	Instruction (Mnemonic)	
0000	A9	LDA	#$FF
0001	FF		
0002	8D	STA	VIADDRB
0003 0004	VIADDRB		
0005	A9	LDA	#%10100000
0006	A0		
0007	8D	STA	VIAPCR
0008 0009	VIAPCR		
000A	A5	LDA	$40
000B	40		
000C	8D	STA	VIAORB
000D 000E	VIAORB		
000F	00	BRK	

The pulse for the Latch Enable input is produced automatically when data is stored in Output (Data) Register B. Note, however, that the pulse is a fairly brief one, lasting only one clock cycle; this may be insufficient for some applications.

We could use the level (manual) output from CB2 if the Latch Enable signal were active-high or if the required length were greater. The program would then be.:

```
LDA    #$FF
STA    VIADDRB        ;MAKE PORT BE LINES OUTPUTS
LDA    #%11000000
STA    VIAPCR         ;MAKE LATCH ENABLE A LEVEL (LOW)
LDA    $40            ;GET DATA
STA    VIAORB         ;SEND DATA TO DAC OUTPUT PORT
LDA    #%11100000
STA    VIAPCR         ;OPEN DAC LATCH (ENABLE HIGH)
LDA    #%11000000
STA    VIAPCR         ;LATCH DATA (ENABLE LOW)
BRK
```

Here bit 6 of the Peripheral Control register is set to make CB2 a level with a value given by bit 5 of the Peripheral Control register. This is referred to as the Manual Output mode in 6522 literature. Note how many more instructions are required to pulse the Latch Enable than in the previous example, since no automatic pulse is provided. An inverter gate could also be used to invert the polarity of the strobe.

In the Manual mode, CB2 is completely independent of the parallel data port. It is simply a control output that is available for any purpose. The only problem involved in using it is that you must not accidentally change any of the other bits in the Peripheral Control register, since they may have unrelated functions.

Analog-to-Digital Converter[19-23]

Purpose: Fetch data from an 8-bit analog-to-digital converter that requires a Start Conversion pulse to start the conversion process and provides an End of Conversion output to indicate the completion of the process and the availability of valid data.

Analog-to-digital converters handle the continuous signals produced by various types of sensors and transducers. The converter produces the digital input which the computer requires.

One form of analog-to-digital converter is the successive approximation device, which makes a direct 1-bit comparison during each clock cycle. Such converters are fast but have little noise immunity. Dual slope integrating converters are another form of analog-to-digital converter. These devices take longer but are more resistant to noise. Other techniques, such as the incremental charge balancing technique, are also used.

Analog-to-digital converters usually require some external analog and digital circuitry, although complete units are becoming available at low cost.

Figure 11-30 contains a general description and a timing diagram for the National MM5357 8-bit A/D converter. The device contains output latches and tristate data outputs. A pulse on the Start Conversion (STRT CONV) line starts conversion of the analog input; after about 40 clock cycles (the converter requires a TTL level clock with a minimum pulse width of 400 ns), the result will go to the output latches and the End of Conversion (EOC) output will indicate this by going high. Data is read from the latches by applying a '1' to the Output Enable input. Figure 11-31 shows the connections for the device and some typical applications circuits.

Figure 11-32 shows the interface for the 6502 processor and the 5357 A/D converter. Control line CA2 is used in the Manual (Level) Output mode to provide a Start Conversion

A/D CONVERTER INTERFACE

pulse (active-high) of sufficient length. The End of Conversion signal is tied to control line CA1 so that EOC going high will set bit 1 of the Interrupt Flag register. The important edge on the End of Conversion line is the low-to-high edge, which indicates the completion of the conversion. Note that we are using the 6522 device to handle both control input and control output, since the converter interface involves a complete handshake. The Output Enable pin on the converter is tied high, since we are not placing the data directly on the processor's tri-state data bus. Note (see Figure 11-30) that the converter data outputs are complementary binary (all zeros is full-scale).

NATIONAL
MM5357 8-bit /

General Description

The MM5357 is an 8-bit monolithic A/D converter using P-channel ion-implanted MOS technology. It contains a high input impedance comparator, 256 series resistors and analog switches, control logic and output latches. Conversion is performed using a successive approximation technique where the unknown analog voltage is compared to the resistor tie points using analog switches. When the appropriate tie point voltage matches the unknown voltage, conversion is complete and the digital outputs contain an 8-bit complementary binary word corresponding to the unknown. The binary output is tri-state to permit bussing on common data lines.

Features

- Low cost
- ±5 V, 10 V input ranges
- No missing codes
- High input impedance
- Ratiometric conversion
- Tri-state outputs
- Contains output latches
- TTL compatible

Key Specs

Resolution	8 bits
Linearity	±1/2 LSB
Conversion speed	40μs
Input impedance	> 100 MΩ
Supply voltages	+5 V, -12 V, GND
Clock range	5.0 kHz to 2.0 MHz

Timing Diagram:

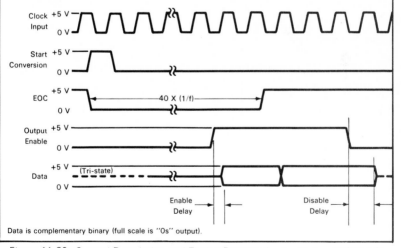

Data is complementary binary (full scale is "0s" output).

Figure 11-30. General Description and Timing Diagram for the National 5357 A/D Converter

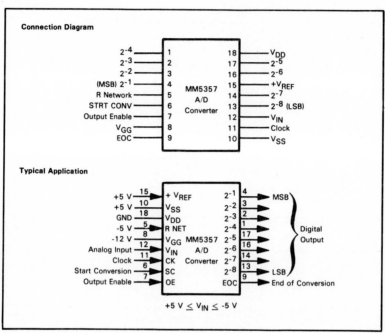

Figure 11-31. Connection Diagram and Typical Application for the National 5357
A/D Converter

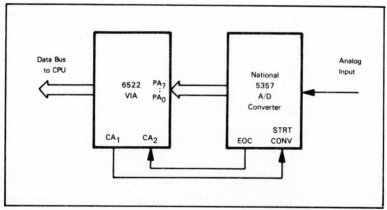

Figure 11-32. Interface for an 8-bit Analog-to-Digital Converter

Task: Input from Converter

Purpose: Start the conversion process, Wait for End of Conversion to go low and then high, and then read the data and store it in memory location 0040.

Flowchart:

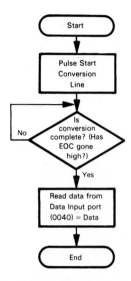

Note that here the VIA serves as a parallel data port, a status port, and a control port.

Source Program:

```
        LDA     #0
        STA     VIADDRA         ;MAKE PORT A LINES INPUTS
        LDA     #%00001101
        STA     VIAPCR          ;BRING START CONV LOW, ENABLE EOC
                                ;  LOW TO HIGH
        LDA     #%00001111
        STA     VIAPCR          ;PULSE START CONVERSION HIGH
        LDA     #%00001101
        STA     VIAPCR          ;PULSE START CONVERSION LOW
WTEOC   LDA     VIAIFR
        AND     #%00000010      ;IS CONVERSION COMPLETE?
        BNE     WTEOC           ;NO, WAIT
        LDA     VIAORA          ;YES, FETCH DATA FROM CONVERTER
        EOR     #%11111111      ;COMPLEMENT DATA FOR TRUE VALUE
        STA     $40             ;SAVE CONVERTER DATA
        BRK
```

Object Program:

Memory Address (Hex)	Memory Contents (Hex)		Instruction (Mnemonic)	
0000	A9		LDA	#0
0001	00			
0002	8D		STA	VIADDRA
0003 0004	VIADDRA			
0005	A9		LDA	#%00001101
0006	0D			
0007	8D		STA	VIAPCR
0008 0009	VIAPCR			
000A	A9		LDA	#%00001111
000B	0F			
000C	8D		STA	VIAPCR
000D 000E	VIAPCR			
000F	A9		LDA	#%00001101
0010	0D			
0011	8D		STA	VIAPCR
0012 0013	VIAPCR			
0014	AD	WTEOC	LDA	VIAIFR
0015 0016	VIAIFR			
0017	29		AND	#%00000010
0018	02			
0019	D0		BNE	WTEOC
001A	F9			
001B	AD		LDA	VIAORA
001C 001D	VIAORA			
001E	49		EOR	#%11111111
001F	FF			
0020	85		STA	$40
0021	40			
0022	00		BRK	

The VIA Peripheral Control register bits are:

Bit 3 = 1 to make CA2 an output
Bit 2 = 1 to make CA2 a level (Manual Output mode)
Bit 1 = value of level on CA2
Bit 0 = 1 to set Status flag on a low-to-high transition on CA1

Note that VIAs can be addressed using the Postindexed mode. The starting address of the VIA (VIAORB) is placed in two memory locations on page zero; all VIA registers can then be reached with appropriate offsets in Index Register Y.

A Teletypewriter (TTY)

Purpose: Transfer data to and from a standard 10-character-per-second serial teleypewriter.

The common teletypewriter transfers data in an asynchronous serial mode. The procedure is as follows:

1) The line is normally in the one state.

2) A Start bit (zero bit) precedes each character.

3) The character is usually 7-bit ASCII with the least significant bit transmitted first.

4) The most significant bit is a Parity bit, which may be even, odd, or fixed at zero or one.

5) Two stop bits (logic one) follow each character.

Figure 11-33 shows the format. Note that each character requires the transmission of eleven bits, of which only seven contain information. Since the data rate is ten characters per second, the bit rate is 10 x 11, or 110 Baud. Each bit therefore has a width of 1/110 of a second, or 9.1 milliseconds. This width is an average; the teletypewriter does not maintain it to any high level of accuracy.

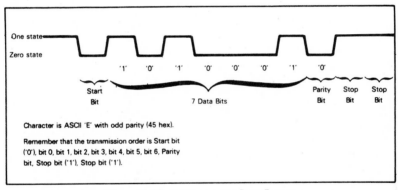

Figure 11-33. Teletypewriter Data Format

For a teletypewriter to communicate properly with a computer, the following procedures are necessary.

Receive (flowcharted in Figure 11-34):

Step 1) Look for a Start bit (a logic zero) on the data line.

Step 2) Center the reception by waiting one-half bit time, or 4.55 milliseconds.

Step 3) Fetch the data bits, waiting one bit time before each one. Assemble the data bits into a word by first shifting the bit to the Carry and then circularly shifting the data with the Carry. Remember that the least significant bit is received first.

Step 4) Generate the received Parity and check it against the transmitted Parity. If they do not match, indicate a "Parity error."

Step 5) Fetch the Stop bits (waiting one bit time between inputs). If they are not correct (if both Stop bits are not one), indicate a "framing error."

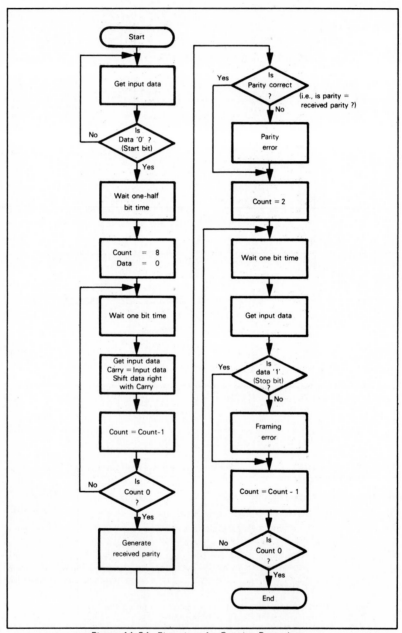

Figure 11-34. Flowchart for Receive Procedure

Task 1. Read Data

Purpose: Fetch data from a teletypewriter through bit 7 of a VIA data port and place the data into memory location 0060. For procedure, see Figure 11-34.

Source Program:

(Assume that the serial port is bit 7 of the VIA and that no parity or framing check is necessary)

```
        LDA     #0
        STA     VIAPCR          ;MAKE ALL CONTROL LINES INPUTS
        STA     VIADDRA         ;MAKE PORT A LINES INPUTS
WAITS   LDA     VIAORA          ;IS THERE A START BIT?
        BMI     WAITS           ;NO, WAIT
        JSR     DLY2            ;YES, DELAY HALF BIT TIME TO CENTER
        LDA     #%10000000      ;COUNT WITH BIT IN MSB
TTYRCV  JSR     DELAY           ;WAIT 1 BIT TIME
        ROL     PIADRA          ;GET DATA BIT
        ROR     A               ;ADD DATA BIT TO DATA WORD
        BCC     TTYRCV          ;CONTINUE IF COUNT BIT NOT IN CARRY
        STA     $60
        BRK
```

(Delay program)

```
DLY2    LDY     #5              ;COUNT FOR 4.55 MS
        BNE     DLY1
DELAY   LDY     #10             ;COUNT FOR 9.1 MS
DLY1    LDX     #$B4            ;GET COUNT FOR 0.91 MS
DLY     DEX
        BNE     DLY
        DEY
        BNE     DLY1
        RTS
```

Remember that bit 0 of the data is received first.

Object Program:

Memory Address (Hex)	Memory Contents (Hex)		Instruction (Mnemonic)	
0000	A9		LDA	#0
0001	00			
0002	8D		STA	VIAPCR
0003 ⎫ 0004 ⎭	VIAPCR			
0005	8D		STA	VIADDRA
0006 ⎫ 0007 ⎭	VIADDRA			
0008	AD	WAITS	LDA	VIAORA
0009 ⎫ 000A ⎭	VIAORA			
000B	30		BMI	WAITS
000C	FB			
000D	20		JSR	DLY2
000E	30			
000F	00			
0010	A9		LDA	#%10000000
0011	80			
0012	20	TTYRCV	JSR	DELAY
0013	34			
0014	00			
0015	2E		ROL	VIAORA
0016 ⎫ 0017 ⎭	VIAORA			
0018	6A		ROR	A
0019	90		BCC	TTYRCV
001A	F7			
001B	85		STA	$60
001C	60			
001D	00		BRK	
• • •				
0030	A0	DLY2	LDY	#5
0031	05			
0032	D0		BNE	DLY1
0033	02			
0034	A0	DELAY	LDY	#10
0035	0A			
0036	A2	DLY1	LDX	#$B4
0037	B4			
0038	CA	DLY	DEX	
0039	D0		BNE	DLY
003A	FD			
003B	88		DEY	
003C	D0		BNE	DLY1
003D	F8			
003E	60		RTS	

This program assumes that the Stack can be used for subroutine calls, i.e., that the monitor has already initialized the Stack Pointer. Otherwise you will have to initialize the Stack Pointer as shown in Chapter 10.

The constants for the delay routine were calculated just as shown earlier in this chapter. You might try determining them for yourself. The delays do not have to be highly accurate because the reception is centered, the messages are short, the bit rate is low, and the teletypewriter is not highly accurate itself.

How would you extend this program to check parity?

Task 2: Write Data

Purpose: Transmit data to a teletypewriter through bit 0 of a VIA Output (Data) register. The data is in memory location 0060.

Transmit (flowcharted in Figure 11-35)

```
┌─────────────┐
│ TTY         │
│ TRANSMIT    │
│ MODE        │
└─────────────┘
```

Step 1)   Transmit a Start bit (i.e., a logic zero).
Step 2)   Transmit the seven data bits, starting with the least significant bit.
Step 3)   Generate and transmit the Parity bit.
Step 4)   Transmit two Stop bits (i.e., logic ones).

The transmission routine must wait one bit time between each operation.

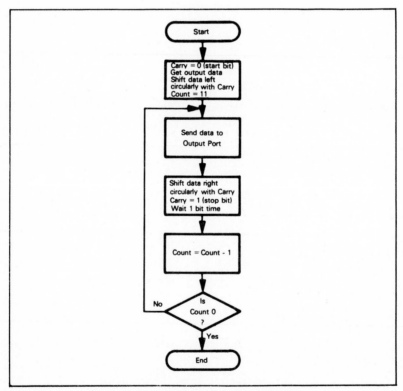

Figure 11-35. Flowchart for Transmit Procedure

11-108

Source Program

(Assume that parity need not be generated)

```
         LDA    #0
         STA    VIAPCR      ;MAKE ALL CONTROL LINES INPUTS
         STA    VIAORB      ;FORM START BIT
         LDA    #$FF
         STA    VIADDRB     ;MAKE PORT B LINES OUTPUTS
         LDA    $60         ;GET DATA
         LDX    #11         ;COUNT = 11 BITS IN CHARACTER
TBIT     JSR    DELAY       ;WAIT 1 BIT TIME
         SEC                ;SET CARRY TO FORM STOP BIT
         ROR    A           ;GET NEXT BIT OF CHARACTER
         ROL    VIAORB      ;SEND NEXT BIT TO TTY
         DEX
         BNE    TBIT
         BRK
```

The DELAY subroutine used here must preserve the Accumulator and Index Register X.
Remember that bit 0 of the data must be transmitted first.

Object Program:

Memory Address (Hex)	Memory Contents (Hex)	Instruction (Mnemonic)	
0000	A9	LDA	#0
0001	00		
0002	8D	STA	VIAPCR
0003 } 0004	VIAPCR		
0005	8D	STA	VIAORB
0006 } 0007	VIAORB		
0008	A9	LDA	#$FF
0009	FF		
000A	8D	STA	VIADDRB
000B } 000C	VIADDRB		
000D	A5	LDA	$60
000E	60		
000F	A2	LDX	#11
0010	0B		
0011	20	TBIT JSR	DELAY
0012	30		
0013	00		
0014	38	SEC	
0015	6A	ROR	A
0016	2E	ROL	VIAORB
0017 } 0018	VIAORB		
0019	CA	DEX	
001A	D0	BNE	TBIT
001B	F5		
001C	00	BRK	

In actual applications, you will find it necessary to place a one on the teletypewriter line after configuration, since that line should normally be in the mark (one) state.

Each character consists of 11 bits, with a Start bit (zero) and ending with two Stop bits (ones).

Note that you can generate parity by counting bits as shown in Chapter 6. The program is:

```
        LDY     #0        ;BIT COUNT = ZERO
        LDA     $60       ;GET DATA
CHBIT   BPL     CHKZ      ;IS NEXT DATA BIT 1?
        INY               ;YES, ADD 1 TO BIT COUNT
CHKZ    ASL     A         ;EXAMINE NEXT BIT POSITION
        BNE     CHBIT     ;UNLESS ALL BITS ARE ZEROS
        BRK
```

Index Register Y contains the number of '1' bits in the data. The least significant bit of Index Register Y is therefore an even Parity bit.

These procedures are sufficiently common and complex to merit a special LSI device: the UART, or Universal Asynchronous Receiver/Transmitter.[24] The UART will perform the reception procedure and provide the data in parallel form and a Data Ready signal. It will also accept data in parallel form, perform the transmission procedure, and provide a Peripheral Ready signal when it can handle more data. UARTs may have many other features, including:

UART

1) Ability to handle various bit lengths (usually 5 to 8), parity options, and numbers of Stop bits (usually 1, 1-1/2, and 2).

2) Indicators for framing errors, parity errors, and "overrun errors" (failure to read a character before another one is received).

3) RS-232[25] compatibility; i.e., a Request-to-Send (RTS) output signal that indicates the presence of data to communications equipment and a Clear-to-Send (CTS) input signal that indicates, in response to RTS, the readiness of the communications equipment. There may be provisions for other RS-232 signals, such as Received Signal Quality, Data Set Ready, or Data Terminal Ready.

4) Tristate outputs and control compatibility with a microprocessor.

5) Clock options that allow the UART to sample incoming data several times in order to detect false Start bits and other errors.

6) Interrupt facilities and controls.

UARTs act as four parallel ports: an input data port, an output data port, an input status port, and an output control port. The status bits include error indicators as well as Ready flags. The control bits select various options. UARTs are inexpensive ($5 to $50, depending on features) and easy to use.

THE 6850 ASYNCHRONOUS COMMUNICATIONS INTERFACE ADAPTER (ACIA)[26, 27]

The 6850 ACIA, or Asynchronous Communications Interface Adapter (see Figure 11-36) **is a UART** specifically designed for use in 6800- and 6502-based microcomputers. It occupies two memory addresses and contains two read-only registers (received data and status) and two write-only registers (transmitted data and control).** Tables 11-16 and 11-17 describe the contents of these registers.

> 6850 ACIA
> REGISTERS

Note the following special features of the 6850 ACIA:

> SPECIAL
> FEATURES
> OF 6850 ACIA

1) Read and write cycles address physically distinct registers. Therefore, you cannot use the ACIA registers as addresses for instructions like Increment, Decrement, or Shift, which involve both read and write cycles.

2) The ACIA Control register cannot be read by the CPU. You will have to save a copy of the Control register in memory if the program needs its value.

3) The ACIA has no Reset input. It can be reset only by placing ones in Control register bits 0 and 1. This procedure (called MASTER RESET) is necessary before the ACIA is used, in order to avoid having a random starting character.

4) The RS-232 signals are all active-low. Request-to-Send (RTS), in particular, should be brought high to make it inactive if it is not in use.

5) The ACIA requires an external clock. Typically 1760 Hz is supplied and the $\div$ 16 mode (Control register bit 1 = 0, bit 0 = 1) is used. The ACIA will use the clock to center the reception in order to avoid false Start bits caused by noise on the lines.

6) The Data Ready (Receive Data Register Full, or RDRF) flag is bit 0 of the Status register. The Peripheral Ready (Transmit Data Register Empty, or TDRE) flag is bit 1 of the Status register.

Table 11-16. Definition of 6850 ACIA Register Contents

Data Bus Line Number	Buffer Address			
	RS·$\overline{R/W}$ Transmit Data Register	RS·R/W Receive Data Register	$\overline{RS}$·$\overline{R/W}$ Control Register	$\overline{RS}$·R/W Status Register
	(Write Only)	(Read Only)	(Write Only)	(Read Only)
0	Data Bit 0*	Data Bit 0	Counter Divide Select 1 (CR0)	Receive Data Register Full (RDRF)
1	Data Bit 1	Data Bit 1	Counter Divide Select 2 (CR1)	Transmit Data Register Empty (TDRE)
2	Data Bit 2	Data Bit 2	Word Select 1 (CR2)	Data Carrier Detect ($\overline{DCD}$)
3	Data Bit 3	Data Bit 3	Word Select 2 (CR3)	Clear-to-Send ($\overline{CTS}$)
4	Data Bit 4	Data Bit 4	Word Select 3 (CR4)	Framing Error (FE)
5	Data Bit 5	Data Bit 5	Transmit Control 1 (CR5)	Receiver Overrun (OVRN)
6	Data Bit 6	Data Bit 6	Transmit Control 2 (CR6)	Parity Error (PE)
7	Data Bit 7***	Data Bit 7**	Receive Interrupt Enable (CR7)	Interrupt Request (IRQ)

* Leading bit = LSB = Bit 0
** Data bit will be zero in 7-bit plus parity modes
*** Data bit is "don't care" in 7-bit plus parity modes

Table 11-17. Meaning of the 6850 ACIA Control Register Bits

CR6	CR5	Function
0	0	$\overline{RTS}$ = low, Transmitting Interrupt Disabled
0	1	$\overline{RTS}$ = low, Transmitting Interrupt Enabled
1	0	$\overline{RTS}$ = high, Transmitting Interrupt Disabled
1	1	$\overline{RTS}$ = low, Transmits a Break level on the Transmit Data Output. Transmitting Interrupt Disabled

CR4	CR3	CR2	Function
0	0	0	7 Bits + Even Parity + 2 Stop Bits
0	0	1	7 Bits + Odd Parity + 2 Stop Bits
0	1	0	7 Bits + Even Parity + 1 Stop Bit
0	1	1	7 Bits + Odd Parity + 1 Stop Bit
1	0	0	8 Bits + 2 Stop Bits
1	0	1	8 Bits + 1 Stop Bit
1	1	0	8 Bits + Even Parity + 1 Stop Bit
1	1	1	8 Bits + Odd Parity + 1 Stop Bit

CR1	CR0	Function
0	0	÷ 1
0	1	÷ 16
1	0	÷ 64
1	1	Master Reset

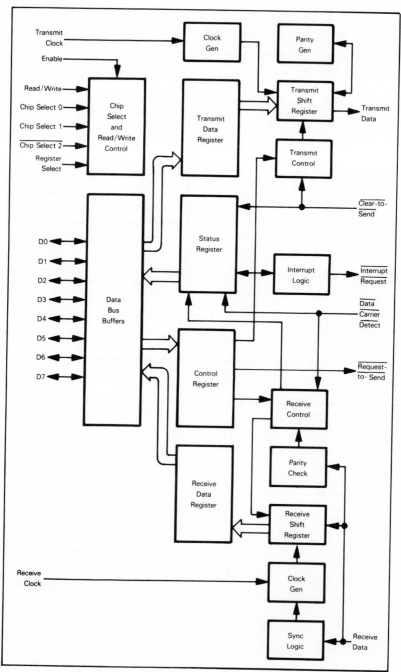

Figure 11-36. Block Diagram of the 6850 ACIA

Task: Receive data from a teletypewriter through a 6850 ACIA and store the data in memory location 0060

Source Program:

```
          LDA    #%00000011   ;MASTER RESET ACIA
          STA    ACIACR
          LDA    #%01000101   ;CONFIGURE ACIA FOR TTY WITH ODD
                              ;  PARITY
          STA    ACIACR
WAITD     LDA    ACIASR       ;GET ACIA STATUS
          LSR    A            ;HAS DATA BEEN RECEIVED?
          BCC    WAITD        ;NO, WAIT
          LDA    ACIADR       ;YES, FETCH DATA FROM ACIA
          STA    $60          ;SAVE DATA
          BRK
```

Object Program:

Memory Address (Hex)	Memory Contents (Hex)		Instruction (Mnemonic)	
0000	A9		LDA	#%00000011
0001	03			
0002	8D		STA	ACIACR
0003⎫ 0004⎭	ACIACR			
0005	A9		LDA	#%01000101
0006	45			
0007	8D		STA	ACIACR
0008⎫ 0009⎭	ACIACR			
000A	AD	WAITD	LDA	ACIASR
000B⎫ 000C⎭	ACIASR			
000D	4A		LSR	A
000E	90		BCC	WAITD
000F	FA			
0010	AD		LDA	ACIADR
0011⎫ 0012⎭	ACIADR			
0013	85		STA	$60
0014	60			
0015	00		BRK	

The program must reset the ACIA originally by placing ones in Control register bits 0 and 1. The ACIA does have an internal power-on reset which holds the ACIA in the reset state until Master Reset is applied.

The program configures the ACIA Control Register as follows:

EXAMPLE OF 6850 ACIA CONFIGURATION

Bit 7 = 0 to disable the receiver interrupt

Bit 6 = 1 to make Request-to-Send ($\overline{RTS}$) high (inactive)

Bit 5 = 0 to disable the transmitter interrupt

Bit 4 = 0 for 7-bit words

Bit 3 = 0, Bit 2 = 1 for odd parity with 2 Stop bits

Bit 1 = 0, Bit 0 = 1 for ÷ 16 clock (1760 Hz must be supplied)

The Received Data Status flag is Status register bit 0. Suppose we tried to replace

LDA	ACIASR
LSR	A

with the single instruction

LSR	ACIASR

What would happen?

Remember that the Status and Control registers share an address but are physically distinct.

Try adding an error-checking routine to the program. Set.

(0061) = 0 if no errors occurred
= 1 if a parity error occurred
(Status register bit 6 = 1)
= 2 if an overrun error occurred
(Status register bit 5 = 1)
= 3 if a framing error occurred
(Status register bit 4 = 1)

Assume that the priority of the errors is from MSB to LSB in the ACIA Status register (i.e., parity errors have priority over overrun errors which, in turn, have priority over framing errors if more than one error has occurred).

Task: Send data from memory location 0060 to a teletypewriter through a 6850 ACIA

Source Program:

```
        LDA    #%00000011    ;MASTER RESET ACIA
        STA    ACIACR
        LDA    #%01000101    ;CONFIGURE ACIA FOR TTY WITH ODD
                             ;  PARITY
        STA    ACIACR
        LDA    #%00000010
WAITR   BIT    ACIASR        ;IS ACIA READY FOR DATA?
        BEQ    WAITR         ;NO, WAIT UNTIL IT IS
        LDA    $60           ;YES, GET DATA
        STA    ACIADR        ;AND TRANSMIT IT
        BRK
```

Object Program:

Memory Address (Hex)	Memory Contents (Hex)	Instruction (Mnemonic)	
0000	A9	LDA	#%00000011
0001	03		
0002	8D	STA	ACIACR
0003 0004	ACIACR		
0005	A9	LDA	#%01000101
0006	45		
0007	8D	STA	ACIACR
0008 0009	ACIACR		
000A	A9	LDA	#%00000010
000B	02		
000C	2C	WAITR BIT	ACIASR
000D 000E	ACIASR		
000F	F0	BEQ	WAITR
0010	FB		
0011	A5	LDA	$60
0012	60		
0013	8D	STA	ACIADR
0014 0015	ACIADR		
0016	00	BRK	

The Transmitter Status flag is Status register bit 1. How could you modify the receive program to use the Bit Test Instruction?

THE 6551 ASYNCHRONOUS COMMUNICATIONS INTERFACE ADAPTER (ACIA)

The 6551 ACIA is a variation of the 6850 device that can also be used in 6800- or 6502-based systems. Figure 11-37 is a block diagram of this device. **It has most of the features of the 6850 ACIA and also has an on-chip baud rate generator that can provide 15 programmable baud rates derived from a standard 1.8432 MHz external crystal. Thus the 6551 ACIA can provide virtually any of the common baud rates without an external timer or baud rate generator.** The device has four internal registers addressed as described by Table 11-18. Its operation is controlled by two registers:

6551 ACIA REGISTERS

1) The Control register (see Figure 11-38) controls the baud rate generator, the word length, the number of stop bits, and the receiver clock source.

2) The Command register (see Figure 11-39) controls parity checking and generation, interrupt enabling, and the RS-232 handshake signals. Note that the program may reset the 6551 ACIA at any time by writing any data into

EXAMPLE OF 6551 ACIA CONFIGURATION

the address of the Status register (see Figure 11-40). For example, the following program resets a 6551 ACIA and configures it for a 10 character per second teletypewriter with odd parity and two stop bits:

```
        LDA     #%10110011
        STA     ACIASR      ;RESET 6551 ACIA
        STA     ACIAMR      ;CONFIGURE MODE FOR TTY (7 BITS, 2 STOP
                            ;  BITS)
        LDA     #%00100011
        STA     ACIACR      ;CONFIGURE FOR ODD PARITY, NO
                            ;  INTERRUPTS
```

We have given the name ACIAMR to the Control (Mode) Register.

The program configures the 6551 ACIA Control (Mode) register as follows:

Bit 7 = 1 for 2 stop bits
Bit 6 = 0, bit 5 = 1 for 7-bit words
Bit 4 = 1 to generate receiver clock from the on-board baud rate generator
Bits 0-3 = 0011 for 109.92 Baud (10 characters per second) from the internal baud rate generator

The program configures the 6551 ACIA Command register as follows:

Bit 7 = 0, bit 6 = 0, bit 5 = 1 for odd parity on both receiver and transmitter
Bit 4 = 0 so characters are not automatically echoed back through the transmitter
Bit 3 = 0, bit 2 = 0 to disable the transmitter interrupt and bring $\overline{RTS}$ high (inactive)
Bit 1 = 1 to disable the receiver interrupt (this is a mask bit)
Bit 0 = 1 to enable the Receiver/Transmitter

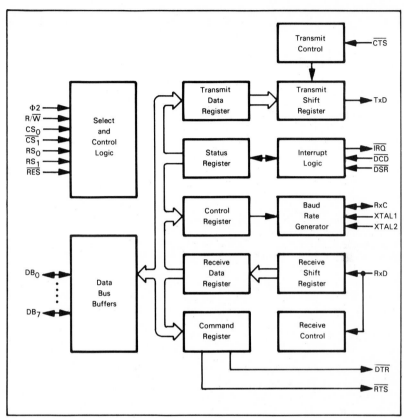

Figure 11-37. Block Diagram of the 6551 ACIA

Table 11-18. Addressing 6551 ACIA Internal Registers

RS$_1$	RS$_0$	Write	Read
0	0	Transmit Data Register	Receiver Data Register
0	1	Programmed Reset (Data is "Don't Care")	Status Register
1	0	Command Register	
1	0	Control Register	

The table shows that only the Command and Control registers are read/write. The Programmed Reset operation does not cause any data transfer, but is used to clear the SY6551 registers. The Programmed Reset is slightly different from the Hardware Reset (RES) and these differences are described in the individual register definitions.

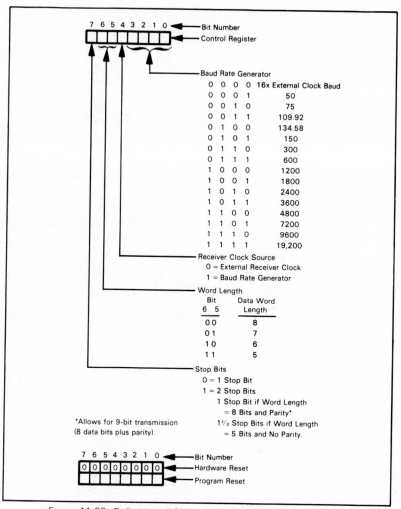

Figure 11-38. Definition of 6551 ACIA Control Register Contents

11-120

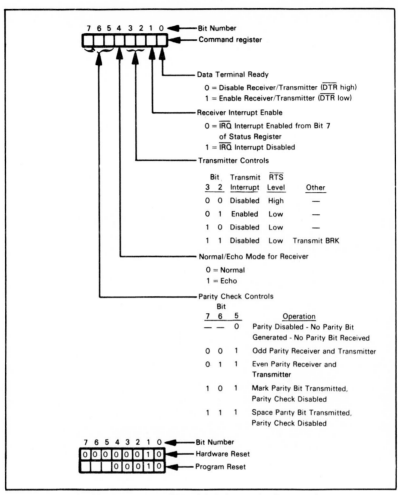

Figure 11-39. Definition of 6551 ACIA Command Register Contents

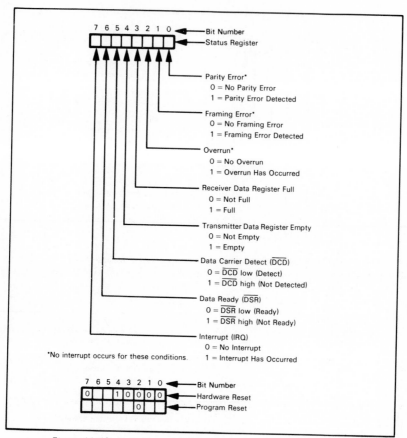

Figure 11-40. Definition of 6551 ACIA Status Register Contents

LOGICAL AND PHYSICAL DEVICES[28]

An important goal in writing I/O routines is to make them | LOGICAL DEVICES |
independent of particular physical hardware. The routines
can then transfer data to or from I/O devices, with the actual addresses being sup-
plied as parameters. The I/O device that can actually be accessed through a partic-
ular interface is referred to as a physical device. The I/O device to which the pro-
gram transfers data is referred to as a logical device. The operating system or
supervisor program must provide a mapping of logical devices on to physical
devices, that is, assign actual physical I/O addresses and characteristics to be
used by the I/O routines.

Note the advantages of this approach:

1) The operating system can vary the assignments under user control. Now the user can easily substitute a test panel or a development system interface for the actual I/O devices. This is useful in field maintenance as well as in debugging and testing. Furthermore, the user can change the I/O devices for different situations; typical examples are directing intermediate output to a video display and final output to a printer or obtaining some input from a remote communications line rather than from a local keyboard.

2) The same I/O routines can handle several identical or similar devices. The operating system or user only has to supply the address of a particular teletypewriter, RS-232 terminal, or printer, for example.

3) Changes, corrections, or additions to the I/O configuration are easy to make since only the assignments (or mapping) must be changed.

On the 6502 microprocessor, either the Preindexed (Indexed Indirect) or Postindexed (Indirect Indexed) addressing mode can be used in the I/O routines to provide independence of specific physical addresses. Preindexing is convenient since it allows the choice of a physical device address from a table.

If a table of I/O addresses is maintained on page zero, all that | I/O DEVICE |
an I/O routine needs is an index into that table. It can then ac- | TABLE |
cess the I/O device by using the Preindexed (or Indexed In-
direct) addressing mode. If, for example, the device number is in memory location DEV, the program to calculate the index would be:

```
        LDA    DEV          ;GET DEVICE NUMBER
        ASL    A            ;MULTIPLY BY 2 FOR 2-BYTE ADDRESS TABLE
        TAX
```

Data may now be transferred to or from the appropriate I/O device with the instructions
```
        LDA    DATA         ;GET DATA
        STA    (IOTBL,X)    ;SEND TO LOGICAL I/O DEVICE
```
or
```
        LDA    (IOTBL,X)    ;GET DATA FROM LOGICAL I/O DEVICE
        STA    DATA         ;SAVE DATA
```

The same I/O routine can transfer data to or from many different I/O devices merely by being supplied with different indexes. Compare the flexibility of this approach with the inflexibility of I/O routines that use direct addressing and are therefore tied to specific physical addresses.

STANDARD INTERFACES

Other standard interfaces besides the TTY current-loop and RS-232 can also be used to connect peripherals to the microcomputer. Popular ones include:

STANDARD INTERFACES

1) The serial RS-449, RS-422, and RS-423 interfaces.[29]

2) The 8-bit parallel General Purpose Interface Bus, also known as IEEE-488 or Hewlett-Packard Interface Bus (HPIB).[30]

3) The S-100 or Altair/Imsai hobbyist bus.[31] This is also an 8-bit bus.

4) The Intel Multibus.[32] This is another 8-bit bus that can, however, be expanded to handle 16 bits in parallel.

PROBLEMS

1) Separating Closures from an Unencoded Keyboard

Purpose: The program should read entries from an unencoded 3 x 3 keyboard and save them in an array. The number of entries is in memory location 0040 and the array starts in memory location 0041.

Separate one closure from the next by waiting for the current closure to end. Remember to debounce the keyboard (this can be simply a 1 ms wait).

Sample Problem:

$$(0040) = 04$$
Entries are 7, 2, 2, 4

Result:	(0041)	=	07
	(0042)	=	02
	(0043)	=	02
	(0044)	=	04

2) Read a Sentence from an Encoded Keyboard

Purpose: The program should read entries from an ASCII keyboard (7 bits with a zero Parity bit) and place them in an array until it receives an ASCII period $2E_{16}$. The array starts in memory location 0040. Each entry is marked by a strobe as in the example given under An Encoded Keyboard.

Sample Problem:

Entries are H, E, L, L, O.

Result:	(0040)	=	48	H
	(0041)	=	45	E
	(0042)	=	4C	L
	(0043)	=	4C	L
	(0044)	=	4F	O
	(0045)	=	2E	

3) A Variable Amplitude Square Wave Generator

Purpose: The program should generate a square wave, as shown in the next figure, using a D/A converter. Memory location 0040 contains the scaled amplitude of the wave, memory location 0041 the length of a half cycle in milliseconds, and memory location 0042 the number of cycles.

Assume that a digital output of 80_{16} to the converter results in an analog output of zero volts. In general, a digital output of D results in an analog output of $(D-80)/80 \times -V_{REF}$ volts.

Sample Problem:

$$(0040) = A0 \text{ (hex)}$$
$$(0041) = 04$$
$$(0042) = 03$$

Result:

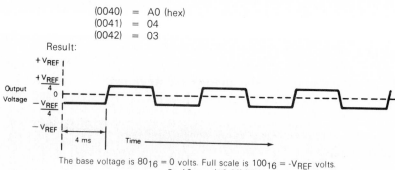

The base voltage is $80_{16} = 0$ volts. Full scale is $100_{16} = -V_{REF}$ volts.
So $A0_{16} = (A0-80)/80 \times -V_{REF} = -V_{REF}/4$

The program produces 3 pulses of amplitude $V_{REF}/4$ with a half cycle length of 4 ms.

4) Averaging Analog Readings

Purpose: The program should take four readings from an A/D converter 10 milliseconds apart and place the average in memory location 0040. Assume that the A/D conversion time can be ignored.

Sample Problem:

Readings are (hex) 86, 89, 81, 84
Result: (0040) = 85

5) A 30 Character-per-Second Terminal

Purpose: Modify the transmit and receive routines of the example given under A Teletypewriter to handle a 30 cps terminal that transfers ASCII data with one stop bit and even parity. How could you write the routines to handle either terminal depending on a flag bit in memory location 0060; e.g., (0060) = 0 for the 30 cps terminal, (0060) = 1 for the 10 cps terminal?

REFERENCES

1. J. Barnes, and V. Gregory, "Use Microprocessors to Enhance Performance with Noisy Data," EDN, August 20, 1976, pp. 71-72.

2. J. E. McNamara, Technical Aspects of Data Communications (Maynard, Mass.: Digital Equipment Corporation, 1977), Chapter 13.

    R. Swanson,"Understanding Cyclic Redundancy Codes," Computer Design, November 1975, pp. 93-99.

    J. Wong, et al., "Software Error Checking Procedures for Data Communications Protocols," Computer Design, February 1979, pp. 122-125.

    The last article contains some 6800 assembly language programs for CRC generation.

3. For example, the 6844 Direct Memory Access Controller for 6800- or 6502-based microcomputers is described in An Introduction to Microcomputers: Volume 2 - Some Real Microprocessors, pp. 9-106 through 9-123.

4. A. Osborne, et al., An Introduction to Microcomputers: Volume 2 - Some Real Microprocessors, pp. 9-45 through 9-54.

    J. Gilmore, and R. Huntington, "Designing with the 6820 Peripheral Interface Adapter," Electronics, December 23, 1976, pp. 85-86.

5. L. Leventhal, 6800 Assembly Language Programming, pp. 11-31 through 11-47, 11-49 through 11-74.

6. A. Osborne, et al., An Introduction to Microcomputers: Volume 2 - Some Real Microprocessors, pp. 10-29 through 10-47.

7. R6500 Microcomputer System Hardware Manual (Anaheim, Calif.: Rockwell International), pp. 1-65 through 1-97.

8. W. C. Mavity, "Megabit Bubble Modules in on Mass Storgage," Electronics, March 29, 1979, pp. 99-103.

9. J. Gieryic, "SYM-1 6522-Based Timer," Micro, April 1979, pp. 11:31 through 11:32. The magazine Micro is dedicated exclusively to 6502-based personal computers; it is available (monthly publication) from the COMPUTERIST, Inc., P. O. Box 3, South Chelmsford, MA 01824.

10. M. L. DeJong, "A Simple 24-Hour Clock for the AIM 65," Micro, March 1979, pp. 10:5 through 10:7.

11. A. Osborne et al., An Introduction to Microcomputers: Volume 2 - Some Real Microprocessors, pp. 10-47 through 10-55.

12. C. Foster, Programming a Microcomputer: 6502 (Reading, Mass.: Addison-Wesley, 1978). This is a very elementary introduction to computers based on the KIM microcomputer.

13. R. C. Camp, et al., Microcomputer Systems Principles Featuring the 6502/KIM (Portland: Matrix Publishers, 1978).

14. A. Caprihan, et al., "A Simple Microcomputer for Biomedical Signal Processing," 4th Annual Conference on Industrial Applications of Microprocessors, 1978, pp. 18-23. Proceedings (since 1975) are available from IEEE, 445 Hoes Lane, Piscataway, NJ 08854.

15. The TTL Data Book for Design Engineers, Texas Instruments Inc., P. O. Box 5012, Dallas, TX 75222, 1976, pp. 7-151 through 7-156.

16. E. Dilatush, "Special Report: Numeric and Alphanumeric Displays," EDN, February 5, 1978, pp. 26-35.

17. See Reference 15, pp. 7-22 through 7-34.

18. M. L. DeJong, "6502 Interfacing for Beginners: an ASCII Keyboard Input Port," Micro, February 1979, pp. 9-11 through 9-13.

19. E. R. Hnatek, A User's Handbook of D/A and A/D Converters (New York: Wiley, 1976).

20. J. Kane et al., An Introduction to Microcomputers: Volume 3 - Some Real Support Devices, Section E.

21. M. L. DeJong, "Digital-Analog and Analog-Digital Conversion Using the KIM-1," The Best of Micro, Volume 1, pp. 30-33.

22. P. H. Garrett, Analog Systems for Microprocessors and Minicomputers (Reston, VA.: Reston Publishing Co., 1978).

23. G. L. Zick and T. T. Sheffer, "Remote Failure Analysis of Micro-based Instrumentation," Computer, September 1977, pp. 30-35.

24. For a discussion of UARTs, see P. Rony et al., "The Bugbook IIa," E and L Instruments Inc., 61 First Street, Derby, CT. 06418 or D. G. Larsen et al., "INWAS: Interfacing with Asynchronous Serial Mode," IEEE Transactions on Industrial Electronics and Control Instrumentation, February 1977, pp. 2-12. See also McNamara, Reference 2.

25. The official RS-232 standard is available as "Interface Between Data Terminal Equipment and Data Communications Equipment Employing Serial Binary Data Interchange" EIA RS-232C August 1969. You can find introductory descriptions of RS-232 in G. Pickles, "Who's Afraid of RS-232?", Kilobaud, May 1977, pp. 50-4 and in C. A. Ogdin, "Microcomputer Buses - Part II," Mini-Micro Systems, July 1978, pp. 76-80. Ogdin also describes the new RS-449 standard.

26. A. Osborne et al., An Introduction to Microcomputers: Volume 2 - Some Real Microprocessors, pp. 9-55 through 9-61.

27. K. Fronheiser, "Device Operation and System Implementation of the Asynchronous Communications Interface Adapter," Motorola Semiconductor Products Application Note AN-754, 1975.

28. C. W. Gear, Computer Organization and Programming 2/E (New York: McGraw-Hill, 1974), Chapter 6.

29. D. Morris, "Revised Data Interface Standards," Electronic Design, September 1, 1977, pp. 138-141.

30. Institute of Electrical and Electronics Engineers, "IEEE Standard Digital Interface for Programmable Instrumentation," IEEE Std488-1978, IEEE, 445 Hoes Lane, Piscataway, NJ 08854.

J. B. Peatman, Microcomputer-Based Design (New York: McGraw-Hill, 1977).

D. C. Loughry, and M. S. Allen, "IEEE Standard 488 and Microprocessor Synergism," Proceedings of the IEEE, February 1978, pp. 162-172.

31. G. Morrow, and H. Fullmer, "Proposed Standard for the S-100 Bus," Computer, May 1978, pp. 84-89.

   M. L. Smith, "Build Your Own Interface," Kilobaud, June 1977, pp. 22-28.

32. T. Rolander, "Intel Multibus Interfacing," Intel Application Note AP-28, Intel Corporation, Santa Clara, CA, 1977. See also An Introduction to Microcomputers: Volume 3 - Some Real support Devices, Section J.

Chapter 12
INTERRUPTS

Interrupts are inputs that the CPU examines as part of each instruction cycle. These inputs allow the CPU to react to asynchronous events in a more efficient manner than polling each device. The use of interrupts generally involves more hardware than does ordinary (programmed) I/O, but interrupts provide a faster and more direct response.[1]

Why use interrupts? **Interrupts allow events** such as alarms, power failure, the passage of a certain amount of time, and peripherals having data or being ready to accept data **to get the immediate attention of the CPU. The program does not have to examine (poll) every potential source, nor need the programmer worry about the system completely missing events.** An interrupt system is like the bell on a telephone — it rings when a call is received so that you don't have to pick up the receiver occasionally to see if someone is on the line. The CPU can go about its normal business (and get a lot more done). When something happens, the interrupt rouses the CPU and forces it to service the input before resuming normal operations. Of course, this simple description becomes more complicated (just like a telephone switchboard) when there are many interrupts of varying importance and there are tasks that cannot be interrupted.

> **REASONING BEHIND INTERRUPTS**

The implementation of interrupt systems varies greatly. Among the questions that must be answered to characterize a particular system are:

> **CHARACTERISTICS OF INTERRUPT SYSTEMS**

1) How many interrupt inputs are there?
2) How does the CPU respond to an interrupt?
3) How does the CPU determine the source of an interrupt if the number of sources exceeds the number of inputs?
4) Can the CPU differentiate between important and unimportant interrupts?
5) How and when is the interrupt system enabled and disabled?

There are many different answers to these questions. **The aim of all the implementations,** however, **is to have the CPU respond rapidly to interrupts and resume normal activity afterwards.**

The number of interrupt inputs on the CPU chip determines the number of different responses that the CPU can produce without any additional hardware or software. Each input can produce a different internal response. Unfortunately, most microprocessors have a very small number (one or two, typically) of separate interrupt inputs.

The ultimate response of the CPU to an interrupt must be to transfer control to the correct interrupt service routine and to save the current value of the Program Counter. The CPU must therefore execute a Jump-to-Subroutine or Call instruction with the beginning of the interrupt service routine as its address. This action will save the return address in the Stack and transfer control to the interrupt service routine. The amount of external hardware required to produce this response varies greatly. Some CPUs internally generate the instruction and the address; others require external hardware to form them. The CPU can only generate a different instruction or address for each separate input.

If the number of interrupting devices exceeds the number of inputs, the CPU will need extra hardware or software to identify the source of the interrupt. In the simplest case, the software can be a polling routine which checks the status of the

POLLING

VECTORING

devices that may be interrupting. The only advantage of such a system over normal polling is that the CPU knows that at least one device is active. The alternative solution is for additional hardware to provide a unique data input (or "vector") for each source. The two alternatives can be mixed; the vectors can identify groups of inputs from which the CPU can identify a particular one by polling.

An interrupt system that can differentiate between important and unimportant interrupts is called a "priority interrupt

PRIORITY

system." Internal hardware can provide as many priority levels as there are inputs. External hardware can provide additional levels through the use of a Priority register and comparator. The external hardware does not allow the interrupt to reach the CPU unless its priority is higher than the contents of the Priority register. A priority interrupt system may need a special way to handle low-priority interrupts that may be ignored for long periods of time.

Most interrupt systems can be enabled or disabled. In fact, most CPUs automatically disable interrupts when a RESET is performed (so that the programmer can configure the interrupt system) and on accepting an interrupt (so that the interrupt will not interrupt its own service routine). The programmer may wish

ENABLING
AND
DISABLING
INTERRUPTS

to disable interrupts while preparing or processing data, performing a timing loop, or executing a multi-byte operation.

An interrupt that cannot be disabled (sometimes called a "non-maskable interrupt") may be useful to warn of power failure, an event that obviously must take precedence over all other activities.

NON-MASKABLE
INTERRUPT

The advantages of interrupts are obvious, but there are also disadvantages:

DISADVANTAGES
OF INTERRUPTS

1) Interrupt systems may require a large amount of extra hardware.

2) Interrupts still require data transfers under program control through the CPU. There is no speed advantage as there is with DMA.

3) Interrupts are random inputs, which makes debugging and testing difficult. Errors may occur sporadically, and therefore may be very hard to find.[2]

4) Interrupts may involve a large amount of overhead if many registers must be saved and the source must be determined by polling.

6502 INTERRUPT SYSTEM

The 6502 microprocessor's internal response to an interrupt is moderately complex. The interrupt system consists of:

1) **An active-low maskable interrupt input ($\overline{IRQ}$) and an active-low nonmaskable interrupt input ($\overline{NMI}$).**

6502
INTERRUPT
INPUTS

2) **An interrupt disable (or mask) bit which disables the maskable interrupt.** If the Interrupt Disable bit is 1, no maskable interrupts are allowed; the I bit is stored in bit 2 of the Processor Status (or P) register.

The 6502 checks the current status of the interrupt system at the end of each instruction. If an interrupt is active and enabled, the response is as follows:

6502
INTERRUPT
RESPONSE

1) **The CPU saves the Program Counter (most significant bits first) and the Status register in the Stack.** Figure 12-1 shows the order in which these registers are saved. Note that the Accumulator and Index registers are not saved automatically.

2) **The CPU disables the maskable interrupt ($\overline{IRQ}$);** that is, it sets bit 2 of the Status register.

3) **The CPU fetches an address from a specified pair of memory addresses and puts that address in the Program Counter.** Table 12-1 contains the pairs of addresses assigned to the various inputs and to the Break instruction.

Note the following special features of the 6502 interrupt system:

SPECIAL FEATURES
OF 6502 INTERRUPT
SYSTEM

1) The 6502 automatically saves the Program Counter and the Status register in the Stack. Remember that the Status register includes the Interrupt Disable flag and the Break Command flag.

2) The 6502 provides no external signals to indicate that it has accepted an interrupt other than the address that it places on the Address Bus.

3) The 6502 has no special internal provisions for determining the source of an interrupt when there are several sources tied to the same input.

The 6502 has the following special instructions to manipulate its interrupt system:

1) **CLI (Clear Interrupt Disable Bit)** clears bit 2 of the Status register and thus enables the maskable interrupt.

2) **SEI (Set Interrupt Disable Bit)** sets bit 2 of the Status register and thus disables the maskable interrupt.

3) **BRK (Force Break)** sets the Break Command flag, saves the Program Counter and Status register in the Stack, disables the maskable interrupt, and places the contents of addresses FFFE and FFFF in the Program Counter.

4) **RTI (Return from Interrupt) restores the Status register and the Program Counter from the Stack.** The result is that the old values are returned to the Program Counter and the Status register (including the Interrupt bit). RTI differs from RTS (Return from Subroutine) in that RTI restores the Status register as well as the Program Counter and **RTI does not add 1 to the return address as RTS does** (see Chapter 11 for a discussion of RTS).

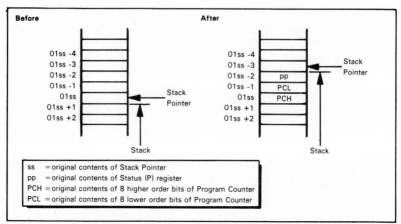

Figure 12-1. Saving the Status of the Microprocessor in the Stack

Table 12-1. Memory Map for 6502 Addresses Used in
Response to Interrupts and Reset

Source	Address Used (Hexadecimal)
Interrupt Request (IRQ) and BRK Instruction	FFFE and FFFF
Reset (RESET)	FFFC and FFFD
Nonmaskable Interrupt (NMI)	FFFA and FFFB

The addresses are stored in the usual 6502 fashion with the least significant bits at the lower address.

The BRK (Force Break) instruction produces almost exactly the same response as an interrupt input (IRQ). The only difference is that the Break Command flag (bit 4 of the Status register) is set. Thus a service routine can differentiate between a BRK instruction and an IRQ input by examining bit 4 of the top byte in the Stack (remember Figure 12-1). A typical program would be:

BRK INSTRUCTION

```
PLA              ;GET STATUS REGISTER FROM STACK
AND   #%00010000 ;IS BREAK COMMAND FLAG SET?
BNE   BREAK      ;YES, GO TO BREAK ROUTINE
```

The BRK instruction is useful for debugging (see Chapter 14) and for returning control to a monitor or operating system. See Chapter 3 for more information about the BRK instruction.

The non-maskable interrupt is an edge-sensitive input. The processor therefore reacts only to the edge of a pulse on this line, and the pulse will not interrupt its own service routine. Non-maskable interrupts are useful for applications that must respond to loss of power (i.e., must save data in a low-power memory or switch to a backup battery). Typical applications are communications equipment that must retain codes and partial messages, and test equipment that must keep track of partially completed tests. We will not discuss the non-maskable interrupt any further. We will assume that all interrupt inputs are tied to IRQ.

NON-MASKABLE INTERRUPT

6520 PIA Interrupts[3]

Most 6502 interrupt systems involve programmable interface chips or multifunction devices such as the 6520 Peripheral Interface Adapter, the 6522 Versatile Interface Adapter, or the 6530

and 6532 Multifunction Devices. **Each side of the 6520 PIA has the following features for use with interrupts:**

1) **An active-low interrupt output.**
2) **Interrupt enable bits** (bit 0 of the Control register for control line 1, bit 3 for control line 2).
3) **Interrupt status bits** (bit 7 of the Control register for control line 1, bit 6 for control line 2).

Bits 1 and 4 of the Control register determine whether a rising edge (low-to-high transition) or falling edge (high-to-low transition) on the control line causes an interrupt.

Note that:

1) **The PIA interrupt enable bits have the opposite polarity from the 6502 I (or Interrupt Disable) flag;** that is, they must be '1' to enable an interrupt.
2) **$\overline{\text{RESET}}$ clears the PIA Control registers and thus disables all the interrupts.**
3) **The CPU can check bits 6 and 7 of the Control register to see if a PIA has an interrupt pending. Once set, these bits will remain set until the CPU reads the PIA Data register.**
4) **The PIA will remember an interrupt that occurs while PIA interrupts are disabled and will output an interrupt request as soon as the PIA interrupt is enabled.**

6522 VIA INTERRUPTS

The 6522 Versatile Interface Adapter may also be used as a source of interrupts. This device has an Interrupt Enable register (IER) which can be used to enable the various interrupt sources **and an Interrupt Flag register (IFR)** which contains the status of the various sources. Figure 12-2 shows the positions of the various enabling bits in the Interrupt Enable register and Figure 12-3 describes the Interrupt Flag register.

An interrupt source can be enabled by setting the corresponding enable bit. Note that the most significant bit controls how the other enable bits are affected:

1) If IER7 = 0, each '1' in a bit position clears an enable bit and thus disables that interrupt.

2) If IER7 = 1, each '1' in a bit position sets an interrupt bit and thus enables that interrupt.

Zeros in the enabling bit positions leave the enable bits unchanged.

Some examples of enabling and disabling 6522 VIA interrupts are:

1) Enable CA1 interrupt, disable all others.

```
        LDA     #%01111101      ;DISABLE ALL OTHER INTERRUPTS
        STA     VIAIER
        LDA     #%10000010      ;ENABLE CA1 INTERRUPT
        STA     VIAIER
```

The first operation sets IER7 to zero, so that the '1's in bit positions 0, 2, 3, 4, 5, and 6 clear the corresponding enable bits and thus disable those interrupts. The second operation sets IER7 to one, so that the '1' in bit position 1 sets the corresponding enable bit (CA1 interrupt) and thus enables that interrupt.

2) Enable CB1 and CB2 interrupts, disable all others.

```
        LDA     #%01100111      ;DISABLE ALL OTHER INTERRUPTS
        STA     VIAIER
        LDA     #%10011000      ;ENABLE CB1, CB2 INTERRUPTS
        STA     VIAIER
```

The first operation sets IER7 to zero, so that the '1's in bit positions 0, 1, 2, 5, and 6 clear the corresponding enable bits and thus disable those interrupts. The second operation sets IER7 to one, so that the '1's in bit positions 3 and 4 set the corresponding enable bits (bit 3 for CB2, bit 4 for CB1) and thus enable those interrupts.

Besides the conditions described in Figure 12-3, **the bits in the Interrupt Flag register can also be cleared by writing '1's into the required bit positions in that address.** This procedure is useful for clearing flags that are being used in the independent modes and for eliminating undesired interrupts that may have been caused accidentally during reset or startup. Note that the Interrupt Flag register bit positions are the same as the Interrupt Enable register bit positions so that we can easily extend the previous examples to eliminate stray interrupts. This can be done with either enabling or disabling operations, since the value of bit 7 does not matter. The extended examples are:

1) Enable CA1 interrupt, disable all others, clear CA1 interrupt flag.

```
        LDA     #%01111101      ;DISABLE ALL OTHER INTERRUPTS
        STA     VIAIER
        LDA     #%10000010
        STA     VIAIFR          ;CLEAR CA1 INTERRUPT FLAG
        STA     VIAIER          ;ENABLE CA1 INTERRUPT
```

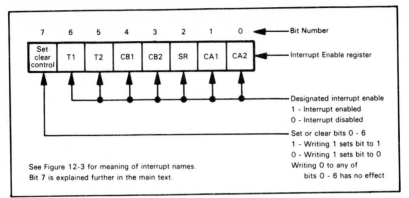

Figure 12-2. Description of the 6522 VIA Interrupt Enable Register

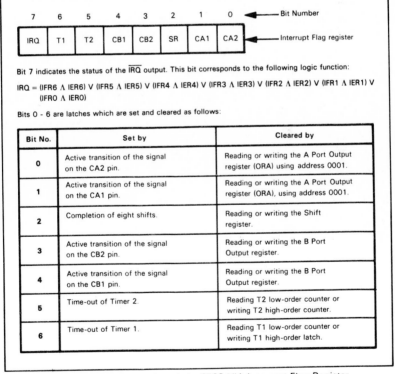

Bit 7 indicates the status of the $\overline{IRQ}$ output. This bit corresponds to the following logic function:

$$IRQ = (IFR6 \wedge IER6) \vee (IFR5 \wedge IER5) \vee (IFR4 \wedge IER4) \vee (IFR3 \wedge IER3) \vee (IFR2 \wedge IER2) \vee (IFR1 \wedge IER1) \vee$$
$$(IFR0 \wedge IER0)$$

Bits 0 - 6 are latches which are set and cleared as follows:

Bit No.	Set by	Cleared by
0	Active transition of the signal on the CA2 pin.	Reading or writing the A Port Output register (ORA) using address 0001.
1	Active transition of the signal on the CA1 pin.	Reading or writing the A Port Output register (ORA), using address 0001.
2	Completion of eight shifts.	Reading or writing the Shift register.
3	Active transition of the signal on the CB2 pin.	Reading or writing the B Port Output register.
4	Active transition of the signal on the CB1 pin.	Reading or writing the B Port Output register.
5	Time-out of Timer 2.	Reading T2 low-order counter or writing T2 high-order counter.
6	Time-out of Timer 1.	Reading T1 low-order counter or writing T1 high-order latch.

Figure 12-3. Description of the 6522 VIA Interrupt Flag Register

2) Enable CB1 and CB2 interrupts, disable all others, clear CB1 and CB2 flags.

```
LDA     #%01100111   ;DISABLE ALL OTHER INTERRUPTS
STA     VIAIER
LDA     #%10011000
STA     VIAIFR       ;CLEAR CB1, CB2 INTERRUPT FLAGS
STA     VIAIER       ;ENABLE CB1, CB2 INTERRUPTS
```

Note that bit 7 of the Interrupt Flag register and bit 7 of the Interrupt Enable register are both special. Bit 7 of the Interrupt Flag register indicates the status of the IRQ output — that is, it is 1 if any of the interrupts are both active and enabled. **Bit 7 of the Interrupt Enable register is the Set/Clear control** mentioned earlier. Note that bit 7 of the Interrupt Flag register cannot be cleared directly; it can only be cleared by either clearing all the active interrupt flags or by disabling all the active interrupts.

Note the following about VIA interrupts:

1) **The VIA interrupt enable bits have the opposite polarity from the 6502 I (or Interrupt Disable) flag;** that is, they must be '1' to enable an interrupt.

2) **RESET disables all the interrupts.**

3) **The CPU can check bit 7 of the Interrupt Flag register to see if any interrupts are both active and enabled.** That bit will remain set until no interrupt is both active and enabled.

4) **The VIA will remember an interrupt that occurs when VIA interrupts are disabled and will output a request via IRQ as the VIA is enabled.**

There are several examples of VIA interrupts later in this chapter.

6530 and 6532 Multifunction Device Interrupts

The 6530 device can provide an interrupt from its interval timer. The $\overline{IRQ}$ output is also pin PB7 from Port B and should be set up as an input if it is to be used to cause an interrupt. The interrupt can be enabled by writing to the

6530 AND 6532
MULTIFUNCTION
DEVICE INTERRUPTS

timer with address line A3 high. The interrupt can be disabled by writing to the timer with address line A3 low. It can be cleared by reading or writing the timer after an interrupt has occurred.

The 6532 device can provide a timer interrupt like the 6530 device. It can also provide an interrupt based on the occurrence of an edge on PA7; PA7 thus operates much like CA1 or CB1 on a 6520 PIA or a 6522 VIA. The interrupt can occur either on a low-to-high transition (positive edge) or on a high-to-low transition (negative edge).

6532 interrupts are controlled and examined by writing to and reading from specific addresses (see Table 12-2 for a description of the addresses in a 6532 device). Note the following:

1) To control the PA7 interrupt, you simply write any data whatsoever into the address in the 6532 I/O section given by:

   $\overline{RS} = 1$ to activate I/O rather than the on-board RAM

   A2 = 1, A4 = 0

The two least significant address bits (not the data) then control the PA7 mode as follows:

   A1 = 1 to enable PA7 interrupt, 0 to disable it

   A0 = 1 for a positive (low-to-high) edge detect, 0 for a negative (high-to-low) edge detect.

2) To read and clear the Interrupt flags, read from the address in the 6532 I/O section given by:

   $\overline{RS} = 1$ to activate I/O rather than the on-board RAM

   A2 = 1, A0 = 1

Bit 7 is the Timer Interrupt flag and bit 6 is the PA7 Interrupt flag. These can easily be read by means of the Bit Test instruction (Bit 7 is transferred to the Sign flag and bit 6 to the Overflow flag).

ACIA Interrupts

The 6850 ACIA can also serve as a source for interrupts. You should note the following features of the ACIA in interrupt-based systems:

6850 ACIA
INTERRUPTS

1) **The transmitter interrupt (ACIA is ready for data) is enabled only if Control register bit 6 = 0 and Control register bit 5 = 1.**

2) **The receiver interrupt (ACIA has received new data) is enabled only if Control register bit 7 = 1.**

3) **Master reset does not affect the interrupt enable bits.**

4) **Bit 7 of the Status register is set if an interrupt has occurred.** This bit can be cleared either by reading data from the ACIA or by writing data into the ACIA.

Table 12-2. Addressing the 6532 Multifunction Device

$\overline{RS}$	R/$\overline{W}$	A4	A3	A2	A1	A0	Address Mode
		Selection Lines					
0	1(0)	X	X	X	X	X	**RAM Addressing** Read (Write) RAM. A0 - A6 select RAM address.
1	1(0)	X	X	0	0	0	**I/O Addressing** Read (Write) Port A data
1	1(0)	X	X	0	0	1	Read (Write) Port A Data Direction Register
1	1(0)	X	X	0	1	0	Read (Write) Port B data
1	1(0)	X	X	0	1	1	Read (Write) Port B Data Direction Register
1	0	0	X	1	0	X	**Edge-Detection Control** Disable interrupt from PA7
1	0	0	X	1	1	X	Enable interrupt from PA7
1	0	0	X	1	X	0	Negative edge detect
1	0	0	X	1	X	1	Positive edge detect
1	1	X	X	1	X	1	**Read and Clear Interrupt Flags** Bit 7 is the Timer Flag Bit 6 is the PA7 Flag
1	0	1	0	1	X	X	**Write Count to Interval Timer** and disable timer interrupt
1	0	1	1	1	X	X	and enable timer interrupt
1	0	1	X	1	0	0	and decrement every $\Phi2$ pulse
1	0	1	X	1	0	1	and decrement every 8 $\Phi2$ pulses
1	0	1	X	1	1	0	and decrement every 64 $\Phi2$ pulses
1	0	1	X	1	1	1	and decrement every 1024 $\Phi2$ pulses

For all operations CS1 = 1, $\overline{CS2}$ = 0.

Logic levels: 0 means low level

1 means high level

X means level of that signal does not matter (either 0 or 1)

6502 Polling Interrupt Systems

Most 6502 interrupt systems must poll each PIA, VIA, ACIA, or other device to determine which one caused an interrupt. The polling method is:

POLLING INTERRUPTS

1) Check each PIA by examining Control register bits 6 and 7:

```
BIT     PIACR   ;CHECK PIA STATUS BITS
BMI     INT1    ;BRANCH TO INTERRUPT 1 IF BIT 7 SET
BVS     INT2    ;BRANCH TO INTERRUPT 2 IF BIT 6 SET
```

2) Check each VIA by examining Interrupt Flag register bit 7:

```
BIT     VIAIFR  ;ARE ANY INTERRUPTS ACTIVE ON THIS VIA?
BMI     INTV    ;YES, GO EXAMINE ALL OF FLAG REGISTER
```

You must still examine the Interrupt Flag register if there is more than one potential interrupt source from a particular VIA. All that bit 7 tells you is that at least one source is both active and enabled.

3) Check each ACIA by examining Status register bit 7:

```
BIT     ACIASR  ;ARE ANY INTERRUPTS ACTIVE ON THIS ACIA?
BMI     INTA    ;YES, GO DETERMINE WHICH ONE IF NECESSARY
```

The interrupt could still be either a receiver or a transmitter interrupt.

The important features of a 6502 polling system are:

1) **The first interrupt examined has the highest priority, since the remaining interrupts will not be examined if the first one is active.** The second interrupt has the next highest priority, and so on.

2) **The service routine must clear the interrupt flags from PIAs, VIAs, ACIAs, or other devices if the clearing is not performed automatically.**

The programmer should be particularly careful of:

PIAs being used as interrupting output ports.

A dummy read of the port is necessary, since the Interrupt flag is not cleared automatically when data is written into the port. PIA Status (Interrupt) flags are cleared only when the Data registers are read.

• **VIAs being used in the independent input mode or through addresses that do not affect the Interrupt flags.**

The Interrupt flag must then be explicitly cleared by writing a logic '1' into the appropriate bit of the Interrupt Flag register.

Polling routines are adequate if there are only a few inputs. However, if there are many inputs, polling routines are slow and awkward because:

DISADVANTAGES OF POLLING INTERRUPTS

1) The average number of polling operations increases linearly with the number of inputs. On the average, of course, you'll have to poll half of the inputs before finding the correct one. You can reduce the average number of polling operations somewhat by checking the most frequent inputs first.

2) PIA, VIA, and ACIA addresses are rarely consecutive or evenly spaced; therefore, separate instructions are necessary to examine each input. Polling routines are therefore difficult to expand. Tables of I/O addresses could be used by placing the base address on page zero and using the post-indexed addressing mode or by placing the entire table on page zero and using the pre-indexed addressing mode.

3) Interrupts that are polled first may shut out those that are polled later unless the order of polling is varied. However, the lack of consecutive addresses makes varying the order of polling difficult.

6502 Vectored Interrupt Systems

The problem of polling in 6502-based systems has typically been solved by special methods, unique to a particular application or microcomputer. **Note that there is no way to know that the 6502 has accepted an interrupt other than by recognizing the addresses FFFE and FFFF when they appear on the Address Bus. Special hardware can then substitute the vector provided by the actual source.**[4] We will not discuss 6502 vectored interrupt systems any further.

| 6502 |
| VECTORED |
| INTERRUPTS |

EXAMPLES

A Startup Interrupt

Purpose: The computer waits for a VIA interrupt to occur before starting actual operations.

Many systems remain inactive until the operator actually starts them or until a Data Ready signal is received. On RESET, such systems must initialize the Stack Pointer, enable the startup interrupt, and execute an endless loop or jump-to-self instruction. Remember that RESET disables the processor interrupt (by setting I to 1) as well as all the VIA interrupts (by clearing all the VIA interrupt enable bits). In the flowchart, the decision as to whether startup is active is made in hardware (i.e., by the CPU examining the interrupt input internally) rather than in software.

Flowchart:

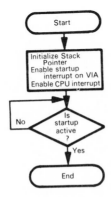

Source Program:

Main Program:

```
          LDX     #$FF            ;PUT STACK AT END OF PAGE 1
          TXS
          LDA     #0
          STA     VIAPCR          ;MAKE ALL CONTROL LINES INPUTS
          LDA     #%10000010
          STA     VIAIFR          ;CLEAR CA1 INTERRUPT FLAG
          STA     VIAIER          ;ENABLE CA1 INTERRUPT
          CLI                     ;ENABLE CPU INTERRUPT
HERE      JMP     HERE            ;WAIT FOREVER
```

Interrupt Service Routine:

```
          *=INTRP
          LDA     #%10000010
          STA     VIAIFR          ;CLEAR CA1 INTERRUPT FLAG
          LDX     #$FF            ;REINITIALIZE STACK POINTER
          TXS
          JMP     START
```

Object Program:

Memory Address (Hex)	Memory Contents (Hex)		Instruction (Mnemonic)	
Main Program:				
0000	A2		LDX	#$FF
0001	FF			
0002	9A		TXS	
0003	A9		LDA	#0
0004	00			
0005	8D		STA	VIAPCR
0006 } 0007 }	VIAPCR			
0008	A9		LDA	#%10000010
0009	82			
000A	8D		STA	VIAIFR
000B } 000C }	VIAIFR			
000D	8D		STA	VIAIER
000E } 000F }	VIAIER			
0010	58		CLI	
0011	4C	HERE	JMP	HERE
0012	11			
0013	00			
Interrupt Service Routine:				
INTRP	A9		LDA	#%10000010
INTRP+1	82			
INTRP+2	8D		STA	VIAIFR
INTRP+3 } INTRP+4 }	VIAIFR			
INTRP+5	A2		LDX	#$FF
INTRP+6	FF			
INTRP+7	9A		TXS	
INTRP+8	4C		JMP	START
INTRP+9 } INTRP+A }	START			

The exact location of the interrupt service routine varies with the microcomputer. If your microcomputer has no monitor, you can simply place whatever address you want in memory locations FFFE and FFFF (or whatever locations respond to those addresses). You must then start the interrupt service routine at the address you chose. Of course, you should place the routine so that it does not interfere with fixed addresses or with other programs.

INTERRUPTS ON PARTICULAR MICROCOMPUTERS

If your microcomputer has a monitor, the monitor will occupy addresses FFFE and FFFF. Those addresses will either contain a starting address at which you must place your interrupt service routine, or will contain the starting address of a routine that allows you to choose the starting address of the interrupt service routine. A typical monitor routine would be:

INTERRUPT HANDLING BY MONITORS

```
MONINT  JMP     (USRINT)    ;JUMP TO USER SUPPLIED INTERRUPT ADDRESS
```

You must then place the address of your service routine in memory locations USRINT and USRINT+1. Remember that MONINT is an address in the monitor program and its value is in addresses FFFE and FFFF.

You can include the loading of memory locations USRINT and USRINT+1 in your main program.

```
        LDA     #USRL       ;LOAD LSB'S OF USER INTERRUPT ADDRESS
        STA     USRINT
        LDA     #USRM       ;LOAD MSB'S OF USER INTERRUPT ADDRESS
        STA     USRINT+1
```

These instructions must precede the enabling of the interrupts.

The main program only enables the interrupt from the startup VIA. We have assumed that the startup line is attached to VIA input CA1 and that the active edge is the trailing one (i.e., a high-to-low transition). Other configurations would merely require different values in the VIA Peripheral Control register.

Note that the VIA interrupt is enabled and the Stack Pointer is loaded before the CPU interrupt is enabled (by clearing the I bit). What would happen if you cleared the I bit before loading the Stack Pointer? This will not be a potential problem if the monitor already places a value in the Stack Pointer.

In this example, the return address and Status register that the 6502 stores in the Stack on accepting an interrupt are not useful. Thus the service routine simply reinitializes the Stack Pointer.

Note that we could replace the JMP HERE instruction with a conditional branch that provided a guaranteed jump, such as BNE HERE. The Zero flag is not zero since the last operation was the one that enabled the CA1 interrupt. This shortcut is often helpful to make up for the fact that the 6502 has no unconditional branch with relative addressing.

Remember that RESET and accepting an interrupt automatically disable the interrupt system. This allows the real startup routine to configure all the VIAs and other interrupt sources without being interrupted. Note that you must explicitly clear the CA1 Interrupt flag or else it will interrupt again as soon as the interrupt system is re-enabled. You could also clear the flag by reading the VIA's Output Register A from the handshaking address (see Table 11-7).

A Keyboard Interrupt

Purpose: The computer waits for a keyboard interrupt and places the data from the keyboard into memory locaton 0040.

KEYBOARD INTERRUPT

Sample Problem:

Keyboard data   =   06
Result: (0040)   =   06

Flowchart:

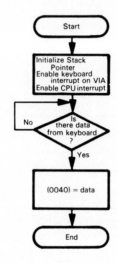

Source Program:

Main Program:

```
        LDX     #$FF            ;PUT STACK AT END OF PAGE 1
        TXS
        LDA     #0
        STA     VIAPCR          ;MAKE ALL CONTROL LINES INPUTS
        STA     VIADDRA         ;MAKE PORT A LINES INPUTS
        LDA     #%10000010
        STA     VIAIFR          ;CLEAR KEYBOARD INTERRUPT FLAG
        STA     VIAIER          ;ENABLE KEYBOARD INTERRUPT FROM VIA
        CLI                     ;ENABLE CPU INTERRUPT
HERE    JMP     HERE            ;DUMMY MAIN PROGRAM
```

Interrupt Service Routine:

```
        *=INTRP
        PHA                     ;SAVE ACCUMULATOR IN STACK
        LDA     VIAORA          ;GET KEYBOARD DATA
        STA     $40             ;SAVE KEYBOARD DATA
        PLA                     ;RESTORE ACCUMULATOR FROM STACK
        RTI
```

Object Program:

Memory Address (Hex)	Memory Contents (Hex)		Instruction (Mnemonic)	
Main Program:				
0000	A2		LDX	#$FF
0001	FF			
0002	9A		TXS	
0003	A9		LDA	#0
0004	00			
0005	8D		STA	VIAPCR
0006 0007 }	VIAPCR			
0008	8D		STA	VIADDRA
0009 000A }	VIADDRA			
000B	A9		LDA	#%10000010
000C	82			
000D	8D		STA	VIAIFR
000E 000F }	VIAIFR			
0010	8D		STA	VIAIER
0011 0012 }	VIAIER			
0013	58		CLI	
0014	4C	HERE	JMP	HERE
0015	14			
0016	00			
Interrupt Service Routine:				
INTRP	48		PHA	
INTRP+1	AD		LDA	VIAORA
INTRP+2 INTRP+3 }	VIAORA			
INTRP+4	85		STA	$40
INTRP+5	40			
INTRP+6	68		PLA	
INTRP+7	40		RTI	

You must configure the VIA completely before enabling the interrupts. This includes establishing the directions of ports, determining the transitions to be recognized on strobe lines, and enabling latches (remember that setting bit 0 of the Auxiliary Control register enables the Port A latch).

The JMP HERE is an endless loop (jump-to-self) instruction that is used to represent the main program. After interrupts are enabled in a working system, the main program goes about its business until an interrupt occurs and then resumes execution after the interrupt service routine is completed.

The RTI instruction at the end of the service routine transfers control back to the JMP instruction in the main program. If you want to avoid this, you can simply change the Program Counter in the Stack. Remember that the Stack is always located on page 1 (addresses 0100 - 01FF), the Stack Pointer

contains the address of the next empty location, and the interrupt response places the Program Counter in the Stack underneath the Status register. Thus **the following program will increment the Program Counter in the Stack without removing it.**

```
        TXS                     ;MAKE STACK POINTER INTO INDEX
        INC     $0102,X         ;INCREMENT LSB'S OF RETURN ADDRESS
        BNE     DONE
        INC     $0103,X         ;AND CARRY TO MSB'S IF NECESSARY
DONE    (next instruction)
```

Since the 6502 does not automatically save its registers (other than the Status register), you can use them to pass parameters and results between the main program and the interrupt service routine. So, you could leave the data in the Accumulator instead of in memory location 0040. This is, however, a dangerous practice that should be avoided in all but the most trivial systems. In most applications, the processor is using its registers during normal program execution; having the interrupt service routines randomly change the contents of those registers would surely cause havoc. **In general, no interrupt service routine should ever alter any register unless that register's contents have been saved prior to its alteration and will be restored at the completion of the routine.**

Note that you need not explicitly re-enable the interrupts at the end of the service routine. The reason is that **the RTI instruction automatically restores the old Status (P) register with the Interrupt Disable bit in its original state.** In fact, you will have to alter the Interrupt Disable bit in the Stack (bit 2 of the top location) if you do not want the interrupts to be re-enabled.

Using the Stack is the most general approach to saving and restoring registers. The instruction PHA saves the contents of the Accumulator in the Stack and the instruction PLA restores the contents of the Accumulator from the Stack. This method can be expanded indefinitely (as long as there is room in the Stack) since nested service routines will not destroy the data saved by the earlier routines.

You can save all the registers in the Stack (remember that Status is automatically saved) after an interrupt with the sequence:

```
        PHA             ;SAVE ACCUMULATOR
        TXA             ;SAVE INDEX REGISTER X
        PHA
        TYA             ;SAVE INDEX REGISTER Y
        PHA
```

Note that there is no direct way to transfer data between the Stack and the Index registers. The contents of the Accumulator must be saved first (why?).

You can restore the registers from the Stack (remember that RTI automatically restores Status) after an interrupt service routine by removing the data from the Stack in the opposite order from which it was entered:

```
        PLA             ;RESTORE INDEX REGISTER Y
        TAY
        PLA             ;RESTORE INDEX REGISTER X
        TAX
        PLA             ;RESTORE ACCUMULATOR
```

Note that the Accumulator is saved first and restored last.

An alternative approach would be for the interrupt routine to maintain control until it received an entire line of text (e.g., a string of characters ending with a carriage return). The main program would be:

FILLING A
BUFFER VIA
INTERRUPTS

Main Program:

```
        LDX     #$FF        ;PUT STACK AT END OF PAGE 1
        TXS
        LDA     #0
        STA     VIAPCR      ;MAKE ALL CONTROL LINES INPUTS
        STA     VIADDRA     ;MAKE PORT A LINES INPUTS
        STA     $40         ;CLEAR BUFFER INDEX TO START
        LDA     #%10000010
        STA     VIAIFR      ;CLEAR KEYBOARD INTERRUPT FLAG
        STA     VIAIER      ;ENABLE KEYBOARD INTERRUPT FROM VIA
        CLI                 ;ENABLE CPU INTERRUPT
HERE    JMP     HERE        ;DUMMY MAIN PROGRAM
```

Interrupt Service Routine:

```
        *=INTRP
        PHA                 ;SAVE ACCUMULATOR IN STACK
        TXA                 ;SAVE INDEX REGISTER X IN STACK
        PHA
        LDX     $40         ;GET BUFFER INDEX
        LDA     VIAORA      ;GET KEYBOARD DATA
        STA     $41,X       ;SAVE DATA IN BUFFER
        CMP     #CR         ;IS DATA A CARRIAGE RETURN?
        BEQ     ENDL        ;YES, END OF LINE
        INC     $40         ;NO, INCREMENT BUFFER POINTER
        PLA                 ;RESTORE INDEX REGISTER X FROM STACK
        TAX
        PLA                 ;RESTORE ACCUMULATOR FROM STACK
        RTI
ENDL    JMP     LPROC       ;PROCESS LINE WITHOUT INTERRUPTS
```

This program fills a buffer starting at memory location 0041 until it receives a carriage return character (CR). Memory location 0040 holds the current buffer index.

When the processor receives a carriage return, it leaves the interrupt system disabled while it handles the line.

An alternative approach would be to fill another buffer while handling the first one; this approach is called double buffering.

DOUBLE
BUFFERING

The line processing routine is begun at address LPROC with interrupts disabled, and with the original register contents (P, A, and X) and the return address in the Stack.

In a real application, the CPU could perform other tasks between interrupts. It could, for instance, edit, move, or transmit a line from one buffer while the interrupt was filling another buffer.

A Printer Interrupt

Purpose: The computer waits for a printer interrupt and sends the data from memory location 0040 to the printer.

Sample Problem:

$(0040) = 51_{16}$

Result: Printer receives a 51_{16} (ASCII Q) when it is ready.

Flowchart:

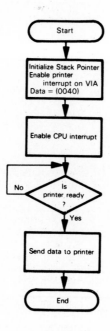

Source Program:

Main Program:

```
          LDX     #$FF           ;PUT STACK AT END OF PAGE 1
          TXS
          STX     VIADDRB        ;MAKE PORT B LINES OUTPUTS
          LDA     #0
          STA     VIAPCR         ;MAKE ALL CONTROL LINES INPUTS
          LDA     #%10000010
          STA     VIAIFR         ;CLEAR PRINTER INTERRUPT FLAG
          STA     VIAIER         ;ENABLE PRINTER INTERRUPT FROM VIA
          CLI                    ;ENABLE CPU INTERRUPTS
HERE      JMP     HERE           ;DUMMY MAIN PROGRAM
```

Interrupt Service Routine:

```
          *=INTRP
          PHA                    ;SAVE ACCUMULATOR IN STACK
          LDA     $40            ;GET DATA
          STA     VIAORB         ;SEND DATA TO PRINTER
          PLA                    ;RESTORE ACCUMULATOR FROM STACK
          RTI
```

Object Program:

Memory Address (Hex)	Memory Contents (Hex)	Instruction (Mnemonic)	
Main Program:			
0000	A2	LDX	#$FF
0001	FF		
0002	9A	TXS	
0003	8E	STX	VIADDRB
0004 0005	VIADDRB		
0006	A9	LDA	#0
0007	00		
0008	8D	STA	VIAPCR
0009 000A	VIAPCR		
000B	A9	LDA	#%10000010
000C	82		
000D	8D	STA	VIAIFR
000E 000F	VIAIFR		
0010	8D	STA	VIAIER
0011 0012	VIAIER		
0013	58	CLI	
0014	4C	HERE JMP	HERE
0015	14		
0016	00		
Interrupt Service Routine:			
INTRP	48	PHA	
INTRP+1	A5	LDA	$40
INTRP+2	40		
INTRP+3	8D	STA	VIAORB
INTRP+4 INTRP+5	VIAORB		
INTRP+6	68	PLA	
INTRP+7	40	RTI	

12-21

Here, as with the keyboard, you could have the printer continue to interrupt until it transferred an entire line of text. The main program and the service routine would be:

EMPTYING A BUFFER WITH INTERRUPTS

Main Program:

```
          LDX     #$FF
          TXS              ;PUT STACK AT END OF PAGE 1
          STX     VIADDRB  ;MAKE PORT B LINES OUTPUTS
          LDA     #0
          STA     VIAPCR   ;MAKE ALL CONTROL LINES INPUTS
          STA     $40      ;INITIALIZE BUFFER INDEX TO ZERO
          LDA     #%10000010
          STA     VIAIFR   ;CLEAR PRINTER INTERRUPT FLAG
          STA     VIAIER   ;ENABLE PRINTER INTERRUPT FROM VIA
          CLI              ;ENABLE CPU INTERRUPT
HERE      JMP     HERE     ;DUMMY MAIN PROGRAM
```

Interrupt Service Routine:

```
          *=INTRP
          PHA              ;SAVE ACCUMULATOR IN STACK
          TXA              ;SAVE INDEX REGISTER X IN STACK
          PHA
          LDX     $40      ;GET BUFFER INDEX
          LDA     $41,X    ;GET A BYTE OF DATA FROM BUFFER
          STA     VIAORB   ;SEND DATA TO PRINTER
          CMP     #CR      ;IS DATA A CARRIAGE RETURN?
          BEQ     ENDL     ;YES, END OF LINE
          INC     $40      ;NO, INCREMENT BUFFER POINTER
          PLA              ;RESTORE INDEX REGISTER X FROM STACK
          TAX
          PLA              ;RESTORE ACCUMULATOR FROM STACK
          RTI
ENDL      JMP     LCOMP    ;HANDLE COMPLETED LINE
```

Again, double buffering could be used to allow I/O and processing to occur at the same time without ever halting the CPU.

A Real-Time Clock Interrupt[5,6]

Purpose: The computer waits for an interrupt from a real-time clock.

REAL-TIME CLOCK

A real-time clock simply provides a regular series of pulses. The interval between the pulses can be used as a time reference. Real-time clock interrupts can be counted to give any multiple of the basic time interval. A real-time clock can be produced by dividing down the CPU clock, by using a separate timer or a programmable timer like the ones available in the 6522 VIA or in the 6530 or 6532 Multifunction devices (see Chapter 11), or by using external sources such as the AC line frequency.

Note the tradeoffs involved in determining the frequency of the real-time clock. A high frequency (say 10 kHz) allows the creation of a wide range of time intervals of high accuracy. On the

FREQUENCY OF REAL-TIME CLOCK

other hand, the overhead involved in counting real-time clock interrupts may be considerable, and the counts will quickly exceed the capacity of a single 8-bit register or memory location. The choice of frequency depends on the precision and timing requirements of your application. The clock may, of course, consist partly of hardware; a counter may count high frequency pulses and interrupt the processor only occasionally. A program will have to read the counter to measure time to high accuracy.

One problem is synchronizing operations with the real-time clock. Clearly, there will be some effect on the precision of the timing interval if the CPU starts the measurement randomly during a clock period, rather than exactly at the beginning. Some ways to synchronize operations are:

SYNCHRONIZATION WITH REAL-TIME CLOCK

1) Start the CPU and clock together. $\overline{\text{RESET}}$ or a startup interrupt can start the clock as well as the CPU.
2) Allow the CPU to start and stop the clock under program control.
3) Use a high-frequency clock so that an error of less than one clock period will be small.
4) Line up the clock (by waiting for an edge or interrupt) before starting the measurement.

A real-time clock interrupt should have very high priority, since the precision of the timing intervals will be affected by any delay in servicing the interrupt. The usual practice is to

PRIORITY OF REAL-TIME CLOCK

make the real-time clock the highest priority interrupt except for power failure. **The clock interrupt service routine is generally kept extremely short so that it does not interfere with other CPU activities.**

a) Wait for Real-Time Clock

Source Program:

Main Program:

```
            LDX     #$FF            ;PUT STACK AT END OF PAGE 1
            TXS
            LDA     #0
            STA     VIAPCR          ;MAKE ALL CONTROL LINES INPUTS
            LDA     #%10000010
            STA     VIAIFR          ;CLEAR CLOCK INTERRUPT FLAG
            STA     VIAIER          ;ENABLE CLOCK INTERRUPT FROM VIA
            CLI                     ;ENABLE CPU INTERRUPT
HERE        JMP     HERE            ;DUMMY MAIN PROGRAM
```

Interrupt Service Routine:

```
            *=INTRP
            PHA                     ;SAVE ACCUMULATOR IN STACK
            LDA     #%10000010
            STA     VIAIFR          ;CLEAR CLOCK INTERRUPT FLAG
            PLA                     ;RESTORE ACCUMULATOR FROM STACK
            BRK
```

Object Program:

Memory Address (Hex)	Memory Contents (Hex)		Instruction (Mnemonic)	
Main Program:				
0000	A2		LDX	#$FF
0001	FF			
0002	9A		TXS	
0003	A9		LDA	#0
0004	00			
0005	8D		STA	VIAPCR
0006⎱ 0007⎰	VIAPCR			
0008	A9		LDA	#%10000010
0009	82			
000A	8D		STA	VIAIFR
000B⎱ 000C⎰	VIAIFR			
000D	8D		STA	VIAIER
000E⎱ 000F⎰	VIAIER			
0010	58		CLI	
0011	4C	HERE	JMP	HERE
0012	11			
0013	00			
Interrupt Service Routine:				
INTRP	48		PHA	
INTRP+1	A9		LDA	#%10000010
INTRP+2	82			
INTRP+3	8D		STA	VIAIFR
INTRP+4⎱ INTRP+5⎰	VIAIFR			
INTRP+6	68		PLA	
INTRp+7	00		BRK	

If bit 0 of the VIA Peripheral Control register is 0, the interrupt will occur on the high-to-low (falling) clock edge. If that bit is 1, the interrupt will occur on the low-to-high (rising) clock edge.

The Clock Interrupt flag must be explicitly cleared in the interrupt service routine since no I/O transfer is required. Note that Port A could still be used for data as long as that data was transferred using the address that does not affect the interrupt flags (see Table 11-7).

We could, of course, generate the pulse itself using one of the 6522 timers. The following example uses timer 1 to produce a single pulse 5000 (1388_{16}) clock cycles in length. Remember the following:

1) The timer 1 counters are loaded from two memory locations (VIAT1L and VIAT1CH); loading the most significant bits of the timer count into VIAT1CH starts the timer and clears the T1 Interrupt flag (bit 6 of the Interrupt Flag register).

2) The mode of operation of timer 1 is controlled by bits 6 and 7 of the Auxiliary Control register:

   bit 6 = 0 for a single pulse and 1 for continuous operation

   bit 7 = 0 to disable output pulses on PB7 and 1 to generate such pulses.

3) The conclusion of the timing interval sets the timer 1 Interrupt flag (bit 6 of the Interrupt Flag register).

Table 11-7 describes the addressing of the VIA, Figure 11-10 describes the Auxiliary Control register, and Figure 12-3 describes the Interrupt Flag register.

Main Program:

```
          LDX      #$FF
          TXS                        ;PUT STACK AT END OF PAGE 1
          LDA      #0
          STA      VIAACR            ;GENERATE ONE PULSE FROM TIMER 1
          LDA      #%11000000
          STA      VIAIFR            ;CLEAR TIMER 1 INTERRUPT
          STA      VIAIER            ;ENABLE TIMER 1 INTERRUPT
          LDA      #$88              ;PULSE LENGTH = 5000 (1388 HEX)
          STA      VIAT1L
          LDA      #$13
          STA      VIAT1CH           ;START TIMING INTERVAL
          CLI                        ;ENABLE CPU INTERRUPT
HERE      JMP      HERE              ;DUMMY MAIN PROGRAM
```

Interrupt Service Routine:

```
          *=INTRP
          PHA                        ;SAVE ACCUMULATOR IN STACK
          LDA      #%11000000
          STA      VIAIFR            ;CLEAR CLOCK INTERRUPT FLAG
          PLA                        ;RESTORE ACCUMULATOR FROM STACK
          BRK
```

The only change in the service routine is the position of the Clock Interrupt flag in the Interrupt Flag register.

b) Wait for 10 Real-Time Clock Interrupts

Source Program:

Main Program:

```
        LDX     #$FF            ;PUT STACK AT END OF PAGE 1
        TXS
        LDA     #0
        STA     VIAPCR          ;MAKE ALL CONTROL LINES INPUTS
        STA     $40             ;CLEAR CLOCK COUNTER
        LDA     #%10000010
        STA     VIAIFR          ;CLEAR CLOCK INTERRUPT FLAG
        STA     VIAIER          ;ENABLE CLOCK INTERRUPT FROM VIA
        LDA     #10             ;NUMBER OF COUNTS = 10
        CLI                     ;ENABLE CPU INTERRUPT
WTTEN   CMP     $40             ;HAVE TEN COUNTS ELAPSED?
        BNE     WTTEN           ;NO, WAIT
        SEI                     ;YES, DISABLE CPU INTERRUPT
        BRK
```

Interrupt Service Routine:

```
        *=INTRP
        PHA                     ;SAVE ACCUMULATOR IN STACK
        INC     $40             ;INCREMENT CLOCK COUNTER
        LDA     #%10000010
        STA     VIAIFR          ;CLEAR CLOCK INTERRUPT FLAG
        PLA                     ;RESTORE ACCUMULATOR FROM STACK
        RTI
```

Clearly we could generate the pulses from the 6522 timer — for example, we could use timer 1 in its continuous mode (bit 6 of the Auxiliary Control register = 1). The only other change would be the bit position of the Interrupt flag.

Object Program:

Memory Address (Hex)	Memory Contents (Hex)		Instruction (Mnemonic)	
Main Program:				
0000	A2		LDX	#$FF
0001	FF			
0002	9A		TXS	
0003	A9		LDA	#0
0004	00			
0005	8D		STA	VIAPCR
0006 } 0007 }	VIAPCR			
0008	85		STA	$40
0009	40			
000A	A9		LDA	#%10000010
000B	82			
000C	8D		STA	VIAIFR
000D } 000E }	VIAIFR			
000F	8D		STA	VIAIER
0010 } 0011 }	VIAIER			
0012	A9		LDA	#10
0013	0A			
0014	58		CLI	
0015	C5	WTTEN	CMP	$40
0016	40			
0017	D0		BNE	WTTEN
0018	FC			
0019	78		SEI	
001A	00		BRK	
Interrupt Service Routine:				
INTRP	48		PHA	
INTRP+1	E6		INC	$40
INTRP+2	40			
INTRP+3	A9		LDA	#%10000010
INTRP+4	82			
INTRP+5	8D		STA	VIAIFR
INTRP+6 } INTRP+7 }	VIAIFR			
INTRP+8	68		PLA	
INTRP+9	40		RTI	

12-28

This interrupt service routine merely updates the counter in memory location 0040. It is transparent to the main program.

A more realistic real-time clock interrupt routine could maintain real time in several memory locations. For example, the following routine uses addresses 0040 through 0043 as follows:

0040 - hundredths of seconds
0041 - seconds
0042 - minutes
0043 - hours

We assume that the routine is triggered by a 100 Hz clock.

Flowchart:

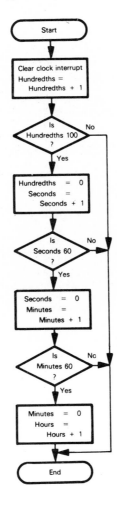

Source Program:

```
            *=INTRP
            PHA                              ;SAVE ACCUMULATOR IN STACK
            LDA     #%10000010
            STA     VIAIFR                   ;CLEAR CLOCK INTERRUPT FLAG
            INC     $40                      ;UPDATE HUNDREDTHS OF SECONDS
            LDA     $40
            SEC                              ;IS THERE A CARRY TO SECONDS?
            SBC     #100
            BNE     ENDINT                   ;NO, DONE
            STA     $40                      ;YES, MAKE HUNDREDTHS ZERO
            INC     $41                      ;UPDATE SECONDS
            LDA     $41
            SBC     #60                      ;IS THERE A CARRY TO MINUTES?
            BNE     ENDINT                   ;NO, DONE
            STA     $41                      ;YES, MAKE SECONDS ZERO
            INC     $42                      ;UPDATE MINUTES
            LDA     $42
            SBC     #60                      ;IS THERE A CARRY TO HOURS?
            BNE     ENDINT                   ;NO, DONE
            STA     $42                      ;YES, MAKE MINUTES ZERO
            INC     $43                      ;UPDATE HOURS
ENDINT      PLA                              ;RESTORE ACCUMULATOR FROM STACK
            RTI
```

Now a wait of 300 ms could be produced in the main program with the routine:

```
            LDA     $40                      ;GET CURRENT REAL TIME
            CLC
            ADC     #30                      ;DESIRED TIME IS 30 COUNTS LATER
            CMP     #100                     ;MOD 100
            BCC     WAIT30
            SBC     #100
WAIT30      CMP     $40                      ;WAIT UNTIL DESIRED TIME
            BNE     WAIT30
```

We do not need explicit SET CARRY (SEC) instructions except in the first operation in the interrupt service routine. The other operations in the interrupt service routine are only performed if the previous subtraction produced a zero result (and hence also produced a Carry of 1 indicating no borrow). In the wait program, the subtraction is only performed at all if the Carry is 1 (otherwise a branch occurs).

Of course, the program could perform other tasks and check the elapsed time only occasionally. How would you produce a delay of seven seconds? Of three minutes?

Sometimes you may want to keep time either as BCD digits or as ASCII characters. How would you revise the last program to handle these alternatives?

When it is no longer needed, you can disable the clock interrupt (or any other interrupt) in any of the following ways:

1) By executing an SEI instruction in the main program. This disables the entire interrupt system. An SEI instruction in the service routine has no effect, since RTI restores the old I flag; anyway, the 6502 automatically disables interrupts during the service routine.

2) By clearing the appropriate bit in the Interrupt Enable register (see Figure 12-2) either during the service routine or during the main program. This disables only the single interrupt source from one VIA.

3) By setting the Interrupt Disable flag in the Stack during the service routine. The following program will do the job (remember that the Interrupt Disable flag is bit 2 of the Status register and that the Status register is the top entry in the Stack — see Figure 12-1):

```
PLA                          ;GET STATUS REGISTER
ORA      #%00000010          ;SET INTERRUPT DISABLE FLAG
PHA                          ;RETURN STATUS REGISTER TO STACK
```

RTI will then cause a return to the main program with the entire interrupt system disabled.

Note, however, that you must be very careful about not re-enabling the interrupts automatically, since the main program would be completely unaware that interrupts were no longer allowed. **In general, all interrupt service routines should re-enable the interrupts before returning; any other policy means that the service routines are not transparent to the main program.**

A Teletypewriter Interrupt

Purpose: The computer waits for data to be received from a teletypewriter and stores the data in memory location 0040.

a) Using a 6850 ACIA

(7-bit characters with odd parity and two stop bits).

```
ACIA
INTERRUPT
ROUTINE
```

Source Program:

Main Program:

```
          LDX     #$FF            ;PUT STACK AT END OF PAGE 1
          TXS
          LDA     #%00000011      ;MASTER RESET ACIA
          STA     ACIACR
          LDA     #%11000101      ;ENABLE ACIA INTERRUPT
          STA     ACIACR
          CLI                     ;ENABLE CPU INTERRUPT
HERE      JMP     HERE            ;DUMMY MAIN PROGRAM
```

Interrupt Service Routine:

```
          *=INTRP
          PHA                     ;SAVE ACCUMULATOR IN STACK
          LDA     ACIADR          ;GET DATA FROM ACIA
          STA     $40             ;SAVE DATA
          PLA                     ;RESTORE ACCUMULATOR FROM STACK
          RTI
```

Object Program:

Memory Address (Hex)	Memory Contents (Hex)	Instruction (Mnemonic)	
Main Program:			
0000	A2	LDX	#$FF
0001	FF		
0002	9A	TXS	
0003	A9	LDA	#%00000011
0004	03		
0005	8D	STA	ACIACR
0006〗 0007〗	ACIACR		
0008	A9	LDA	#%11000101
0009	C5		
000A	8D	STA	ACIACR
000B〗 000C〗	ACIACR		
000D	58	CLI	
000E	4C	HERE JMP	HERE
000F	0E		
0010	00		
Interrupt Service Routine:			
INTRP	48	PHA	
INTRP+1	AD	LDA	ACIADR
INTRP+2〗 INTRP+3〗	ACIADR		
INTRP+4	85	STA	$40
INTRP+5	40		
INTRP+6	68	PLA	
INTRP+7	40	RTI	

Remember that the ACIA has no RESET input, so a Master Reset (making Control register bits 0 and 1 both '1') is necessary before the ACIA is used. The ACIA Control register configuration is:

Bit 7 = 1 to enable the receive interrupt

Bit 6 = 1, Bit 5 = 0 to disable the transmitter interrupt and make $\overline{RTS}$ high (inactive)

Bit 4 = 0, Bit 3 = 0, Bit 2 = 1 to select 7-bit data with odd parity and two stop bits

Bit 1 = 0, Bit 0 = 1 for ÷ 16 clock (1760 Hz)

To determine if a particular ACIA is the source of an interrupt, the CPU must examine the Interrupt Request bit, bit 7 of the Status register. The program must examine the Receive Data Register Full bit (Status register bit 0) and the Transmit Data Register Empty bit (Status register bit 1) to differentiate between receive and transmit interrupts.

Either reading the Receive Data register or writing into the Transmit Data register clears the ACIA Interrupt Request bit.

b) Using a 6522 VIA

(Received data tied to both data bit 7 and to control line 1 of the VIA.)

Source Program:

Main Program:

```
        LDX     #$FF        ;PUT STACK AT END OF PAGE 1
        TXS
        LDA     #0
        STA     VIAPCR      ;MAKE ALL CONTROL LINES INPUTS
        STA     VIADDRA
        LDA     #%10000010
        STA     VIAIFR      ;CLEAR START BIT INTERRUPT FLAG
        STA     VIAIER      ;ENABLE START BIT INTERRUPT FROM VIA
        CLI                 ;ENABLE CPU INTERRUPT
HERE    JUMP    HERE        ;DUMMY MAIN PROGRAM
```

Interrupt Service Routine:

```
        *=INTRP
        PHA                 ;SAVE ACCUMULATOR IN STACK
        LDA     #%00000010
        STA     VIAIFR      ;CLEAR START BIT INTERRUPT FLAG
        STA     VIAIER      ;DISABLE START BIT INTERRUPT
        JSR     TTYRCV      ;FETCH DATA FROM TTY
        LDA     #%10000010
        STA     VIAIER      ;RE-ENABLE START BIT INTERRUPT
        PLA                 ;RESTORE ACCUMULATOR FROM STACK
        RTI
```

Object Program:

Memory Address (Hex)	Memory Contents (Hex)		Instruction (Mnemonic)	
Main Program:				
0000	A2		LDX	#$FF
0001	FF			
0002	9A		TXS	
0003	A9		LDA	#0
0004	00			
0005	8D		STA	VIAPCR
0006 0007	VIAPCR			
0008	8D		STA	VIADDRA
0009 000A	VIADDRA			
000B	A9		LDA	#%10000010
000C	82			
000D	8D		STA	VIAIFR
000E 000F	VIAIFR			
0010	8D		STA	VIAIER
0011 0012	VIAIER			
0013	58		CLI	
0014	4C	HERE	JMP	HERE
0015	14			
0016	00			
Interrupt Service Routine:				
INTRP	48		PHA	
INTRP+1	A9		LDA	#%00000010
INTRP+2	02			
INTRP+3	8D		STA	VIAIFR
INTRP+4 INTRP+5	VIAIFR			
INTRP+6	8D		STA	VIAIER
INTRP+7 INTRP+8	VIAIER			
INTRP+9	20		JSR	TTYRCV
INTRP+10 INTRP+11	TTYRCV			
INTRP+12	A9		LDA	#%10000010
INTRP+13	82			
INTRP+14	8D		STA	VIAIER
INTRP+15 INTRP+16	VIAIER			
INTRP+17	68		PLA	
INTRP+18	40		RTI	

Subroutine TTYRCV is the teletypewriter receive routine shown in the previous chapter.

The edge used to cause the interrupt is very important here. The transition from the normal '1' (MARK) state to the '0' (SPACE) state must cause the interrupt, since this transition identifies the start of the transmission. No '0' to '1' transition will occur until a nonzero data bit is received.

The service routine must disable the VIA interrupt, since otherwise each '1' to '0' transition in the character will cause an interrupt. Of course, you must re-enable the VIA interrupt after the entire character has been read.

Note how VIA interrupts are enabled or disabled. Bit 7 of the Interrupt Enable register is a "Set/Clear Control" bit. If that bit is 0, subsequent '1' bits clear interrupt enable bits and hence disable the corresponding interrupts; if that bit is 1, subsequent '1' bits set interrupt enable bits and hence enable the corresponding interrupts. The processor cannot actually write into bit 7 of the Interrupt Flag register, so either an enabling or a disabling pattern can be used to clear the interrupt flags. Remember the descriptions of the Interrupt Enable register and Interrupt Flag register in Figures 12-2 and 12-3.

MORE GENERAL SERVICE ROUTINES

More general service routines that are part of a complete interrupt-driven system must handle the following tasks:

1) **Saving all registers that are used in the interrupt service routine in the Stack so that the interrupted program can be correctly resumed.**

Remember that the 6502 only has Push instructions for the Accumulator and for the Status (P) register. Pushing the Status register is unnecessary after an interrupt since the interrupt response does this automatically. A routine to save all the registers in the Stack would be (as shown earlier):

```
PHA             ;SAVE ACCUMULATOR IN STACK
TXA             ;SAVE INDEX REGISTER X IN STACK
PHA
TYA             ;SAVE INDEX REGISTER Y IN STACK
PHA
```

In some 6502 programs, certain memory locations on page zero are treated as extra registers. Such locations may have to be saved and restored during interrupt service routines. The procedure to save the contents of memory location 0040 would be, for example:

```
LDA    $40      ;SAVE MEMORY LOCATION 0040 IN STACK
PHA
```

Of course, only those registers that are used by the interrupt service routine must be saved.

2) **Restoring all registers from the Stack after completing the interrupt service routine.** Remember that registers must be restored in the opposite order from that in which they were saved.

3) **Enabling and disabling interrupts appropriately.** Remember that the CPU automatically disables its interrupts upon accepting one.

The service routines should be transparent as far as the interrupt program is concerned (i.e., they should have no incidental effects).

Any standard subroutines that are used by an interrupt service routine must be reentrant. If some subroutines cannot be made reentrant, the interrupt service routine must have separate versions to use.[7]

PROBLEMS

1) A Test Interrupt

Purpose: The computer waits for a VIA interrupt to occur, then executes the endless loop instruction:

HERE   JMP   HERE

until the next interrupt occurs.

2) A Keyboard Interrupt

Purpose: The computer waits for a 4-digit entry from a keyboard and places the digits into memory locations 0040 through 0043 (first one received in 0040). Each digit entry causes an interrupt. The fourth entry should also result in the disabling of the keyboard interrupt.

Sample Problem:

Keyboard data = 04, 06, 01, 07

Result: (0040) = 04
           (0041) = 06
           (0042) = 01
           (0043) = 07

3) A Printer Interrupt

Purpose: The computer sends four characters from memory locations 0040 to 0043 (starting with 0040) to the printer. Each character is requested by an interrupt. The fourth transfer also disables the printer interrupt.

4) A Real-Time Clock Interrupt

Purpose: The computer clears memory location 0040 initially and then complements memory location 0040 each time the real-time clock interrupt occurs.

How would you change the program so that it complements memory location 0040 after every ten interrupts? How would you change the program so that it leaves memory location 0040 at zero for ten clock periods, FF_{16}, for five clock periods, and so on continuously? You may want to use a display rather than memory location 0040 so that it will be easier to see.

5) A Teletypewriter Interrupt

Purpose: The computer receives TTY data from an interrupting 6850 ACIA and stores the characters in a buffer starting in memory location 0040. The process continues until the computer receives a carriage return ($0D_{16}$). Assume that the characters are 7-bit ASCII with odd parity. How would you change your program to use a VIA? Assume that subroutine TTYRCV is available, as in the example. Include the carriage return as the final character in the buffer.

REFERENCES

1. A. Osborne, An Introduction to Microcomputers: Volume 1 — Basic Concepts, (Berkeley: OSBORNE/McGraw-Hill, 1977), pp. 5-14 to 5-34.

2. R. L. Baldridge, "Interrupts Add Power, Complexity to Microcomputer System Design", EDN, August 5, 1977, pp. 67-73.

3. L. Leventhal, 6800 Assembly Language Programming (Berkeley: OSBORNE/McGraw-Hill, 1979), pp. 12-5 to 12-25.

4. MCS6500 Microcomputer Family Hardware Manual, MOS Technology Inc., pp. 104-108.

5. J. Gieryic, "SYM-1 6522-Based Timer", Micro, April 1979, pp. 11:31 to 11:32.

6. M. L. DeJong, "A Simple 24-Hour Clock for the AIM 65", Micro, March 1979, pp. 10:5 to 10:7.

7. For further discussion and some real-life examples of designing 6502- and 6800-based systems with interrupts, see the following:

6502

T. Travis, "Patching a Program into a ROM", Electronics, September 1, 1976, pp. 98 - 101.

G. L. Zick and T. T. Sheffer, "Remote Failure Analysis of Micro-Based Instrumentation", Computer, September 1977, pp. 30-35.

6800

S. C. Baunach, "An Example of an M6800-based GPIB Interface", EDN, September 20, 1977, pp. 125-128.

L. E. Cannon and P. S. Kreager, "Using a Microprocessor: a Real-Life Application. Part 2 - Software", Computer Design, October 1975, pp. 81-89.

D. Fullager et al., "Interfacing Data Converters and Microprocessors", Electronics, December 8, 1976, pp. 81-89.

S. A. Hill, "Multiprocess Control Interface Makes Remote μP Command Possible", EDN, February 5, 1976, pp. 87-89.

W. S. Holderby, "Designing a Microprocessor-based Terminal for Factory Data Collection", Computer Design, March 1977, pp. 81-88.

A. Lange, "OPTACON Interface Permits the Blind to 'Read' Digital Instruments", EDN, February 5, 1976, pp. 84-86.

J. D. Logan and P. S. Kreager, "Using a Microprocessor: a Real-Life Application. Part 1 - Hardware", Computer Design, September 1975, pp. 69-77.

A. Moore and M. Eidson, "Printer Control", Application Note available from Motorola Semiconductor Products, Phoenix, AZ.

M. C. Mulder and P. P. Fasang, "A Microprocessor Controlled Substation Alarm Logger", IECI '78 Proceedings - Industrial Applications of Microprocessors, March 20-22, 1978, pp. 2-6.

P. J. Zsombar-Murray et al., "Microprocessor Based Frequency Response Analyzer", IECI '78 Proceedings - Industrial Applications of Microprocessors, March 20-22, 1978, pp. 36-44.

The Proceedings of the IEEE's Industrial Electronics and Control Instrumentation Group's Annual Meeting on "Industrial Applications of Microprocessors" contains many interesting articles. Volumes (starting with 1975) are available from IEEE Service Center, CP Department, 445 Hoes Lane, Piscataway, NJ 08854.

Chapter 13
PROBLEM DEFINITION AND PROGRAM DESIGN

THE TASKS OF SOFTWARE DEVELOPMENT

In the previous chapters, we have concentrated on the writing of short programs in assembly language. While this is an important topic, it is only a small part of software development. Although writing assembly language programs is a major task for the beginner, it soon becomes simple. By now, you should be familiar with standard methods for programming in assembly language on the 6502 microprocessor. **The next four chapters will describe how to formulate tasks as programs and how to combine short programs to form a working system.**

Software development consists of many stages. Figure 13-1 is a flowchart of the software development process. **Its stages are:**

> STAGES OF
> SOFTWARE
> DEVELOPMENT

- Problem definition
- Program design
- Coding
- Debugging
- Testing
- Documentation
- Maintenance and redesign

Each of these stages is important in the construction of a working system. Note that coding, the writing of programs in a form that the computer understands, is only one of seven stages.

In fact, **coding is usually the easiest stage to define and perform.** The rules for writing computer programs are easy to learn. They vary somewhat from computer to computer, but the basic techniques remain the same. Few software projects run into trouble because of coding; indeed, coding is not the most time-consuming part of software development. Experts estimate that a programmer can write one to ten fully debugged and documented statements per day. Clearly, the mere coding of one to ten statements is hardly a full day's effort. On most software projects, coding occupies less than 25% of the programmer's time.

> RELATIVE
> IMPORTANCE
> OF CODING

Measuring progress in the other stages is difficult. You can say that half of the program has been written, but you can hardly say that half of the errors have been removed or half of the problem has been defined. Timetables for such stages as program design, debugging, and testing are difficult to produce. Many days or weeks of effort may result in no clear progress. Furthermore, an incomplete job in one stage may result in tremendous problems later. For example, poor problem definition or program design can make debugging and testing very difficult. Time saved in one stage may be spent many times over in later stages.

> MEASURING
> PROGRESS
> IN STAGES

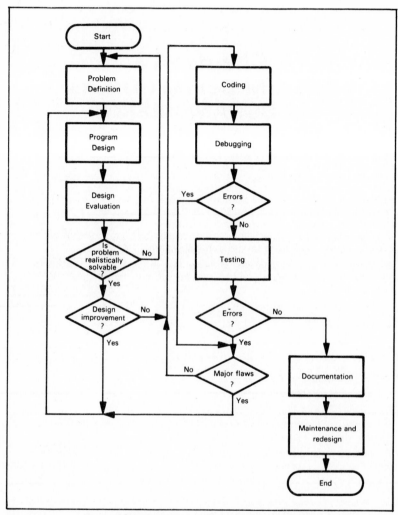

Figure 13-1. Flowchart of Software Development

DEFINITION OF THE STAGES

Problem definition is the formulation of the task in terms of the requirements that it places on the computer. For example, what is necessary to make a computer control a tool, run a series of electrical tests, or handle communications between a central controller and a remote instrument? Problem definition requires that you determine the forms and rates of inputs and outputs, the amount and speed of processing that is needed, and the types of possible errors and their handling. Problem definition takes a vague idea of building a computer-controlled system and defines the tasks and requirements for the computer.

```
PROBLEM
DEFINITION
```

Program design is the outline of the computer program which will perform the tasks that have been defined. In the design stage, the tasks are described in a way that can easily be converted into a program. **Among the useful techniques in this stage are flowcharting, structured programming, modular programming, and top-down design.**

```
PROGRAM
DESIGN
```

Coding is the writing of the program in a form that the computer can either directly understand or translate. The form may be machine language, assembly language, or a high-level language.

```
CODING
```

Debugging, also called program verification, **is making the program do what the design specified that it would do.** In this stage, you use such tools as breakpoints, traces, simulators, logic analyzers, and in-circuit emulators. The end of the debugging stage is hard to define, since you never know when you have found the last error.

```
DEBUGGING
```

Testing, also referred to as program validation, **is ensuring that the program performs the overall system tasks correctly.** The designer uses simulators, exercisers, and various statistical techniques to measure the program's performance. This stage is like quality control for hardware.

```
TESTING
```

Documentation is the description of the program in the proper form for users and maintenance personnel. Documentation also allows the designer to develop a program library so that subsequent tasks will be far simpler. Flowcharts, comments, memory maps, and library forms are some of the tools used in documentation.

```
DOCUMENTATION
```

Maintenance and redesign are the servicing, improvement, and extension of the program. Clearly, the designer must be ready to handle field problems in computer-based equipment. Special diagnostic modes or programs and other maintenance tools may be required. Upgrading or extension of the program may be necessary to meet new requirements or handle new tasks.

```
MAINTENANCE
AND
REDESIGN
```

The rest of this chapter will consider only the problem definition and program design stages. Chapter 14 will discuss debugging and testing, and Chapter 15 will discuss documentation, extension, and redesign. We will bring all the stages together in some simple systems examples in Chapter 16.

PROBLEM DEFINITION

Typical microprocessor tasks require a lot of definition. For example, what must a program do to control a scale, a cash register, or a signal generator? Clearly, we have a long way to go just to define the tasks involved.

DEFINING THE INPUTS

How do we start the definition? The obvious place to begin is with the inputs. **We should begin by listing all the inputs that the computer may receive in this application.**

Examples of inputs are:

- Data blocks from transmission lines
- Status words from peripherals
- Data from A/D converters

Then, we may ask the following questions about each input:

1) What is its form; i.e., what signals will the computer actually receive?
2) When is the input available and how does the processor know it is available? Does the processor have to request the input with a strobe signal? Does the input provide its own clock?
3) How long is it available?
4) How often does it change, and how does the processor know that it has changed?
5) Does the input consist of a sequence or block of data? Is the order important?
6) What should be done if the data contains errors? These may include transmission errors, incorrect data, sequencing errors, extra data, etc.
7) Is the input related to other inputs or outputs?

DEFINING THE OUTPUTS

The next step to define is the output. **We must list all the outputs that the computer must produce.** Examples of outputs include:

- Data blocks to transmission lines
- Control words to peripherals
- Data to D/A converters

Then, we may ask the following questions about each output:

1) What is its form; i.e., what signals must the computer produce?
2) When must it be available, and how does the peripheral know it is available?
3) How long must it be available?
4) How often must it change, and how does the peripheral know that it has changed?
5) Is there a sequence of outputs?
6) What should be done to avoid transmission errors or to sense and recover from peripheral failures?
7) How is the output related to other inputs and outputs?

PROCESSING SECTION

Between the reading of input data and the sending of output results is the processing section. Here **we must determine exactly how the computer must process the input data. The questions are:**

1) What is the basic procedure (algorithm) for transforming input data into output results?

 FACTORS IN PROCESSING

2) What time constraints exist? These may include data rates, delay times, the time constants of input and output devices, etc.

3) What memory constraints exist? Do we have limits on the amount of program memory or data memory, or on the size of buffers?

4) What standard programs or tables must be used? What are their requirements?

5) What special cases exist, and how should the program handle them?

6) How accurate must the results be?

7) How should the program handle processing errors or special conditions such as overflow, underflow, or loss of significance?

ERROR HANDLING

An important factor in many applications is the handling of errors. Clearly, the designer must make provisions for recovering from common errors and for diagnosing malfunctions. **Among the questions that the designer must ask at the definition stage are:**

1) What errors could occur?

 ERROR CONSIDERATIONS

2) Which errors are most likely? If a person operates the system, human error is the most common. Following human errors, communications or transmission errors are more common than mechanical, electrical, mathematical, or processor errors.

3) Which errors will not be immediately obvious to the system? A special problem is the occurrence of errors that the system or operator may not recognize as incorrect.

4) How can the system recover from errors with a minimum loss of time and data and yet be aware that an error has occurred?

5) Which errors or malfunctions cause the same system behavior? How can these errors or malfunctions be distinguished for diagnostic purposes?

6) Which errors involve special system procedures? For example, do parity errors require retransmission of data?

Another question is: How can the field technician systematically find the source of malfunctions without being an expert? Built-in test programs, special diagnostics, or signature analysis can help.[1]

HUMAN FACTORS

Many microprocessor-based systems involve human interaction. **Human factors must be considered throughout the development process for** such **systems. Among the questions that the designer must ask are:**

```
OPERATOR
INTERACTION
```

1) What input procedures are most natural for the human operator?
2) Can the operator easily determine how to begin, continue and end the input operations?
3) How is the operator informed of procedural errors and equipment malfunctions?
4) What errors is the operator most likely to make?
5) How does the operator know that data has been entered correctly?
6) Are displays in a form that the operator can easily read and understand?
7) Is the response of the system adequate for the operator?
8) Is the system easy for the operator to use?
9) Are there guiding features for an inexperienced operator?
10) Are there shortcuts and reasonable options for the experienced operator?
11) Can the operator always determine or reset the state of the system after interruptions or distractions?

Building a system for people to use is difficult. The microprocessor can make the system more powerful, more flexible, and more responsive. However, the designer still must add the human touches that can greatly increase the usefulness and attractiveness of the system and the productivity of the human operator.[2]

EXAMPLES

Response to a Switch

Figure 13-2 shows a simple system in which the input is from a single SPST switch and the output is to a single LED display. In response to a switch closure, the processor turns the display on for one second. This system should be easy to define.

DEFINING
SWITCH AND
LIGHT SYSTEM

SWITCH AND
LIGHT INPUT

Let us first examine the input and answer each of the questions previously presented:

1) The input is a single bit, which may be either '0' (switch closed) or '1' (switch open).

2) The input is always available and need not be requested.

3) The input is available for at least several milliseconds after the closure.

4) The input will seldom change more than once every few seconds. The processor has to handle only the bounce in the switch. The processor must monitor the switch to determine when it is closed.

5) There is no sequence of inputs.

6) The obvious input errors are switch failure, failure in the input circuitry, and the operator attempting to close the switch again before a sufficient amount of time has elapsed. We will discuss the handling of these errors later.

7) The input does not depend on any other inputs or outputs.

The next requirement in defining the system is to examine the output. The answers to our questions are:

SWITCH
AND LIGHT
OUTPUTS

1) The output is a single bit, which is '0' to turn the display on, '1' to turn it off.

2) There are no time constraints on the output. The peripheral does not need to be informed of the availability of data.

3) If the display is an LED, the data need be available for only a few milliseconds at a pulse rate of about 100 times per second. The observer will see a continuously lit display.

4) The data must change (go off) after one second.

5) There is no sequence of outputs.

6) The possible output errors are display failure and failure in the output circuitry.

7) The output depends only on the switch input and time.

The processing section is extremely simple. As soon as the switch input becomes a logic '0', the CPU turns the light on (a logic '0') for one second. No time or memory constraints exist.

Let us now look at the possible errors and malfunctions. These are:

SWITCH AND
LIGHT ERROR
HANDLING

- Another switch closure before one second has elapsed
- Switch failure
- Display failure
- Computer failure

Surely the first error is the most likely. The simplest solution is for the processor to ignore switch closures until one second has elapsed. This brief unresponsive period will hardly be noticeable to the human operator. Furthermore, ignoring the switch during this period means that no debouncing circuitry or software is necessary, since the system will not react to the bounce anyway.

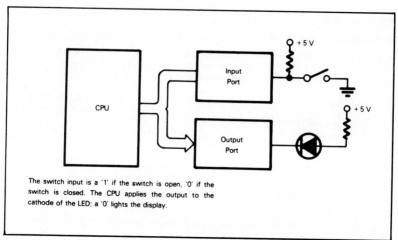

The switch input is a '1' if the switch is open, '0' if the switch is closed. The CPU applies the output to the cathode of the LED; a '0' lights the display.

Figure 13-2. The Switch and Light System

Clearly, the last three failures can produce unpredictable results. The display may stay on, stay off, or change state randomly. Some possible ways to isolate the failures would be:

- Lamp-test hardware to check the display; i.e., a button that turns the light on independently of the processor
- A direct connection to the switch to check its operation
- A diagnostic program that exercises the input and output circuits

If both the display and switch are working, the computer is at fault. A field technician with proper equipment can determine the cause of the failure.

A Switch-Based Memory Loader

Figure 13-3 shows a system that allows the user to enter data into any memory location in a microcomputer. One input port, DPORT, reads data from eight toggle switches. The other input port, CPORT, is used to read control information.

DEFINING A SWITCH-BASED MEMORY LOADER

There are three momentary switches: High Address, Low Address and Data. The output is the value of the last completed entry from the data switches; eight LEDs are used for the display.

The system will also, of course, require various resistors, buffers, and drivers.

We shall first examine the inputs. The characteristics of the switches are the same as in the previous example; however, here there is a distinct sequence of inputs, as follows:

1) The operator must set the data switches according to the eight most significant bits of an address, then

2) press the High Address button. The high address bits will appear on the lights, and the program will interpret the data as the high byte of the address.

3) Then the operator must set the data switches with the value of the least significant byte of the address and

4) press the Low Address button. The low address bits will appear on the lights, and the program will consider the data to be the low byte of the address.

5) Finally, the operator must set the desired data into the data switches and

6) press the Data button. The display will now show the data, and the program stores the data in memory at the previously entered address.

The operator may repeat the process to enter an entire program. Clearly, even in this simplified situation, we will have many possible sequences to consider. How do we cope with erroneous sequences and make the system easy to use?

Output is no problem. After each input, the program sends to the displays the complement (since the displays are active-low) of the input bits. The output data remains the same until the next input operation.

The processing section remains quite simple. There are no time or memory constraints. The program can debounce the switches by waiting for a few milliseconds, and must provide complemented data to the displays.

The most likely errors are operator mistakes. These include:

MEMORY LOADER ERROR HANDLING

- Incorrect entries
- Incorrect order
- Incomplete entries; for example, forgetting the data

The system must be able to handle these problems in a reasonable way, since they are certain to occur in actual operation.

The designer must also consider the effects of equipment failure. Just as before, the possible difficulties are:

- Switch failure
- Display failure
- Computer failure

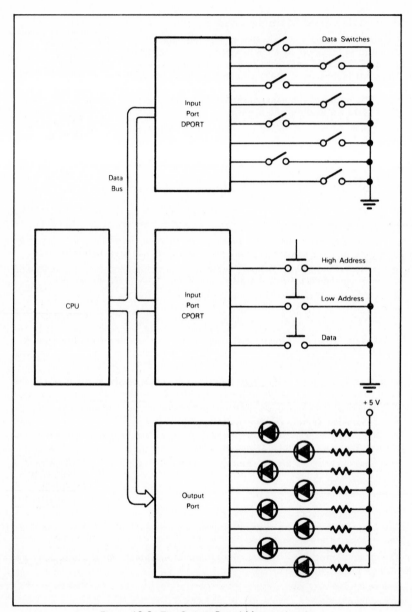

Figure 13-3. The Switch-Based Memory Loader

In this system, however, we must pay more attention to how these failures affect the system. A computer failure will presumably cause very unusual behavior by the system, and will be easy to detect. A display failure may not be immediately noticeable; here a Lamp Test feature will allow the operator to check the operation. Note that we would like to test each LED separately, in order to diagnose the case in which output lines are shorted together. In addition, the operator may not immediately detect switch failure; however, the operator should soon notice it and establish which switch is faulty by a process of elimination.

Let us look at some of the possible operator errors. Typical errors will be:

| **OPERATOR ERROR CORRECTION IN MEMORY LOADER** |

- Erroneous data
- Wrong order of entries or switches
- Trying to go on to the next entry without completing the current one

The operator will presumably notice erroneous data as soon as it appears on the displays. What is a viable recovery procedure for the operator? Some of the options are:

1) The operator must complete the entry procedure; i.e., enter Low Address and Data if the error occurs in the High Address. Clearly, this procedure is wasteful and would only serve to annoy the operator.

2) The operator may restart the entry process by returning to the high address entry steps. This solution is useful if the error was in the High Address, but forces the operator to re-enter earlier data if the error was in the Low Address or Data stage.

3) The operator may enter any part of the sequence at any time simply by setting the Data switches with the desired data and pressing the corresponding button. This procedure allows the operator to make corrections at any point in the sequence.

This type of procedure should always be preferred over one that does not allow immediate error correction, has a variety of concluding steps, or enters data into the system without allowing the operator a final check. Any added complication in hardware or software will be justified in increased operator efficiency. You should always prefer to let the microcomputer do the tedious work and recognize arbitrary sequences; it never gets tired and never forgets what was in the operating manual.

A further helpful feature would be status lights that would define the meaning of the display. Three status lights, marked "High Address", "Low Address", and "Data", would let the operator know what had been entered without having to remember which button was pressed. The processor would have to monitor the sequence, but the added complication in software would simplify the operator's task. Clearly, three separate sets of displays plus the ability to examine a memory location would be even more helpful to the operator.

We should note that, although we have emphasized human interaction, machine or system interaction has many of the same characteristics. The microprocessor should do the work. If complicating the microprocessor's task makes error recovery simple and the causes of failure obvious, the entire system will work better and be easier to maintain. Note that you should not wait until after the software has been completed to consider system use and maintenance: instead, you should include these factors in the problem definition stage.

A Verification Terminal

Figure 13-4 is a block diagram of a simple credit-verification terminal. One input port derives data from a keyboard (see Figure 13-5); the other input port accepts verification data from a transmission line. One output port sends data to a set of

displays (see Figure 13-6); another sends the credit card number to the central computer. A third output port turns on one light whenever the terminal is ready to accept an inquiry, and another light when the operator sends the information. The "Busy" light turns off when the response returns. Clearly, the input and output of data will be more complex than in the previous case, although the processing is still simple.

Additional displays may be useful to emphasize the meaning of the response. Many terminals use a green light for "Yes", a red light for "No", and a yellow light for "Consult Store Manager." Note that these lights will still have to be clearly marked with their meanings to allow for a color-blind operator.

Let us first look at the keyboard input. This is, of course, different from the switch input, since the CPU must have some way of distinguishing new data. We will assume that each key closure provides a unique hexadecimal code (we can code

each of the 12 keys into one digit) and a strobe. The program will have to recognize the strobe and fetch the hexadecimal number that identifies the key. There is a time constraint, since the program cannot miss any data or strobes. The constraint is not serious, since keyboard entries will be at least several milliseconds apart.

The transmission input similarly consists of a series of characters, each identified by a strobe (perhaps from a UART). The program will have to recognize each strobe and fetch the character. The data being sent across the transmission lines is usually organized into messages. A possible message format is:

- Introductory characters, or header
- Terminal destination address
- Coded yes or no
- Ending characters, or trailer

The terminal will check the header, read the destination address, and see if the message is intended for it. If the message is for the terminal, the terminal accepts the data. The address could be (and often is) hard-wired into the terminal so that the terminal receives only messages intended for it. This approach simplifies the software at the cost of some flexibility.

The output is also more complex than in the earlier examples. If the displays are multiplexed, the processor must not only send the data to the display port but must also direct the data to a particular display. We will need either a separate control port

or a counter and decoder to handle this. Note that hardware blanking controls can blank leading zeros as long as the first digit in a multi-digit number is never zero. Software can also handle this task. Time constraints include the pulse length and frequency required to produce a continuous display for the operator.

The communications output will consist of a series of characters with a particular format. The program will also have to consider the time required between characters. A possible format for the output message is:

- Header
- Terminal address
- Credit card number
- Trailer

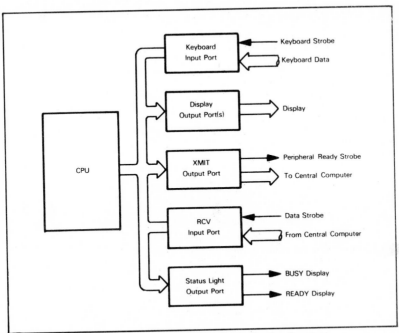

Figure 13-4. Block Diagram of a Verification Terminal

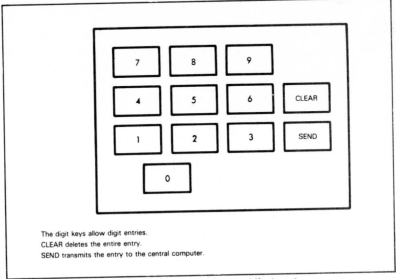

The digit keys allow digit entries.
CLEAR deletes the entire entry.
SEND transmits the entry to the central computer.

Figure 13-5. Verification Terminal Keyboard

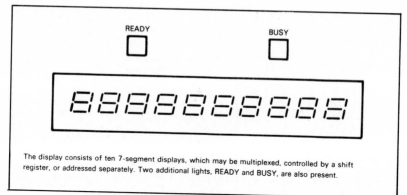

The display consists of ten 7-segment displays, which may be multiplexed, controlled by a shift register, or addressed separately. Two additional lights, READY and BUSY, are also present.

Figure 13-6. Verification Terminal Display

A central communications computer may poll the terminals, checking for data ready to be sent.

The processing in this system involves many new tasks, such as:

- Identifying the control keys by number and performing the proper actions
- Adding the header, terminal address, and trailer to the outgoing message
- Recognizing the header and trailer in the returning message
- Checking the incoming terminal address

Note that none of the tasks involve any complex arithmetic or any serious time or memory constraints.

```
VERIFICATION
TERMINAL
ERROR
HANDLING
```

The number of possible errors in this system is, of course, much larger than in the earlier examples. Let us first consider the possible operator errors. These include:

- Entering the credit card number incorrectly
- Trying to send an incomplete credit card number
- Trying to send another number while the central computer is processing one
- Clearing non-existent entries

Some of these errors can be easily handled by correctly structuring the program. For example, the program should not accept the Send key until the credit card number has been completely entered, and it should ignore any additional keyboard entries until the response comes back from the central computer. Note that the operator will know that the entry has not been sent, since the Busy light will not go on. The operator will also know when the keyboard has been locked out (the program is ignoring keyboard entries), since entries will not appear on the display and the Ready light will be off.

Incorrect entries are an obvious problem. If the operator recog- **CORRECTING KEYBOARD ERRORS**
nizes an error, he can use the Clear key to make corrections. The
operator would probably find it more convenient to have two Clear
keys, one that cleared the most recent key and one that cleared
the entire entry. This would allow both for the situation in which the operator recognizes the error immediately and for the situation in which the operator recognizes the
error late in the procedure. The operator should be able to correct errors immediately
and have to repeat as few keys as possible. The operator will, however, make a certain
number of errors without recognizing them. Most credit card numbers include a self-
checking digit; the terminal could check the number before permitting it to be sent to
the central computer. This step would save the central computer from wasting precious
processing time checking the number.

This requires, however, that the terminal have some way of informing the operator of
the error, perhaps by flashing one of the displays or by providing some other special indicator that the operator is sure to notice.

Still another problem is how the operator knows that an entry has been lost or pro-
cessed incorrectly. Some terminals simply unlock after a maximum time delay. The
operator notes that the Busy light has gone off without an answer being received. The
operator is then expected to try the entry again. After one or two retries, the operator
should report the failure to supervisory personnel.

**Many equipment failures are also possible. Besides the displays, keyboard, and
processor, there now exist the problems of communications errors or failures and
central computer failures.**

The data transmission will probably have to include error checking and correcting procedures. Some possibilities are:

1) Parity provides an error detection facility but no correction   **CORRECTING TRANSMISSION ERRORS**
   mechanism. The receiver will need some way of request-
   ing retransmission, and the sender will have to save a copy
   of the data until proper reception is acknowledged. Parity
   is, however, very simple to implement.

2) Short messages may use more elaborate schemes. For example, the yes/no
   response to the terminal could be coded so as to provide error detection and correction capability.

3) An acknowledgement and a limited number of retries could trigger an indicator
   that would inform the operator of a communications failure (inability to transfer a
   message without errors) or central computer failure (no response at all to the
   message within a certain period of time). Such a scheme, along with the Lamp
   Test, would allow simple failure diagnosis.

A communications or central computer failure indicator should also "unlock" the terminal, i.e., allow it to accept another entry. This is necessary if the terminal will not accept entries while a verification is in progress. The terminal may also unlock after a certain maximum time delay. Certain entries could be reserved for diagnostics; i.e., certain
credit card numbers could be used to check the internal operation of the terminal and
test the displays.

REVIEW OF PROBLEM DEFINITION

Problem definition is as important a part of software development as it is of any other engineering task. Note that it does not require any programming or knowledge of the computer; rather, it is based on an understanding of the system and sound engineering judgment. Microprocessors can offer flexibility that the designer can use to provide a range of features which were not previously available.

Problem definition is independent of any particular computer, computer language, or development system. It should, however, provide guidelines as to what type or speed of computer the application will require and what kind of hardware/software trade-offs the designer can make. The problem definition stage is in fact independent of whether or not a computer is used at all, although a knowledge of the capabilities of the computer can help the designer in suggesting possible implementations of procedures.

PROGRAM DESIGN

Program design is the stage in which the problem definition is formulated as a program. If the program is small and simple, this stage may involve little more than the writing of a one-page flowchart. If the program is larger or more complex, the designer should consider more elaborate methods

We will discuss flowcharting, modular programming, structured programming, and top-down design. We will try to indicate the reasoning behind these methods, and their advantages and disadvantages. We will not, however, advocate any particular method since there is no evidence that one method is always superior to all others. You should remember that the goal is to produce a good working system, not to follow religiously the tenets of one methodology or another.

All the methodologies do, however, **have some** obvious **principles in common.** Many of these are the same principles that apply to any kind of design, **such as:**

BASIC PRINCIPLES OF PROGRAM DESIGN

1) Proceed in small steps. Do not try to do too much at one time.

2) Divide large jobs into small, logically separate tasks. Make the sub-tasks as independent of one another as possible, so that they can be tested separately and so that changes can be made in one without affecting the others.

3) Keep the flow of control as simple as possible so as to make it easier to find errors.

4) Use pictorial or graphic descriptions as much as possible. They are easier to visualize than word descriptions. This is the great advantage of flowcharts.

5) Emphasize clarity and simplicity at first. You can improve performance (if necessary) once the system is working.

6) Proceed in a thorough and systematic manner. Use checklists and standard procedures.

7) Do not tempt fate. Either do not use methods that you are not sure of, or use them very carefully. Watch for situations that might cause confusion, and clarify them as soon as possible.

8) Keep in mind that the system must be debugged, tested and maintained. Plan for these later stages.

9) Use simple and consistent terminology and methods. Repetitiveness is no fault in program design, nor is complexity a virtue.

10) Have your design completely formulated before you start coding. Resist the temptation to start writing down instructions: it makes no more sense than making parts lists or laying out circuit boards before you know exactly what will be in the system.

11) Be particularly careful of factors that may change. Make the implementation of likely changes as simple as possible.

FLOWCHARTING

Flowcharting is certainly the best-known of all program design methods. Programming textbooks describe how programmers first write complete flowcharts and then start writing the actual program. In fact, few programmers have ever worked this way, and flowcharting has often been more of a joke or a nuisance to programmers than a design method. We will try to describe both the advantages and disadvantages of flowcharts, and show the place of this technique in program design.

The basic advantage of the flowchart is that it is a pictorial `ADVANTAGES OF FLOWCHARTING`
representation. People find such representations much more meaningful than written descriptions. The designer can visualize the whole system and see the relationships of the various parts. Logical errors and inconsistencies often stand out instead of being hidden in a printed page. **At its best, the flowchart is a picture of the entire system.**

Some of the more specific advantages of flowcharts are:

1) Standard symbols exist (see Figure 13-7) so that flowcharting forms are widely recognized.
2) Flowcharts can be understood by someone without a programming background.
3) Flowcharts can be used to divide the entire project into sub-tasks. The flowchart can then be examined to measure overall progress.
4) Flowcharts show the sequence of operations and can therefore aid in locating the source of errors.
5) Flowcharting is widely used in other areas besides programming.
6) There are many tools available to aid in flowcharting, including programmer's templates and automated drawing packages.

These advantages are all important. There is no question that `DISADVANTAGES OF FLOWCHARTING`
flowcharting will continue to be widely used. But **we should note some of the disadvantages of flowcharting as a program design method, e.g.:**

1) Flowcharts are difficult to design, draw, or change in all except the simplest situations.
2) There is no easy way to debug or test a flowchart.
3) Flowcharts tend to become cluttered. Designers find it difficult to balance between the amount of detail needed to make the flowchart useful and the amount that makes the flowchart little better than a program listing.
4) Flowcharts show only the program organization. They do not show the organization of the data or the structure of the input/output modules.
5) Flowcharts do not help with hardware or timing problems or give hints as to where these problems might occur.
6) Flowcharts allow for highly unstructured design. Lines and arrows backtracking and looping all over the chart are the antithesis of good structured design principles.

Thus, **flowcharting is a helpful technique** that you should not try to extend too far. **Flowcharts are useful as program documentation, since they have standard forms and are comprehensible to non-programmers.** As a design tool, **however,** flowcharts cannot provide much more than a starting outline; **the programmer cannot debug a detailed flowchart** and the flowchart is often more difficult to design than the program itself.

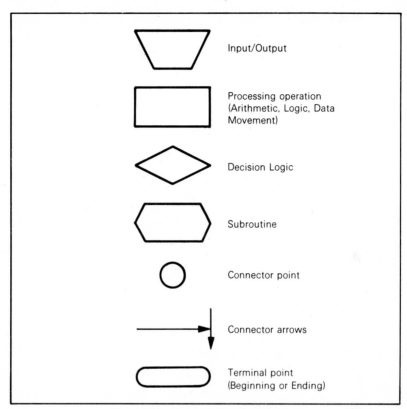

Figure 13-7. Standard Flowchart Symbols

EXAMPLES

Response to a Switch

This simple task, in which a single switch turns on a light for one second, is easy to flowchart. In fact, such tasks are typical examples for flowcharting books, although they form a small part of most systems. The data structure here is so simple that it can be safely ignored.

```
FLOWCHARTING
SWITCH AND
LIGHT SYSTEM
```

Figure 13-8 is the flowchart. There is little difficulty in deciding on the amount of detail required. The flowchart gives a straightforward picture of the procedure, which anyone could understand.

Note that the most useful flowcharts may ignore program variables and ask questions directly. Of course, compromises are often necessary here. **Two versions of the flowchart are sometimes helpful — one general version in layman's language, which will be useful to non-programmers, and one programmer's version in terms of the program variables, which will be useful to other programmers.**

A third type of flowchart, a data flowchart, may also be helpful. This flowchart serves as a cross-reference for the other flowcharts, since it shows how the program handles a particular type of data. Ordinary flowcharts show how the program proceeds, handling different types of data at different points. Data flowcharts, on the other hand, show how particular types of data move through the system, passing from one part of the program to another. Such flowcharts are very useful in debugging and maintenance, since errors most often show up as a particular type of data being handled incorrectly.

```
DATA
FLOWCHARTS
```

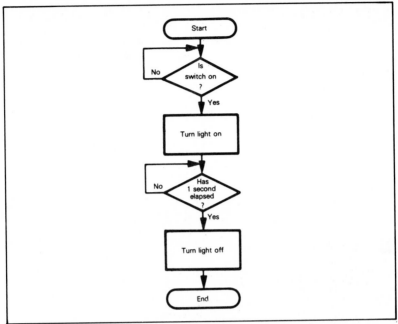

Figure 13-8. Flowchart of One-Second Response to a Switch

The Switch-Based Memory Loader

This system (see Figure 13-3) is considerably more complex than the previous example, and involves many more decisions. **The flowchart (see Figure 13-9) is more difficult to write and is not as straightforward as the previous example.** In this example, we face the problem that there is no way to debug or test the flowchart.

The flowchart in Figure 13-9 includes the improvements we suggested as part of the problem definition. Clearly, **this flowchart is beginning to get cluttered and lose its advantages over a written description.** Adding other features that define the meaning of the entry with status lights and allow the operator to check entries after completion would make the flowchart even more complex. Writing the complete flowchart from scratch could quickly become a formidable task. However, once the program has been written, the flowchart is useful as documentation.

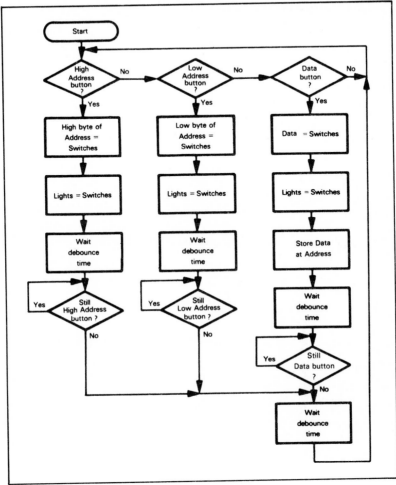

Figure 13-9. Flowchart of Switch-Based Memory Loader

The Credit-Verification Terminal

In this application (see Figures 13-4 through 13-6), the flowchart will be even more complex than in the switch-based memory loader case. Here, **the best idea is to flowchart sections separately so that the flowcharts remain manageable.** However, the presence of data structures (as in the multi-digit display and the messages) will make the gap between flowchart and program much wider.

Let us look at some of the sections. **Figure 13-10 shows the keyboard entry process for the digit keys.** The program must fetch the data after each strobe and place the digit into the display array if there is room for it. If there are already ten digits in the array, the program simply ignores the entry.

The actual program will have to handle the displays at the same time. Note that either software or hardware must de-activate the keyboard strobe after the processor reads a digit.

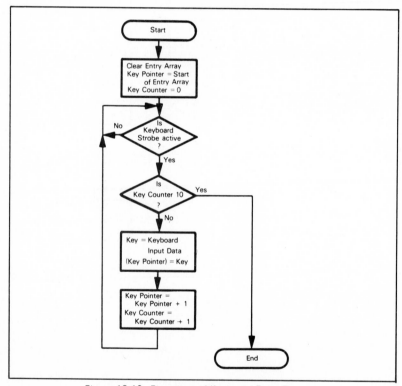

Figure 13-10. Flowchart of Keyboard Entry Process

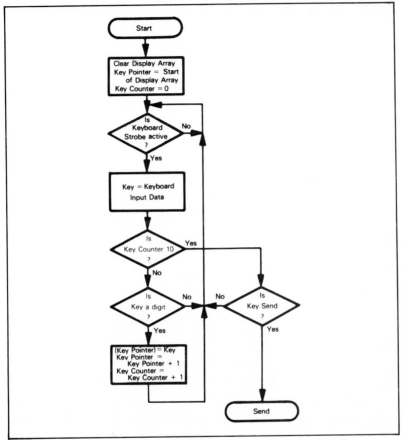

Figure 13-11. Flowchart of Keyboard Entry Process with Send Key

Figure 13-11 adds the Send key. This key, of course, is optional. The terminal could just send the data as soon as the operator enters a complete number. However, that procedure would not give the operator a chance to check the entire entry. The flowchart with the Send key is more complex because there are two alternatives.

1) If the operator has not entered ten digits, the program must ignore the Send key and place any other key into the entry.

2) If the operator has entered ten digits, the program must respond to the Send key by transferring control to the Send routine, and ignore all other keys.

Note that the flowchart has become much more difficult to organize and to follow. There is also no obvious way to check the flowchart.

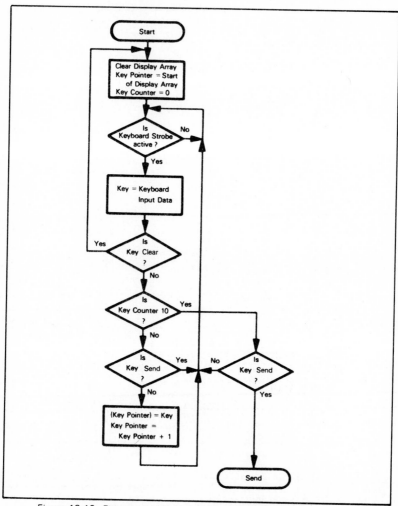

Figure 13-12. Flowchart of Keyboard Entry Process with Function Keys

Figure 13-12 shows the flowchart of the keyboard entry process with all the function keys. In this example, the flow of control is not simple. Clearly, some written description is necessary. The organization and layout of complex flowcharts requires careful planning. We have followed the process of adding features to the flowchart one at a time, but this still results in a large amount of redrawing. Again we should remember that throughout the keyboard entry process, the program must also refresh the displays if they are multiplexed and not controlled by shift registers or other hardware.

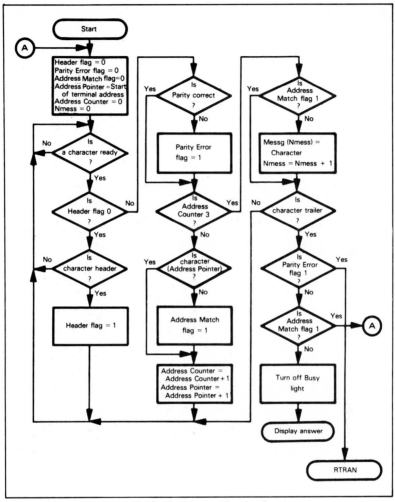

Figure 13-13. Flowchart of Receive Routine

13-27

Figure 13-13 is the flowchart of a receive routine. We assume that the serial/parallel conversion and error checking are done in hardware (e.g., by a UART). The processor must:

1) Look for the header (we assume that it is a single character).
2) Read the destination address (we assume that it is three characters long) and see if the message is meant for this terminal; i.e., if the three characters agree with the terminal address.
3) Wait for the trailer character.
4) If the message is meant for the terminal, turn off the Busy light and go to Display Answer routine.
5) In the event of any errors, request retransmission by going to RTRANS routine.

This routine involves a large number of decisions, and the flowchart is neither simple nor obvious.

Clearly, we have come a long way from the simple flowchart (Figure 13-8) of the first example. A complete set of flowcharts for the transaction terminal would be a major task. It would consist of several interrelated charts with complex logic, and would require a large amount of effort. Such an effort would be just as difficult as writing a preliminary program, and not as useful, since you could not check it on the computer.

MODULAR PROGRAMMING

Once programs become large and complex, flowcharting is no longer a satisfactory design tool. However, the problem definition and the flowchart can give you some idea as to how to divide the program into reasonable sub-tasks. **The division of the entire program into sub-tasks or modules is called "modular programming."** Clearly, most of the programs we presented in earlier chapters would typically be modules in a large system program. **The problems that the designer faces in modular programming are how to divide the program into modules and how to put the modules together.**

The advantages of modular programming are obvious:

> **ADVANTAGES OF MODULAR PROGRAMMING**

1) A single module is easier to write, debug, and test than an entire program.

2) A module is likely to be useful in many places and in other programs, particularly if it is reasonably general and performs a common task. You can build up a library of standard modules.

3) Modular programming allows the programmer to divide tasks and use previously written programs.

4) Changes can be incorporated into one module rather than into the entire system.

5) Errors can often be isolated and then attributed to a single module.

6) Modular programming gives an idea of how much progress has been made and how much of the work is left.

The idea of modular programming is such an obvious one that its disadvantages are often ignored. These include:

> **DISADVANTAGES OF MODULAR PROGRAMMING**

1) Fitting the modules together can be a major problem, particularly if different people write the modules.

2) Modules require very careful documentation, since they may affect other parts of the program, such as data structures used by all the modules.

3) Testing and debugging modules separately is difficult, since other modules may produce the data used by the module being debugged and still other modules may use the results. You may have to write special programs (called "drivers") just to produce sample data and test the programs. These drivers require extra programming effort that adds nothing to the system.

4) Programs may be very difficult to modularize. If you modularize the program poorly, integration will be very difficult, since almost all errors and changes will involve several modules.

5) Modular programs often require extra time and memory, since the separate modules may repeat functions.

Therefore, while modular programming is certainly an improvement over trying to write the entire program from scratch, it does have some disadvantages as well.

Important considerations include restricting the amount of information shared by modules, limiting design decisions that are subject to change to a single module and restricting the access of one module to another.[3]

An obvious problem is that there are no proven, systematic methods for modularizing programs. We should mention the following principles:[4]

1) Modules that reference common data should be parts of the same overall module.

2) Two modules in which the first uses or depends on the second, but not the reverse, should be separate.

3) A module that is used by more than one other module should be part of a different overall module than the others.

4) Two modules in which the first is used by many other modules and the second is used by only a few other modules should be separate.

5) Two modules whose frequencies of usage are significantly different should be part of different modules.

6) The structure or organization of related data should be hidden within a single module.

If a program is difficult to modularize, you may need to redefine the tasks that are involved. Too many special cases or too many variables that require special handling are typical signs of inadequate problem definition.

EXAMPLES

Response to a Switch

This simple program can be divided into two modules:

Module 1 waits for the switch to be turned on and turns the light on in response.

Module 2 provides the one-second delay.

MODULARIZING THE SWITCH AND LIGHT SYSTEM

Module 1 is likely to be specific to the system, since it will depend on how the switch and light are attached. Module 2 will be generally useful, since many tasks require delays. Clearly, it would be advantageous to have a standard delay module that could provide delays of varying lengths. The module will require careful documentation so that you will know how to specify the length of the delay, how to call the module, and what registers and memory locations the module affects.

A general version of Module 1 would be far less useful, since it would have to deal with different types and connections of switches and lights.

You would probably find it simpler to write a module for a particular configuration of switches and lights rather than try to use a standard routine. Note the difference between this situation and Module 2.

The Switch-Based Memory Loader

The switch-based memory loader is difficult to modularize, since all the programming tasks depend on the hardware configuration and the tasks are so simple that modules hardly seem worthwhile. The flowchart in Figure 13-9 suggests that one module might be the one that waits for the operator to press one of the three pushbuttons.

MODULARIZING THE SWITCH- BASED MEMORY LOADER

Some other modules might be:

- A delay module that provides the delay required to debounce the switches
- A switch and display module that reads the data from the switches and sends it to the displays
- A Lamp Test module

Highly system-dependent modules such as the last two are unlikely to be generally useful. This example is not one in which modular programming offers great advantages.

The Verification Terminal

The verification terminal, on the other hand, lends itself very well to modular programming. The entire system **can easily be divided into three main modules:**

MODULARIZING THE VERIFICATION TERMINAL

- **Keyboard and display module**
- **Data transmission module**
- **Data reception module**

A general keyboard and display module could handle many keyboard- and display-based systems. The sub-modules would perform such tasks as:

- Recognizing a new keyboard entry and fetching the data
- Clearing the array in response to a Clear key
- Entering digits into storage
- Looking for the terminator or Send key
- Displaying the digits

Although the key interpretations and the number of digits will vary, the basic entry, data storage, and data display processes will be the same for many programs. Such function keys as Clear would also be standard. Clearly, **the designer must consider which modules will be useful in other applications, and pay careful attention to those modules.**

The data transmission module could also be divided into such sub-modules as:

1) Adding the header character.
2) Transmitting characters as the output line can handle them.
3) Generating delay times between bits or characters.
4) Adding the trailer character.
5) Checking for transmission failures; i.e., no acknowledgement or inability to transmit without errors.

The data reception module could include sub-modules which:

1) Look for the header character.
2) Check the message destination address against the terminal address.
3) Store and interpret the message.
4) Look for the trailer character.
5) Generate bit or character delays.

Note here how important it is that each design decision (such as the bit rate, message format, or error-checking procedure) be implemented in only one module. A change in any of these decisions will then require changes only to that single module. The other

INFORMATION HIDING PRINCIPLE

modules should be written so that they are totally unaware of the values chosen or the methods used in the implementing module. **An important concept here is the "information-hiding principle,"[5] whereby modules share only information that is absolutely essential to getting the task done. Other information is hidden within a single module.**

Error handling is a typical context in which this principle should be employed. When a module detects a lethal error, it should not try to recover; instead, it should inform the calling module of the error status and allow that module to decide how to proceed. The reason is that the lower level module often lacks sufficient information to establish recovery procedures. For example, suppose that the lower level module is one that accepts numeric input from a user. This module expects a string of numeric digits terminated by a carriage return. Entry of a non-numeric character causes the module to terminate abnormally. Since the module does not know the context (i.e., is the numeric string an operand, a line number, an I/O unit number, or the length of a file?), it cannot decide how to handle an error. If the module always followed a single error recovery procedure, it would lose its generality and only be usable in those situations where that procedure was required.

REVIEW OF MODULAR PROGRAMMING

Modular programming can be very helpful if you abide by the following rules:

```
RULES FOR
MODULAR
PROGRAMMING
```

1) **Use modules of 20 to 50 lines.** Shorter modules are usually a waste of time, while longer modules are seldom general and may be difficult to integrate.

2) **Try to make modules reasonably general.** Differentiate between common features like ASCII code or asynchronous transmission formats, which will be the same for many applications, and key identifications, number of displays, or number of characters in a message, which are likely to be unique to a particular application. Make the changing of the latter parameters simple. Major changes like different character codes should be handled by separate modules.

3) **Take extra time on modules** like delays, display handlers, keyboard handlers, etc. **that will be useful in other projects or in many different places in the present program.**

4) **Try to keep modules as distinct and logically separate as possible.** Restrict the flow of information between modules and implement each design decision in a single module.

5) **Do not try to modularize simple tasks** where rewriting the entire task may be easier than assembling or modifying the module.

STRUCTURED PROGRAMMING

How do you keep modules distinct and stop them from interacting? How do you write a program that has a clear sequence of operations so that you can isolate and correct errors? One answer is to use the methods known as "structured programming", whereby each part of the program consists of elements from a limited set of structures and each structure has a single entry and a single exit.

Figure 13-14 shows a flowchart of an unstructured program. If an error occurs in Module B, we have five possible sources for that error. Not only must we check each sequence, but we also have to make sure that any changes made to correct the error do not affect any of the other sequences. The usual result is that debugging becomes like wrestling an octopus. Every time you think the situation is under control, there is another loose tentacle somewhere.

The solution is to establish a clear sequence of operations so that you can isolate errors. Such a sequence uses single-entry, single-exit modules. **The basic modules that are needed are:**

> **BASIC STRUCTURES OF STRUCTURED PROGRAMMING**

1) **An ordinary sequence;** i.e., a linear structure in which statements or structures are executed consecutively. In the sequence:

S1

S2

S3

the computer executes S1 first, S2 second, and S3 third. S1, S2, and S3 may be single instructions or entire programs.

2) **A conditional structure.**

The common one is "if C then S1 else S2," where C is a condition and S1 and S2 are statements or sequences of statements. The computer executes S1 if C is true, and S2 if C is false. Figure 13-15 shows the logic of this structure. Note that the structure has a single entry and a single exit; there is no way to enter or leave S1 or S2 other than through the structure.

3) **A loop structure.**

The common loop structure is "while C do S," where C is a condition and S is a statement or sequence of statements. The computer checks C and executes S if C is true. This structure (see Figure 13-16) also has a single entry and a single exit. Note that the computer will not execute S at all if C is originally false, since the value of C is checked before S is executed.

In most structured programming languages, an alternative looping construct is provided. This construct is known as the do-until clause. Its basic structure is "do S until C", where C is a condition and S is a statement or sequence of statements. It is similar to the do-while construct except that the test of the looping condition C is performed at the end of the loop. This has the effect of guaranteeing that the loop is always executed at least once. This is illustrated by the flowchart in Figure 13-17. The common index-controlled or DO loop can be implemented as a special case of either of these two basic looping constructs.

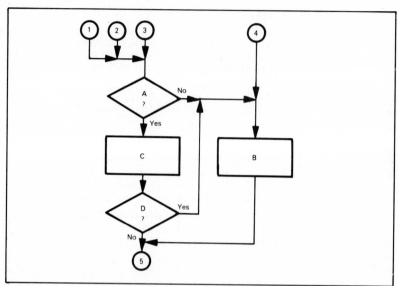

Figure 13-14. Flowchart of an Unstructured Program

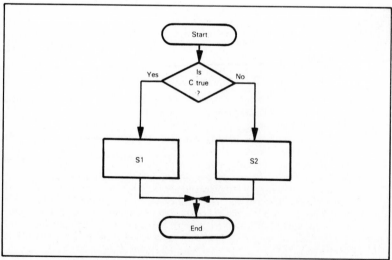

Figure 13-15. Flowchart of the If-Then-Else Structure

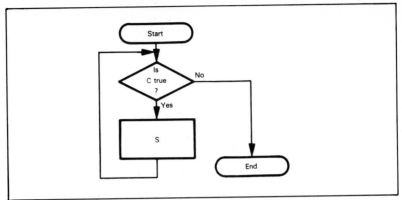

Figure 13-16. Flowchart of the Do-While Structure

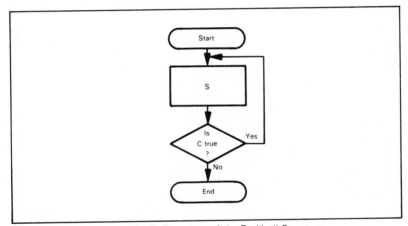

Figure 13-17. Flowchart of the Do-Until Structure

4) **A case structure.**

Although not a primitive structure like sequential, if-then-else, and do-while, the case structure is so commonly used that we include it here as an adjunct to the basic structure descriptions. The case structure is "case I of S0, S1, . . .Sn", where I is an index and S0, S1, . . . Sn are statements or sequences of statements. If I is equal to zero then statement S0 is executed, if I is equal to 1 then statement S1 is executed, etc. Only one of the n statements is executed. After its execution, control passes to the next sequential statement following the case statement group. If I is greater than n (i.e., the number of statements in the case statement), then none of the statements in the case statement is executed, and control is passed directly to the next sequential statement following the case statement. This is illustrated by the flowchart in Figure 13-18.

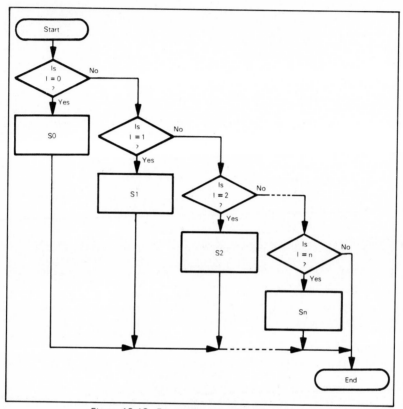

Figure 13-18. Flowchart of the Case Structure

Note the following features of structured programming:

1) **Only the three basic structures, and possibly a small number of auxiliary structures, are permitted.**

2) **Structures may be nested to any level of complexity so that any structure can, in turn, contain any of the structures.**

3) **Each structure has a single entry and a single exit.**

Some examples of the conditional structure illustrated in Figure 13-15 are:

EXAMPLES OF STRUCTURES

1) S2 included:

if $X \geq 0$ then NPOS = NPOS + 1
   else NNEG = NNEG + 1

Both S1 and S2 are single statements.

2) S2 omitted:

if $X \neq 0$ then Y = 1/X

Here no action is taken if C $(X \neq 0)$ is false. S2 and "else" can be omitted in this case.

13-38

Some examples of the loop structure illustrated in Figure 13-16 are:

1) Form the sum of integers from 1 to N.

```
I = 0
SUM = 0
do while I < N
   I = I + 1
   SUM = SUM + I
end
```

The computer executes the loop as long as I < N. If N = 0, the program within the "do-while" is not executed at all.

2) Count characters in an array SENTENCE until you find an ASCII period.

```
NCHAR = 0
do while SENTENCE (NCHAR) ≠ PERIOD
   NCHAR = NCHAR + 1
end
```

The computer executes the loop as long as the character in SENTENCE is not an ASCII period. The count is zero if the first character is a period.

The advantages of structured programming are:

> ADVANTAGES OF STRUCTURED PROGRAMMING

1) The sequence of operations is simple to trace. This allows you to test and debug easily.
2) The number of structures is limited and the terminology is standardized.
3) The structures can easily be made into modules.
4) Theoreticians have proved that the given set of structures is complete; that is, all programs can be written in terms of the three structures.
5) The structured version of a program is partly self-documenting and fairly easy to read.
6) Structured programs are easy to describe with program outlines.
7) Structured programming has been shown in practice to increase programmer productivity.

Structured programming basically forces much more discipline on the programmer than does modular programming. The result is more systematic and better-organized programs.

The disadvantages of structured programming are:

> DISADVANTAGES OF STRUCTURED PROGRAMMING

1) Only a few high-level languages (e.g., PL/M, PASCAL) will directly accept the structures. The programmer therefore has to go through an extra translation stage to convert the structures to assembly language code. The structured version of the program, however, is often useful as documentation.
2) Structured programs often execute more slowly and use more memory than unstructured programs.
3) Limiting the structures to the three basic forms makes some tasks very awkward to perform. The completeness of the structures only means that all programs can be implemented with them; it does not mean that a given program can be implemented efficiently or conveniently.
4) The standard structures are often quite confusing, e.g., nested "if-then-else" structures may be very difficult to read, since there may be no clear indication of where inner structures end. A series of nested "do-while" loops can also be difficult to read.

5) Structured programs consider only the sequence of program operations, not the flow of data. Therefore, the structures may handle data awkwardly.

6) Few programmers are accustomed to structured programming. Many find the standard structures awkward and restrictive.

We are neither advocating nor discouraging the use of structured programming. It is one way of systematizing program design. In general, structured programming is most useful in the following situations:

- Larger programs, perhaps exceeding 1000 instructions.
- Applications in which memory usage is not critical.
- Low-volume applications where software development costs, particularly testing and debugging, are important factors.
- Applications involving string manipulation, process control, or other algorithms rather than simple bit manipulations.

WHEN TO USE STRUCTURED PROGRAMMING

In the future, we expect the cost of memory to decrease, the average size of microprocessor programs to increase, and the cost of software development to increase. Therefore, methods like structured programming, which decrease software development costs for larger programs but use more memory, will become more valuable.

Just because structured programming concepts are usually expressed in high-level languages does not mean that structured programming is not applicable to assembly language programming. To the contrary, **the assembly language programmer, with the total freedom of expression that assembly level programming allows, needs the structuring concepts provided by structured programming. Creating modules with single entry and exit points, using simple control structures and keeping the complexity of each module minimal makes assembly language coding more efficient.**

EXAMPLES

Response to a Switch

The structured version of this example is:

```
STRUCTURED
PROGRAMMING
IN THE
SWITCH AND
LIGHT SYSTEM
```

```
SWITCH = OFF
do while SWITCH = OFF
   READ SWITCH
   end
LIGHT = ON
DELAY 1
LIGHT = OFF
```

ON and OFF must have the proper definitions for the switch and light. We assume that DELAY is a module that provides a delay given by its parameter in seconds.

A statement in a structured program may actually be a subroutine. However, in order to conform to the rules of structured programming, the subroutine cannot have any exits other than the one that returns control to the main program.

Since "do-while" checks the condition before executing the loop, we set the variable SWITCH to OFF before starting. The structured program is straightforward, readable, and easy to check by hand. However, it would probably require somewhat more memory than an unstructured program, which would not have to initialize SWITCH and could combine the reading and checking procedures.

The Switch-Based Memory Loader

The switch-based memory loader is a more complex structured programming problem. We may implement the flowchart of Figure 13-9 as follows (a · indicates a comment):

```
·
· INITIALIZE VARIABLES
·
HIADDRESS = 0
LOADDRESS = 0
·
· THIS PROGRAM USES A DO-WHILE CONSTRUCT WITH NO CONDITION
· (CALLED SIMPLY DO-FOREVER). THEREFORE, THE SYSTEM CONTINUALLY
· EXECUTES THE PROGRAM CONTAINED IN THIS DO-WHILE LOOP.
·
do forever
·
· TEST FOR HIADDRESS BUTTON; PERFORM THE REQUIRED PROCESSING
· IF IT IS ON.
·
    if HIADDRBUTTON = 1 then
      begin
        HIADDRESS = SWITCHES
        LIGHTS = SWITCHES
        do
          DELAY (DEBOUNCE TIME)
        until HIADDRBUTTON ≠ 1
      end
·
· TEST FOR LOADDRESS BUTTON; PERFORM LOW ADDRESS PROCESSING
· IF IT IS ON.
·
    if LOADDRBUTTON = 1 then
      begin
        LOADDRESS = SWITCHES
        LIGHTS = SWITCHES
        do
          DELAY (DEBOUNCE TIME)
        until LOADDRBUTTON ≠ 1
      end
·
· TEST FOR DATABUTTON, AND STORE DATA INTO MEMORY
· IF IT IS ON.
·
    if DATABUTTON = 1 then
      begin
        DATA = SWITCHES
        LIGHTS = SWITCHES
        (HIADDRESS, LOADDRESS) = DATA
        do
          DELAY (DEBOUNCE TIME)
        until DATABUTTON ≠ 1
      end
end
```

```
.
. THE LAST END ABOVE TERMINATES THE
.     do forever LOOP
.
```

Structured programs are not easy to write, but they can give a great deal of insight into the overall program logic. You can check the logic of the structured program by hand before writing any actual code.

The Credit-Verification Terminal

Let us look at the keyboard entry for the transaction terminal.
We will assume that the display array is ENTRY, the keyboard
strobe is KEYSTROBE, and the keyboard data is KEYIN. **The structured program without the function keys is:**

STRUCTURED
PROGRAM FOR
THE CREDIT-
VERIFICATION
TERMINAL

STRUCTURED
KEYBOARD
ROUTINE

```
NKEYS = 10
•
• CLEAR ENTRY TO START
•
  do while NKEYS > 0
    NKEYS = NKEYS - 1
    ENTRY(NKEYS) = 0
  end
•
• FETCH A COMPLETE ENTRY FROM KEYBOARD
•
  do while NKEYS < 10
    if KEYSTROBE = ACTIVE then
      begin
        KEYSTROBE = INACTIVE
        ENTRY(NKEYS) = KEYIN
        NKEYS = NKEYS + 1
    end
  end
```

**Adding the SEND key means that the program must ignore extra digits after it has
a complete entry, and must ignore the SEND key until it has a complete entry. The
structured program is:**

```
NKEYS = 10
•
• CLEAR ENTRY TO START
•
  do while NKEYS > 0
    NKEYS = NKEYS - 1
    ENTRY(NKEYS) = 0
  end
•
• WAIT FOR COMPLETE ENTRY FOLLOWED BY SEND KEY
•
  do while KEY ≠ SEND OR NKEYS ≠ 10
    if KEYSTROBE = ACTIVE then
      begin
        KEYSTROBE = INACTIVE
        KEY = KEYIN
        if NKEYS ≠ 10 AND KEY ≠ SEND then
          begin
            ENTRY(NKEYS) = KEY
            NKEYS = NKEYS + 1
          end
    end
  end
```

Note the following features of this structured program.

1) The second if-then is nested within the first one, since keys are only entered after a strobe is recognized. If the second if-then were on the same level as the first, a single key could fill the entry, since its value would be entered into the array during each iteration of the do-while loop.

2) KEY need not be defined initially, since NKEYS is set to zero as part of the clearing of the entry.

Adding the CLEAR key allows the program to clear the entry originally by simulating the pressing of CLEAR; i.e., by setting NKEYS to 10 and KEY to CLEAR before starting. The structured program must also only clear digits that have previously been filled. **The new structured program is:**

```
•
• SIMULATE COMPLETE CLEARING
•
NKEYS = 10
KEY = CLEAR

•
• WAIT FOR COMPLETE ENTRY AND SEND KEY
•
do while KEY ≠ SEND OR NKEYS ≠ 10
•
• CLEAR WHOLE ENTRY IF CLEAR KEY STRUCK
•
    if KEY = CLEAR then
      begin
        KEY = 0
        do while NKEYS > 0
          NKEYS = NKEYS - 1
          ENTRY(NKEYS) = 0
        end
      end

•
• GET DIGIT IF ENTRY INCOMPLETE
•
    if KEYSTROBE = INACTIVE then
      begin
        KEYSTROBE = INACTIVE
        KEY = KEYIN
        if KEY < 10 AND NKEYS ≠ 10 then
          begin
            ENTRY(NKEYS) = KEY
            NKEYS = NKEYS + 1
          end
      end
end
```

Note that the program resets KEY to zero after clearing the array, so that the operation is not repeated.

We can similarly build a structured program for the receive routine. An initial program could just look for the header and trailer characters. We will assume that RSTB is the indicator that a character is ready. **The structured program is:**

```
•
• CLEAR HEADER FLAG TO START
•
HFLAG = 0
•
• WAIT FOR HEADER AND TRAILER
•
do while HFLAG = 0 OR CHAR ≠ TRAILER
•
• GET CHARACTER IF READY, LOOK FOR HEADER
•
    if RSTB = ACTIVE then
      begin
        RSTB = INACTIVE
        CHAR = INPUT
        if CHAR = HEADER then HFLAG = 1
      end
```

Now we can add the section that checks the message address against the three digits in TERMINAL ADDRESS (TERMADDR). If any of the corresponding digits are not equal, the ADDRESS MATCH flag (ADDRMATCH) is set to 1.

```
•
• CLEAR HEADER FLAG, ADDRESS MATCH FLAG, ADDRESS COUNTER TO START
•
HFLAG = 0
ADDRMATCH = 0
ADDRCTR = 0
•
• WAIT FOR HEADER, DESTINATION ADDRESS AND TRAILER
•
do while HFLAG = 0 OR CHAR ≠ TRAILER OR ADDRCTR ≠ 3
•
• GET CHARACTER IF READY
•
    if RSTB = ACTIVE then
      begin
        RSTB = INACTIVE
        CHAR = INPUT
      end
•
• CHECK FOR TERMINAL ADDRESS AND HEADER
•
    if HFLAG = 1 AND ADDRCTR ≠ 3 then
      begin
        ADDRMATCH = 1
        ADDRCTR = ADDRCTR + 1
      end
    if CHAR = HEADER then HFLAG = 1
end
```

The program must now wait for a header, a three-digit identification code, and a trailer. You must be careful of what happens during the iteration when the program finds the header, and of what happens if an erroneous identification code character is the same as the trailer.

A further addition can store the message in MESSG. NMESS is the number of characters in the message; if it is not zero at the end, the program knows that the terminal has received a valid message. We have not tried to minimize the logic expressions in this program.

```
.
. CLEAR FLAGS, COUNTERS TO START
.
HFLAG = 0
ADDRMATCH = 0
ADDRCTR = 0
NMESS = 0
.
. WAIT FOR HEADER, DESTINATION ADDRESS AND TRAILER
.
do while HFLAG = 0 OR CHAR ≠ TRAILER or ADDRCTR ≠ 3
.
. GET CHARACTER IF READY
.
    if RSTB = ACTIVE then
      begin
        RSTB = INACTIVE
        CHAR = INPUT
      end
.
. READ MESSAGE IF DESTINATION ADDRESS = TERMINAL ADDRESS
.
    if HFLAG = 1 AND ADDRCTR = 3 then
      if ADDRMATCH = 0 and CHAR ≠ TRAILER then
        begin
          MESSG(NMESS) = CHAR
          NMESS = NMESS + 1
        end
.
. CHECK FOR TERMINAL ADDRESS
.
    if HFLAG = 1 AND ADDRCTR ≠ 3 then
      if CHAR ≠ TERMADDR(ADDRCTR) then
        begin
          ADDRMATCH = 1
          ADDRCTR = ADDRCTR + 1
        end
.
. LOOK FOR HEADER
.
    if CHAR = HEADER then HFLAG = 1
end
```

The program checks for the identification code only if it found a header during a previous iteration. It accepts the message only if it has previously found a header and a complete, matching destination address. The program must work properly during the iterations when it finds the header, the trailer and the last digit of the destination address. It must not try to match the header with the terminal address or place the trailer or the final digit of the destination address in the message. **You might try adding the rest of the logic from the flowchart (Figure 13-13) to the structured program. Note that the order of operations is often critical. You must be sure that the program does not complete one phase and start the next one during the same iteration.**

REVIEW OF STRUCTURED PROGRAMMING

Structured programming brings discipline to program design. It forces you to limit the types of structures you use and the sequence of operations. It provides single-entry, single-exit structures, which you can check for logical accuracy. Structured programming often makes the designer aware of inconsistencies or possible combinations of inputs. Structured programming is not a cure-all, but it does bring some order into a process that can be chaotic. The structured program should also aid in debugging, testing, and documentation.

Structured programming is not simple. The programmer must not only define the problem adequately, but must also work through the logic carefully. This is tedious and difficult, but it results in a clearly written, working program.

The particular structures we have presented are not ideal and are often awkward. In addition, it can be difficult to distinguish where one structure ends and another begins, particularly if they are nested. Theorists may provide better structures in the future, or designers may wish to add some of their own. Some kind of terminator for each structure seems necessary, since indenting does not always clarify the situation. "End" is a logical terminator for the "do-while" loop. There is no obvious terminator, however, for the "if-then-else" statement; some theorists have suggested "endif" or "fi" ("if" backwards), but these are both awkward and detract from the readability of the program.

TERMINATORS FOR STRUCTURES

We suggest the following rules for applying structured programming:

RULES FOR STRUCTURED PROGRAMMING

1) **Begin by writing a basic flowchart** to help define the logic of the program.

2) **Start with the "sequential," "if-then-else," and "do-while" constructs.** They are known to be a complete set, i.e., any program can be written in terms of these structures.

3) **Indent each level** a few spaces from the previous level, so that you will know which statements belong where.

4) **Use terminators for each structure;** e.g., "end" for the "do-while" and "endif" or "fi" for the "if-then-else". The terminators plus the indentation should make the program reasonably clear.

5) **Emphasize simplicity and readability.** Leave lots of spaces, use meaningful names, and make expressions as clear as possible. Do not try to minimize the logic at the cost of clarity.

6) **Comment the program** in an organized manner.

7) **Check the logic.** Try all the extreme cases or special conditions and a few sample cases. Any logical errors you find at this level will not plague you later.

TOP-DOWN DESIGN

The remaining problem is how to check and integrate modules or structures. Certainly we want to divide a large task into sub-tasks. But how do we check the sub-tasks in isolation and put them together? The standard procedure, called "bottom-up design," requires extra work in testing and debugging and leaves the entire integration task to the end. What we need is a method that allows testing and debugging in the actual program environment and modularizes system integration.

BOTTOM-UP DESIGN

This method is "top-down design." Here we start by writing the overall supervisor program. We replace the undefined sub-programs by program "stubs," temporary programs that may either record the entry, provide the answer to a selected test problem, or do nothing. We then test the supervisor program to see that its logic is correct.

TOP-DOWN DESIGN METHODS

STUBS

We proceed by expanding the stubs. Each stub will often contain sub-tasks, which we will temporarily represent as stubs. This process of expansion, debugging, and testing continues until all the stubs are replaced by working programs. Note that testing and integration occur at each level, rather than all at the end. No special driver or data generation programs are necessary. We get a clear idea of exactly where we are in the design. **Top-down design assumes modular programming, and is compatible with structured programming as well.**

EXPANDING STUBS

ADVANTAGES OF TOP-DOWN DESIGN

The disadvantages of top-down design are:

DISADVANTAGES OF TOP-DOWN DESIGN

1) The overall design may not mesh well with system hardware.
2) It may not take good advantage of existing software.
3) Stubs may be difficult to write, particularly if they must work correctly in several different places.
4) Top-down design may not result in generally useful modules.
5) Errors at the top level can have catastrophic effects, whereas errors in bottom-up design are usually limited to a particular module

In large programming projects, top-down design has been shown to greatly improve programmer productivity. However, almost all of these projects have used some bottom-up design in cases where the top-down method would have resulted in a large amount of extra work.

Top-down design is a useful tool that should not be followed to extremes. It provides the same discipline for system testing and integration that structured programming provides for module design. The method, however, has more general applicability, since it does not assume the use of programmed logic. However, top-down design may not result in the most efficient implementation.

EXAMPLES

Response to a Switch

The first structured programming example actually demon-strates top-down design as well. The program was:

TOP-DOWN DESIGN OF SWITCH AND LIGHT SYSTEM

```
SWITCH = OFF
do while SWITCH = OFF
  READ SWITCH
end
LIGHT = ON
DELAY 1
LIGHT = OFF
```

These statements are really stubs, since none of them is fully defined. For example, what does READ SWITCH mean? If the switch were one bit of input port SPORT, it really means:

```
SWITCH = SPORT AND SMASK
```

where SMASK has a '1' bit in the appropriate position. The masking may, of course, be implemented with a Bit Test instruction.

Similarly, DELAY 1 actually means (if the processor itself provides the delay):

```
REG = COUNT
do while REG ≠ 0
  REG = REG - 1
end
```

COUNT is the appropriate number to provide a one-second delay. **The expanded version of the program is:**

```
SWITCH = 0
do while SWITCH = 0
  SWITCH = SPORT AND MASK
end
LIGHT = ON
REG = COUNT
do while REG ≠ 0
  REG = REG - 1
end
LIGHT = NOT (LIGHT)
```

Certainly this program is more explicit, and could more easily be translated into actual instructions or statements.

The Switch-Based Memory Loader

This example is more complex than the first example, so we must proceed systematically. Here again, **the structured program contains stubs.**

TOP-DOWN
DESIGN OF
SWITCH-BASED
MEMORY
LOADER

For example, if the HIGH ADDRESS button is one bit of input port CPORT, "if HIADDRBUTTON = 1" really means:

1) Input from CPORT
2) Complement
3) Logical AND with HAMASK

where HAMASK has a '1' in the appropriate bit position and '0s' elsewhere. Similarly the condition "if DATABUTTON = 1" really means:

1) Input from CPORT
2) Complement
3) Logical AND with DAMASK

So, the initial stubs could just assign values to the buttons, e.g.,

```
HIADDRBUTTON = 0
LOADDRBUTTON = 0
DATABUTTON = 0
```

A run of the supervisor program should show that it takes the implied "else" path through the "if-then-else" structures, and never reads the switches. Similarly, if the stub were:

```
HIADDRBUTTON = 1
```

the supervisor program should stay in the "do while HIADDRBUTTON = 1" loop waiting for the button to be released. These simple runs check the overall logic.

Now **we can expand each stub and see if the expansion produces a reasonable overall result. Note how debugging and testing proceed in a straightforward and modular manner.** We expand the HIADDRBUTTON = 1 stub to:

```
READ CPORT
HIADDRBUTTON = NOT (CPORT) AND HAMASK
```

The program should wait for the HIGH ADDRESS button to be closed. The program should then display the values of the switches on the lights. This run checks for the proper response to the HIGH ADDRESS button.

We then expand the LOW ADDRESS button module to:

```
READ CPORT
LOADDRBUTTON = NOT (CPORT) AND LAMASK
```

With the LOW ADDRESS button in the closed position, the program should display the values of the switches on the lights. This run checks for the proper response to the LOW ADDRESS button.

Similarly, we can expand the DATA button module and check for the proper response to that button. The entire program will then have been tested.

When all the stubs have been expanded, the coding, debugging, and testing stages will all be complete. Of course, we must know exactly what results each stub should produce. However, many logical errors will become obvious at each level without any further expansion.

The Transaction Terminal

This example, of course, will have more levels of detail. **We could start with the following program** (see Figure 13-19 for a flowchart):

```
KEYBOARD
ACK = 0
do while ACK = 0
    TRANSMIT
    RECEIVE
end
DISPLAY
```

Here KEYBOARD, TRANSMIT, RECEIVE, and DISPLAY are program stubs that will be expanded later. KEYBOARD, for example, could simply place a ten-digit verified number into the appropriate buffer.

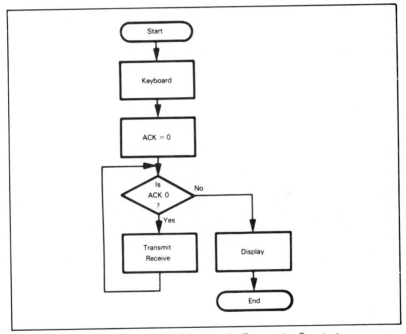

Figure 13-19. Initial Flowchart for Transaction Terminal

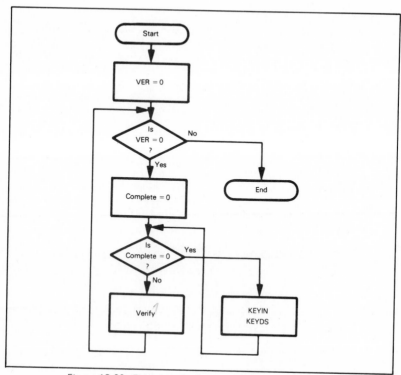

Figure 13-20. Flowchart for Expanded KEYBOARD Routine

The next stage of expansion could produce the following program for KEYBOARD (see Figure 13-20):

```
VER = 0
do while VER = 0
   COMPLETE = 0
   do while COMPLETE = 0
      KEYIN
      KEYDS
   end
   VERIFY
end
```

Here VER = 0 means that an entry has not been verified; COMPLETE = 0 means that
the entry is incomplete. KEYIN and KEYDS are the keyboard input and display routines
respectively. VERIFY checks the entry. A stub for KEYIN would simply place a random
entry (from a random number table or generator) into the buffer and set COMPLETE to
1.

We would continue by similarly expanding, debugging, and testing TRANSMIT,
RECEIVE, and DISPLAY. Note that you should expand each program by one level
so that you do not perform the integration of an entire program at any one time.
You must use your judgment in defining levels. Too small a step wastes time,
while too large a step gets you back to the problems of system integration that
top-down design is supposed to solve.

REVIEW OF TOP-DOWN DESIGN

Top-down design brings discipline to the testing and integration stages of program design. It provides a systematic method for expanding a flowchart or problem definition to the level required to actually write a program. Together with structured programming, it forms a complete set of design techniques.

Like structured programming, top-down design is not simple. The designer must have defined the problem carefully and must work systematically through each level. Here again the methodology may seem tedious, but the payoff can be substantial if you follow the rules.

We recommend the following approach to top-down design:

FORMAT FOR
TOP-DOWN
DESIGN

1) Start with a basic flowchart.

2) Make the stubs as complete and as separate as possible.

3) Define precisely all the possible outcomes from each stub and select a test set.

4) Check each level carefully and systematically.

5) Use the structures from structured programming.

6) Expand each stub by one level. Do not try to do too much in one step.

7) Watch carefully for common tasks and data structures.

8) Test and debug after each stub expansion. Do not try to do an entire level at a time.

9) Be aware of what the hardware can do. Do not hesitate to stop and do a little bottom-up design where that seems necessary.

REVIEW OF PROBLEM DEFINITION AND PROGRAM DESIGN

You should note that we have spent an entire chapter without mentioning any specific microprocessor or assembly language, and without writing a single line of actual code. Hopefully, though, you now know a lot more about the examples than you would have if we had just asked you to write the programs at the start. Although we often think of the writing of computer instructions as a key part of software development, it is actually one of the easiest stages.

Once you have written a few programs, coding will become simple. You will soon learn the instruction set, recognize which instructions are really useful, and remember the common sequences that make up the largest part of most programs. You will then find that many of the other stages of software development remain difficult and have few clear rules.

We have suggested here some ways to systematize the important early stages. In the problem definition stage, you must define all the characteristics of the system — its inputs, outputs, processing, time and memory constraints, and error handling. You must particularly consider how the system will interact with the larger system of which it is a part, and whether that larger system includes electrical equipment, mechanical equipment, or a human operator. You must start at this stage to make the system easy to use and maintain.

In the program design stage, several techniques can help you to systematically specify and document the logic of your program. Modular programming forces you to divide the total program into small, distinct modules. Structured programming provides a systematic way of defining the logic of those modules, while top-down design is a systematic method for integrating and testing them. Of course, no one can compel you to follow all of these techniques; they are, in fact, guidelines more than anything else. But they do provide a unified approach to design, and you should consider them a basis on which to develop your own approach.

REFERENCES

1. Ballard, D. R., "Designing Fail-Safe Microprocessor Systems," *Electronics*, January 4, 1979, pp. 139-143.

   "A Designer's Guide to Signature Analysis," Hewlett-Packard Application Note 222, Hewlett-Packard, Inc., Palo Alto, CA, 1977.

   Donn, E. S. and M. D. Lippman, "Efficient and Effective Microcomputer Testing Requires Careful Preplanning," *EDN*, February 20, 1979, pp. 97-107 (includes self-test examples for 6502).

   Gordon, G. and H. Nadig, "Hexadecimal Signatures Identify Troublespots in Microprocessor Systems," *Electronics*, March 3, 1977, pp. 89-96.

   Neil, M. and R. Goodner, "Designing a Serviceman's Needs into Microprocessor-Based Systems," *Electronics*, March 1, 1979, pp. 122-128.

   Schweber, W. and L. Pearce, "Software Signature Analysis Identifies and Checks PROMs," *EDN*, November 5, 1978, pp. 79-81.

   Srini, V. P., "Fault Diagnosis of Microprocessor Systems," *Computer*, January 1977, pp. 60-65.

2. For a brief discussion of human factors considerations, see G. Morris, "Make Your Next Instrument Design Emphasize User Needs and Wants," *EDN*, October 20, 1978, pp. 100-105.

3. D. L. Parnas (see the references below) has been a leader in the area of modular programming.

4. Collected by B. W. Unger (see reference below).

5. Formulated by D. L. Parnas.

The following references provide additional information on problem definition and program design:

Chapin, N., *Flowcharts*, Auerbach, Princeton, N. J., 1971.

Dalton, W. F., "Design Microcomputer Software like Other Systems — Systematically," *Electronics*, January 19, 1978, pp. 97-101.

Dijkstra, E. W., *A Discipline of Programming*, Prentice-Hall, Englewood Cliffs, N. J., 1976.

Halstead, M. H., *Elements of Software Science*, American Elsevier, New York, 1977.

Hughes, J. K. and J. I. Michtom, *A Structured Approach to Programming*, Prentice-Hall, Englewood Cliffs, N. J. 1977.

Morgan, D. E. and D. J. Taylor, "A Survey of Methods for Achieving Reliable Software," *Computer*, February 1977, pp. 44-52.

Myers, W., "The Need for Software Engineering," *Computer*, February 1978, pp. 12-25.

Parnas, D. L., "On the Criteria to be Used in Decomposing Systems into Modules," *Communications of the ACM*, December 1972, pp. 1053-1058.

Parnas, D. L. "A Technique for the Specification of Software Modules with Examples," *Communications of the ACM*, May 1973, pp. 330-336.

Phister, M. Jr., *Data Processing Technology and Economics*, Santa Monica Publishing Co., Santa Monica, CA, 1976.

Schneider, V., "Prediction of Software Effort and Project Duration — Four New Formulas," *SIGPLAN Notices*, June 1978, pp. 49-59.

Shneiderman, B. et al., "Experimental Investigations of the Utility of Detailed Flow-charts in Programming," Communications of the ACM, June 1977, pp. 373-381.

Tausworthe, R. C., Standardized Development of Computer Software, Prentice-Hall, Englewood Cliffs, N. J., 1977.

Unger, B. W., "Programming Languages for Computer System Simulation," Simulation, April 1978, pp. 101-110.

Wirth, N., Algorithms + Data Structures = Programs, Prentice-Hall, Englewood Cliffs, N. J., 1976.

Wirth, N., Systematic Programming; an Introduction, Prentice-Hall, Englewood Cliffs, N. J., 1973.

Yourdon, E. U., Techniques of Program Structure and Design, Prentice-Hall, Englewood Cliffs, N. J., 1975.

Chapter 14
DEBUGGING AND TESTING

As we noted at the beginning of the previous chapter, debugging and testing are among the most time-consuming stages of software development. **Even though such methods as modular programming, structured programming, and top-down design can simplify programs and reduce the frequency of errors, debugging and testing still are difficult** because they are so poorly defined. The selection of an adequate set of test data is seldom a clear or scientific process. Finding errors sometimes seems like a game of "pin the tail on the donkey," except that the donkey is moving and the programmer must position the tail by remote control. Surely, few tasks are as frustrating as debugging programs.

This chapter will first describe the tools available to aid in debugging. It will then discuss basic debugging procedures, describe the common types of errors, and present some examples of program debugging. The last sections will describe how to select test data and test programs.

We will not do much more than describe the purposes of most of the debugging tools. There is very little standardization in this area, and not enough space to discuss all the devices and programs that are currently available. The examples should give you some idea of the uses, advantages, and limitations of particular hardware or software aids.

SIMPLE DEBUGGING TOOLS

The simplest debugging tools available are:

- **A single-step facility**
- **A breakpoint facility**
- **A Register Dump program (or utility)**
- **A Memory Dump program**

The single-step facility allows you to execute the program one step at a time. Most 6502-based microcomputers have this facility, since the circuitry is fairly simple. Of course, **the only things that you will be able to see when the computer executes a single-step are the states of the output lines that you are monitoring.** The most important lines are:

SINGLE-STEP

- Data Bus
- Address Bus
- Control lines
- SYNC (synchronization) and READ/$\overline{\text{WRITE}}$

If you monitor these lines (either in hardware or in software), you will be able to see the progression of addresses, instructions, and data as the program executes. You will be able to tell what kind of operations the CPU is performing. This information will inform you of such errors as incorrect Jump instructions, omitted or incorrect addresses, erroneous operation codes, or incorrect data values. However, you cannot see the contents of registers and flags without some additional debugging facility or a special sequence of instructions. Many of the operations of the program cannot be checked in real time.

There are many errors that a single-step mode cannot help you to find. These include timing errors and errors in the interrupt or DMA systems. Furthermore, the single-step mode is very slow, typically executing a program at less than one millionth of the speed of the processor itself. To single-step through one second of real processor time would take more than ten days. The single-step mode is useful only to check the logic of short instruction sequences.

LIMITATIONS OF SINGLE-STEP MODE

A breakpoint is a place at which the program will automatically halt or wait so that the user can examine the current status of the system. The program will usually not start again until the operator requests a resumption of execution. Breakpoints allow you to check or pass through an entire section of a program. Thus, to see if an initialization routine is correct, you can place a breakpoint at the end of it and run the program. You can then check memory locations and registers to see if the entire section is correct. However, note that if the section is not correct, you'll still have to pin down the error, either with earlier breakpoints or with a single-step mode.

BREAKPOINT

Breakpoints complement the single-step mode. You can use breakpoints either to localize the error or to pass through sections that you know are correct. You can then do the detailed debugging in the single-step mode. In some cases, breakpoints do not affect program timing; they can then be used to check input/output and interrupts.

Breakpoints often use part or all of the microprocessor interrupt system. Some microprocessors have a special Software Interrupt or Trap facility that can act as a breakpoint. The 6502 BRK (Force Break) instruction can be used in this way. If you are not already using the maskable interrupt (IRQ) and the non-maskable interrupt (NMI) in your system, you can use those vectors as externally controlled breakpoints. Table 14-1 gives the address locations of the 6502 interrupt vectors. Chapter 12 describes the vectors in more detail. The breakpoint routine can print register and memory contents, or just wait (by executing a condition jump dependent on a switch input) until the user allows the computer to proceed. But remember that the interrupts (including BRK) use the Stack and Stack Pointer to store the return address and the Status Register. Figure 14-1 shows a routine in which BRK results in an endless loop. The programmer would have to clear this breakpoint with a RESET or interrupt signal.

BRK AS A BREAKPOINT

Table 14-1. 6502 Interrupt Vectors

Input	Vector Addresses (Hexadecimal)
NMI RESET IRQ or BRK	FFFA, FFFB FFFC, FFFD FFFE, FFFF

*=BREAK		;ADDRESS FOR BREAK ROUTINE
JMP	BREAK	;WAIT IN PLACE

The interrupt service routine must force a jump to address BREAK when it finds the Break Command flag set (this differentiates between BRK and an IRQ input).

Figure 14-1. A Simple Breakpoint Routine

The simplest method for inserting breakpoints is to replace the first byte of the instruction with a BRK instruction or to replace the instruction with a JMP or JSR instruction. The BRK instruction is preferable since only a single byte must be replaced and the breakpoint will not overrun the subsequent instructions.

Many monitors have facilities for inserting and removing breakpoints implemented via some type of Jump instruction. Such breakpoints do not affect the timing of the program until

INSERTING BREAKPOINTS

the breakpoint is executed. However, note that this procedure will not work if part or all of the program is in ROM or PROM. Other monitors implement breakpoints by actually checking the address lines or the Program Counter in hardware or in software. This method allows breakpoints on addresses in ROM or PROM, but it may affect the timing if the address must be checked in software. A more powerful facility would allow the user to enter an address to which the processor would transfer control. Another possibility would be a return dependent on a switch:

```
*=BRKPT              ;ADDRESS FOR BREAKPOINT ROUTINE
BIT     VIAORA       ;WAIT FOR SWITCH TO CLOSE
BPL     BRKPT
RTI
```

Of course, other VIA data or control lines could also be used. Remember that RTI automatically restores the Status register and re-enables the interrupt. If the interrupt comes from a VIA control line, the routine would also have to clear the corresponding bit in the Interrupt Flag register.

A **Register Dump utility on a microcomputer is a program that lists the contents of all the CPU registers.** This information is usually not directly obtainable. **The following routine will print the contents of all the registers on the system printer,** if we assume that PRTHEX prints the contents of the Accumulator as two hexadecimal digits. Figure 14-2 is a flowchart of the program and Figure 14-3 shows a typical result. We assume that the routine is entered with a JUMP TO SUBROUTINE instruction that stores the old Program Counter at the top of the Stack. An interrupt or BRK instruction will store both the Program Counter and the Status register at the top of the Stack.

REGISTER
DUMPS

```
;
; PLACE ALL CPU REGISTER CONTENTS IN STACK (PC ALREADY ON STACK)
;

        PHP                     ;SAVE STATUS IF NECESSARY (NOT AFTER IRQ)
        PHA                     ;SAVE CONTENTS OF ACCUMULATOR
        TXA                     ;SAVE INDEX REGISTER X
        PHA
        TYA                     ;SAVE INDEX REGISTER Y
        PHA
        TSX                     ;SAVE ORIGINAL STACK POINTER
        TXA
        CLC
        ADC     #6              ;OFFSET BACK TO ORIGINAL VALUE
        PHA
;
; PRINT CONTENTS OF REGISTERS
; ORDER IS S, Y, X, A, P, PC(LOW), PC(HIGH)
;

        LDY     #7              ;NUMBER OF BYTES = 7
PRNT1   LDA     $0100,X         ;GET A BYTE FROM STACK
        JSR     PRTHEX          ;AND PRINT IT
        INX
        DEY
        BNE     PRNT1
;
; RESTORE REGISTERS FROM STACK
;

        PLA                     ;PULL AND DISCARD STACK POINTER
        PLA                     ;RESTORE INDEX REGISTER Y
        TAY
        PLA                     ;RESTORE INDEX REGISTER X
        TAX
        PLA                     ;RESTORE CONTENTS OF ACCUMULATOR
        PLP                     ;RESTORE STATUS REGISTER IF NECESSARY
        RTS                     ;RESTORE PC AND SP
```

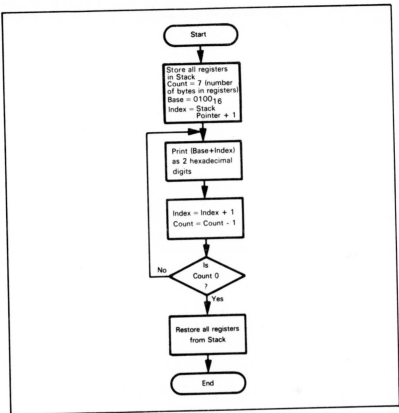

Figure 14-2. Flowchart of Register Dump Program

A6	(S)
05	(Y)
08	(X)
3E	(A)
24	(P)
15	(PCL)
A2	(PCH)

Figure 14-3. Results of a Typical 6502 Register Dump

A Memory Dump is a program that lists the contents of memory on an output device (such as a printer). This is a much more
efficient way to examine data arrays or entire programs than just
looking at single locations. However, very large memory dumps are not useful (except
to supply scrap paper) because of the sheer mass of information that they produce.
They may also take a long time to execute on a slow printer. Small dumps may,
however, provide the programmer with a reasonable amount of information that
can be examined as a unit. Relationships such as regular repetitions of data patterns or offsets of entire arrays may become obvious.

```
MEMORY
DUMP
```

A general dump is often rather difficult to write. The programmer should be careful of
the following situations:

1) The size of the memory area exceeds 256 bytes, so that an 8-bit counter will not
   suffice.

2) The ending location is an address smaller than the starting location. This can be
   treated as an error, or simply cause no output, since the user would seldom want to
   print the entire memory contents in an unusual order.

Since the speed of the Memory Dump depends on the speed of the output device, the
efficiency of the routine seldom matters. The following program will ignore cases
where the starting address is larger than the ending address, and will handle
blocks of any length. We assume that the starting address is in memory addresses
START and START+1 and the ending address is in memory addresses LAST and
LAST+1. We have assumed that addresses START and START+1 are on page zero, so
tht their contents can be used indirectly.

```
;
; PRINT CONTENTS OF SPECIFIED MEMORY LOCATIONS
;
DUMP    LDY     #0          ;KEEP OFFSET AT ZERO ALWAYS
DBYTE   LDA     LAST        ;ARE WE BEYOND FINAL ADDRESS?
        CMP     START
        LDA     LAST+1
        SBC     START+1
        BCC     DONE        ;YES, DUMP COMPLETED
        LDA     (START),Y   ;NO, GET CONTENTS OF NEXT LOCATION
        JSR     PRTHEX      ;PRINT CONTENTS AS 2 HEX DIGITS
        INC     START       ;INCREMENT MEMORY POINTER
        BNE     DBYTE
        INC     START+1
        JMP     DBYTE
DONE    RTS
```

There is no direct way to perform the 16-bit comparison and increment that this routine
requires.

Figure 14-4 shows the output from a dump of memory locations 1000 to 101F.

23	1F	60	54	37	28	3E	00
6E	42	38	17	59	44	98	37
47	36	23	81	E1	FF	FF	5A
34	ED	BC	AF	FE	FF	27	02

Figure 14-4. Results of a Typical Memory Dump

This routine correctly handles the case in which the starting and ending locations are the same (try it!). You will have to interpret the results carefully if the dump area includes the Stack, since the dump subroutine itself uses the Stack. PRTHEX may also change memory and Stack locations.

In a memory dump, the data can be displayed in a number of different ways. Common forms are ASCII characters or pairs of hexadecimal digits for 8-bit values and four hexadecimal digits for 16-bit values. The format should be chosen based on the intended use of the dump. It is almost always easier to interpret an object code dump if it is displayed in hexadecimal form rather than ASCII form.

A common and useful dump format is illustrated here:

        1000   54 68 65 20 64 75 6D 70   The dump

Each line consists of three parts. The line starts with the hexadecimal address of the first byte displayed on the line. Following the address are eight or sixteen bytes displayed in hexadecimal form. Last is the ASCII representation of the same eight or sixteen bytes. Try rewriting the memory dump program so that it will print the address and the ASCII characters as well as the hexadecimal form of the memory contents.

MORE ADVANCED DEBUGGING TOOLS

The more advanced debugging tools that are most widely used are:

- **Simulator programs to check program logic**
- **Logic analyzers to check signals and timing**

Many variations of both these tools exist, and we shall discuss only the standard features.

The simulator is the computerized equivalent of the pencil-and-paper computer. It **is a computer program that goes through the operating cycle of another computer, keeping track of the contents of all the registers, flags, and memory locations.** We could, of course, do this by hand, but it would require a large amount of effort and close attention to the exact effects of each instruction. The simulator program never gets tired or confused, forgets an instruction or register, or runs out of paper.

```
SOFTWARE
SIMULATOR
```

Most simulators are large FORTRAN programs. They can be purchased or used on the time-sharing services. The 6502 simulator is available in several versions from different sources.

Typical simulator features are:

1) **A breakpoint facility.** Usually, breakpoints can be set after a particular number of cycles have been executed, when a memory location or one of a set of memory locations is referenced, when the contents of a location or one of a set of locations are altered, or on other conditions.

2) **Register and memory dump facilities** that can display the values of memory locations, registers, and I/O ports.

3) **A trace facility** that will print the contents of particular registers or memory locations whenever the program changes or uses them.

4) **A load facility** that allows you to set values initially or change them during the simulation.

Some simulators can also simulate input/output, interrupts, and even DMA.

The simulator has many advantages:

1) It can provide a complete description of the status of the computer, since the simulator program is not restricted by pin limitations or other characteristics of the underlying circuitry.

2) It can provide breakpoints, dumps, traces, and other facilities, without using any of the processor's memory space or control system. These facilities will therefore not interfere with the user program.

3) Programs, starting points, and other conditions are easy to change.

4) All the facilities of a large computer, including peripherals and software, are available to the microprocessor designer.

On the other hand, the simulator is limited by its software base and its separation from the real microcomputer. The major limitations are:

1) The simulator cannot help with timing problems, since it operates far more slowly than real time and does not model actual hardware or interfaces.

2) The simulator cannot fully model the input/output section.

3) The simulator is usually quite slow. Reproducing one second of actual processor time may require hours of computer time. Using the simulator can be quite expensive.

The simulator represents the software side of debugging; it has the typical advantages and limitations of a wholly software-based approach. The simulator can provide insight into program logic and other software problems, but cannot help with timing, I/O, and other hardware problems.

The logic or microprocessor analyzer is the hardware solution to debugging. Basically, the analyzer is the parallel digital version of the standard oscilloscope. The analyzer displays information in binary, hexadecimal or mnemonic form on a CRT, and has a variety of triggering events, thresholds, and inputs. Most analyzers also have a memory so that they can display the past contents of the busses.

```
LOGIC
ANALYZER
```

The standard procedure is to set a triggering event, such as the occurrence of a particular address on the Address Bus or instruction on the Data Bus. For example, one might trigger the analyzer if the microcomputer tries to store data in a particular address or execute an input or output instruction. One may then look at the sequence of events that preceded the breakpoint. Common problems you can find in this way include short noise spikes (or glitches), incorrect signal sequences, overlapping wave-forms, and other timing or signaling errors. Of course, a software simulator could not be used to diagnose those errors any more than a logic analyzer could conveniently be used to find errors in program logic.

Logic analyzers vary in many respects. Some of these are:

```
IMPORTANT
FEATURES
OF LOGIC
ANALYZERS
```

1) Number of input lines. At least 24 are necessary to monitor an 8-bit Data Bus and a 16-bit Address Bus. Still more are necessary for control signals, clocks, and other important inputs.

2) Amount of memory. Each previous state that is saved will occupy several bytes.

3) Maximum frequency. It must be several MHz to handle the fastest processors.

4) Minimum signal width (important for catching glitches).

5) Type and number of triggering events allowed. Important features are pre- and post-trigger delays; these allow the user to display events occurring before or after the trigger event.

6) Methods of connecting to the microcomputer. This may require a rather complex interface.

7) Number of display channels.

8) Binary, hexadecimal or mnemonic displays.

9) Display formats.

10) Signal hold time requirements.

11) Probe capacitance.

12) Single or dual thresholds.

All of these factors are important in comparing different logic and microprocessor analyzers, since these instruments are new and unstandardized. A tremendous variety of products is already available and this variety will become even greater in the future.

Logic analyzers, of course, are necessary only for systems with complex timing. Simple applications with low-speed peripherals have few hardware problems that a designer cannot handle with a standard oscilloscope.

DEBUGGING WITH CHECKLISTS

The designer cannot possibly check an entire program by hand; however, there are certain trouble spots that the designer can easily check. **You can use systematic hand checking to find a large number of errors without resorting to any debugging tools.**

The question is where to place the effort. The answer is on points that can be handled with either a yes-no anwer or with a simple arithmetic calculation. Do not try to do complex arithmetic, follow all the flags, or try every conceivable case. Limit

WHAT TO INCLUDE IN CHECKLIST

your hand checking to matters that can be settled easily. Leave the complex problems to be solved with the aid of debugging tools. But proceed systematically; build your checklist, and make sure that the program performs the basic operations correctly.

The first step is to compare the flowchart or other program documentation with the actual code. Make sure that everything that appears in one also appears in the other. A simple checklist will do the job. It is easy to completely omit a branch or a processing section.

Next concentrate on the program loops. Make sure that all registers and memory locations used inside the loops are initialized correctly. This is a common source of errors; once again, a simple checklist will suffice.

Now look at each conditional branch. Select a sample case that should produce a branch and one that should not; try both of them. Is the branch correct or reversed? If the branch involves checking whether a number is above or below a threshold, try the equality case. Does the correct branch occur? Make sure that your choice is consistent with the problem definition.

Look at the loops as a whole. Try the first and last iterations by hand, these are often troublesome special cases. What happens if the number of iterations is zero; i.e., there is no data or the table has no elements? Does the program fall through correctly? Programs often will perform one iteration unnecessarily, or, even worse, decrement counters past zero before checking them.

Check off everything down to the last statement. Don't assume (hopefully) that the first error is the only one in the program. Hand checking will allow you to get the maximum benefit from debugging runs, since you will get rid of many simple errors ahead of time.

A quick review of the hand checking questions:

HAND CHECKING QUESTIONS

1) Is every element of the program design in the program (and vice versa for documentation purposes)?
2) Are all registers and memory locations used inside loops initialized before they are used?
3) Are all conditional branches logically correct?
4) Do all loops start and end properly?
5) Are equality cases handled correctly?
6) Are trivial cases handled correctly?

LOOKING FOR ERRORS

COMMON ERRORS

Of course, despite all these precautions (or if you skip over some of them), programs often still don't work. The designer is left with the problem of how to find the mistakes. The hand checklist provides a starting place if you didn't use it earlier; some of the errors that you may not have eliminated are:

1) **Failure to initialize variables such as counters, pointers, sums, indexes, etc.** Do not assume that the registers, memory locations, or flags necessarily contain zero before they are used.

2) **Inverting the logic of a conditional jump,** such as using Branch on Carry Set when you mean Branch on Carry Clear. Be particularly careful of the fact that the 6502 (unlike most other microprocessors) uses the Carry as an inverted borrow after a subtraction or comparison. So the effects of a comparison or subtraction are as follows (A is the contents of the Accumulator, M the contents of the memory location):

$$\text{Zero flag} = 1 \text{ if } A = M$$
$$\text{Zero flag} = 0 \text{ if } A \neq M$$
$$\text{Carry flag} = 1 \text{ if } A \geq M$$
$$\text{Carry flag} = 0 \text{ if } A < M$$

Note particularly that Carry = 1 if A = M (the equality case). So Branch on Carry Set means jump if $A \geq M$ and Branch on Carry Clear means jump if $A < M$. If you want the equality case on the other side, try either reversing the roles of A and M or adding 1 to M. For example, if you want a jump if $A \geq 10$ use

```
CMP  #10
BCS  ADDR
```

If, on the other hand, you want a jump if $A > 10$ use

```
CMP  #11
BCS  ADDR
```

3) **Updating counters, pointers, and indexes in the wrong place or not at all.** Be sure that there are no paths through a loop that either skip or repeat the updating instructions.

4) **Failure to fall through correctly in trivial cases** such as no data in a buffer, no tests to be run, or no entries in a transaction. Do not assume that such cases will never occur unless the program specifically eliminates them.

Other problems to watch for are:

5) **Reversing the order of operands.** Remember that instructions like TAX move the contents of A to X, not the other way around.

6) **Changing condition flags before you use them.**

Almost all instructions except stores and branches affect the Sign and Zero flags. Note especially that PLP and RTI may change all the flags.

7) **Confusing the Index registers and the indexed memory location.**

Note that INX and INY increment the Index registers while INC ADDR,X and other similar instructions increment the contents of an indexed memory location.

8) **Confusing data and addresses.**

Remember that LDA #$40 loads A with the number 40_{16}, while LDA $40 loads A with the contents of memory location 0040_{16}. Be particularly careful when using the pre-indexed and post-indexed addressing modes in which a pair of addresses on page zero contains the actual or base address of the data.

9) **Accidentally reinitializing a register or memory location.**

Make sure that no Jump instructions transfer control back to initialization statements.

10) **Confusing numbers and characters.**

Remember that the ASCII and EBCDIC representations of digits differ from the digits themselves. For example, ASCII 7 is 37_{16}, whereas hex 07_{16} is the ASCII BELL character.

11) **Confusing binary and decimal numbers.**

Remember that the BCD representation of a number differs from its binary representation. For example, BCD 36, when treated as a simple hexadecimal constant, is equivalent to 54 decimal (try it).

12) **Reversing the order in subtraction. Be careful also with other operations (like division) that do not commute.** Remember that SBC, CMP, CPX, and CPY all subtract the contents of the addressed memory location _from_ the contents of the Accumulator or Index register.

13) **Ignoring the effects of subroutines and macros.**

Don't assume that calls to subroutines or invocations of macros will not change flags, registers, or memory locations. Be sure of exactly what effects subroutines or macros have. Note that it is very important to document these effects so that the user can determine them without going through the entire listing.

14) **Using the Shift instructions improperly.**

Remember the precise effects of ASL, LSR, ROL, and ROR. They are 1-bit shifts that affect the Carry, Sign, and Zero flags. ASL and LSR both clear the empty bit; ROR and ROL are circular shifts that include the Carry in the circular register. Remember that the Carry, Sign, and Zero flags are affected even if these instructions are applied to the data in a memory location.

15) **Counting the length of an array incorrectly.**

Remember that there are five (not four) memory locations included in addresses 0300 through 0304, inclusive.

16) **Confusing 8- and 16-bit quantities.**

Addresses are actually 16 bits long. The only 6502 register that can hold a complete address is the Program Counter.

17) **Forgetting that addresses or 16-bit data occupy two memory locations.**

Absolute direct or absolute indexed addresses occupy two memory locations, as do the addresses that are stored on page zero for use in post-indexing or pre-indexing. The Program Counter also occupies two memory locations when it is stored in the Stack. Note that in the pre-indexed and post-indexed addressing modes, two memory locations are used even though only one is specified. The address immediately following the one specified is also needed to hold the indirect address.

JMP indirect will not work properly if the indirect address crosses a page boundary. See the discussion of indirect addressing in Chapter 3 for a description of this peculiarity.

18) **Confusing the Stack and the Stack Pointer.**

The instruction TXS affects the Stack Pointer, not the contents of the Stack. PHA, PLA, PHP, and PLP transfer data to or from the Stack. Remember that JSR, RTS, RTI, and BRK also use the Stack. Remember also that you must initialize the Stack Pointer before calling any subroutines or allowing any interrupts. The 6502 Stack is always on page one; only the eight least significant bits of the Stack address are actually in the Stack Pointer.

19) **Changing a register or memory location before using it.**

Remember that LDA, STA, LDX, STX, LDY, STY, TAX, TXA, etc. all change the contents of the destination (but not the source).

20) **Forgetting to transfer control past sections of the program that should not be executed in particular situations.**

Remember that the computer will proceed sequentially through the program memory unless specifically ordered not to do so.

21) **Forgetting that the Carry is always included in addition and subtraction operations.**

The 6502 only has Add-with-Carry and Subtract-with Borrow instructions, unlike many other processors which have regular Add and Subtract instructions that do not include the Carry. The Carry must be explicitly cleared before an addition and set before a subtraction if its value is not to affect the operation. Note, however, the comparison instructions (CMP, CPX, CPY) do not include the Carry.

22) **Inverting the significance of the Carry in subtraction.**

In subtraction and comparison instructions, the resulting Carry is an inverted borrow — that is, the Carry is set if no borrow is required. Accordingly, the subtract-with-Borrow instruction subtracts the inverted Carry (1 — Carry) along with the contents of the specified memory location.

23) **Using the decimal mode improperly.**

When the Decimal Mode flag is set, all arithmetic results are decimal. thus the flag must be explicitly cleared after the decimal operations are completed; otherwise it will change the results of operations which were not intended to be decimal. Note that all paths that include a Set Decimal Mode instruction must also include a Clear Decimal Mode instruction; be particularly careful of fall-through cases and error exits.

24) **Using the Bit Test instruction improperly.**

Note that the Bit Test instruction sets the sign and overflow flags according to bits 7 and 6 of the tested memory location, without regard to the contents of the Accumulator. This instruction is convenient for testing status bits in 6520 PIAs and for other bit checking operations, but it requires careful documentation since its results are often unclear to a reader.

Interrupt-driven programs are particularly difficult to debug, since errors may occur randomly. If, for example, the program enables the interrupts a few instructions too early, an error will occur only if an interrupt is received while the program is executing those few instructions. **In fact you can usually assume that randomly occurring errors are caused by the interrupt system.**[2] **Typical errors in interrupt-driven programs are:**

> DEBUGGING
> INTERRUPT-
> DRIVEN
> PROGRAMS

1) **Forgetting to re-enable interrupts after accepting one and servicing it.**

The processor disables the interrupt system automatically on RESET or on accepting an interrupt. Be sure that no possible sequences fail to re-enable the interrupt system. Remember that, in addition to re-enabling interrupts, the program often has to perform some action to cause the interrupting signal to be reset. If this is not done, it will appear as if the interrupting device is constantly requesting service.

2) **Using the Accumulator before saving it;** i.e., PHA must precede any operations that change the Accumulator.

3) **Forgetting to save and restore the Accumulator.**

4) **Restoring registers in the wrong order.**

If the order in which they were saved was:

```
PHA       ;SAVE ACCUMULATOR CONTENTS
TXA       ;SAVE INDEX REGISTER X
PHA
TYA       ;SAVE INDEX REGISTER Y
PHA
```

the order of restoration should be:

```
PLA       ;RESTORE INDEX REGISTER Y
TAY
PLA       ;RESTORE INDEX REGISTER X
TAX
PLA       ;RESTORE ACCUMULATOR CONTENTS
```

5) **Enabling interrupts before establishing all the necessary conditions** such as priority, flags, PIA and VIA configurations, pointers, counters, etc.

A checklist can aid here.

6) **Leaving results in registers and destroying them in the restoration process.**

As noted earlier, registers should not be used to pass information between the program and the interrupt service routines.

7) **Forgetting that the interrupts (including BRK) leave the old Program Counter and Status Register in the Stack whether you use them or not.**

You may have to re-initialize or update the Stack Pointer.

8) **Ignoring the possibility that the service routine may be entered with the Decimal Mode flag set.**

You may have to include a CLD instruction in the service routine if this possibility exists. Note that RTI will automatically restore the original state of the flag at the end of the service routine.

9) **Not disabling the interrupt during multi-word transfers or instruction sequences.**

Watch particularly for situations where the interrupt service routine may use the same memory locations that the program is using.

Hopefully, these lists will at least give you some ideas as to where to look for errors. Unfortunately, even the most systematic debugging can still leave some truly puzzling problems, particularly when interrupts are involved.[3]

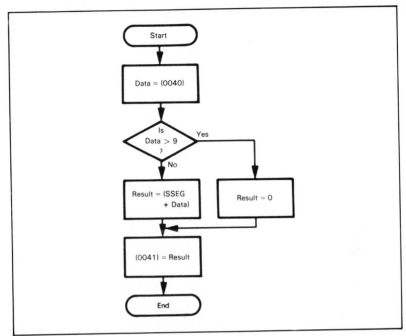

Figure 14-5. Flowchart of Decimal to Seven-Segment Conversion

Debugging Example 1: Decimal to Seven-Segment Conversion

The program converts a decimal number in memory location 0040 to a seven-segment code in memory location 0041. It blanks the display if memory location 0040 does not contain a decimal number.

DEBUGGING
A CODE
CONVERSION
PROGRAM

Initial Program (from flowchart in Figure 14-5):

```
        LDX     #$40            ;GET DATA
        CPX     #9              ;IS DATA GREATER THAN 9?
        BCC     DONE            ;YES, DONE
        LDA     (SSEG,X)        ;GET ELEMENT FROM TABLE
        STX     $41             ;SAVE SEVEN-SEGMENT CODE
DONE    BRK
SSEG    .BYTE   $3F,$06,$5B,$4F,$66
        .BYTE   $6D,$7D,$07,$7D,$6F
```

Using the checklist procedure, we were able to find the following errors:

1) The block that cleared Result had been omitted.

2) The Conditional Branch was incorrect.

For example, if the data is zero, CPX #9 clears the Carry, since 0 < 9 and a borrow is required. However, the Jump utilizing the inverted condition (i.e., BCS DONE) still did not produce the correct result. Now the program handles the equality case incorrectly since, if the data is 9, CPX #9 sets the Carry and causes a jump. The correct version is:

```
        CPX     #10             ;IS DATA A DECIMAL DIGIT?
        BCS     DONE            ;NO, KEEP ERROR CODE
```

Second Program:

```
          LDA      #0              ;GET BLANK CODE FOR DISPLAY
          LDX      #$40            ;GET DATA
          CPX      #10             ;IS DATA A DECIMAL DIGIT?
          BCS      DONE            ;NO, KEEP ERROR CODE
          LDA      (SSEG,X)        ;GET ELEMENT FROM TABLE
          STX      $41             ;SAVE SEVEN-SEGMENT CODE OR ERROR
                                   ;   CODE
DONE      BRK
SSEG      .BYTE    $3F,$06,$5B,$4F,$66
          .BYTE    $6D,$7D,$07,$7D,$6F
```

This version was hand checked successfully.

Since the program was simple, the next stage was to single-step through it with real data. The data selected for the trials was:

$$
\begin{array}{ll}
0 & \text{(the smallest number)} \\
9 & \text{(the largest number)} \\
10 & \text{(a boundary case)} \\
6B_{16} & \text{(a randomly selected case)}
\end{array}
$$

The first trial was with zero in location 0040. The first error was obvious — LDX #$40 loaded the number 40 into X, not the contents of memory location 0040. The correct instruction was LDX $40 (direct rather than immediate addressing). After this correction was made, the program moved along with no apparent errors until it tried to execute the LDA (SSEG,X) instruction.

The contents of the Address Bus during the data fetch was 063F, an address that was not even being used. Clearly, something had gone wrong.

It was now time for some more hand-checking. Since we knew that BCS DONE was correct, the error was clearly in the LDA instruction. A hand check showed:

LDA (SSEG,X) adds the contents of Index Register X to the page-zero address SSEG and uses the sum to fetch the address that contains the actual data. In the present case, since Register X contains zero, the indirect address is in memory locations SSEG and SSEG+1 — that is, it is 063F. The instruction is therefore getting an address from a table that consists of data. The correct instruction is LDA SSEG,X — we want to get data from the table, not the address of the data.

Even with this correction, the program still produced a result of zero, rather than the expected 3F. The error was obviously in the last instruction — it should be STA $41, not STX $41. Note the importance of following through to the very end of the program, rather than quitting after what might seem to be the last error.

The revised program now was:

Third Program:

```
          LDA      #0              ;GET ERROR CODE FOR DISPLAY
          LDX      $40             ;GET DATA
          CPX      #10             ;IS DATA A DECIMAL DIGIT?
          BCS      DONE            ;NO, KEEP ERROR CODE
          LDA      SSEG,X          ;GET ELEMENT FROM TABLE
          STA      $41             ;SAVE SEVEN-SEGMENT CODE OR ER-
                                   ;   ROR CODE
DONE      BRK
SSEG      .BYTE    $3F,$06,$5B,$4F,$66
          .BYTE    $6D,$7D,$07,$7D,$6F
```

The results now were:

Data	Result
00	3F
09	6F
0A	6F
6B	6F

The program was not clearing the result if the data was invalid, i.e., greater than 9. The program never stored the blank code since the destination address DONE was misplaced — it should have been attached to the STA $41 instruction. After these corrections were made, the program produced the correct results for all the test cases.

Since the program was simple, it could be tested for all the decimal digits. The results were:

Data	Result
0	3F
1	06
2	5B
3	4F
4	66
5	6D
6	7D
7	07
8	7D
9	6F

Note that the result for number 8 is wrong — it should be 7F. Since everything else is correct, the error is almost surely in the table. In fact, entry 8 in the table had been miscopied.

The final program is:

```
;
; DECIMAL TO SEVEN-SEGMENT CONVERSION
;
        LDA    #0           ;GET BLANK CODE FOR DISPLAY
        LDX    $40          ;GET DATA
        CPX    #10          ;IS DATA A DECIMAL DIGIT?
        BCS    DONE         ;NO, KEEP ERROR CODE
        LDA    SSEG,X       ;GET SEVEN-SEGMENT CODE FROM
                            ;  TABLE
DONE    STA    $41          ;SAVE SEVEN-SEGMENT CODE OR
                            ;  ERROR CODE
        BRK
SSEG    .BYTE  $3F,$06,$5B,$4F,$66
        .BYTE  $6D, $7D,$07,$7F,$6F
```

The errors encountered in this program are typical of the ones that 6502 assembly language programmers should anticipate. They include:

1) Failing to initialize registers or memory locations.
2) Inverting the logic on conditional branches.
3) Branching incorrectly in the case in which the operands are equal.
4) Confusing immediate and direct addressing, i.e., data and addresses.
5) Failing to keep track of the current contents of registers.
6) Branching to the wrong place so that one path through the program is incorrect.
7) Copying lists of numbers (or instructions) incorrectly.
8) Using the indirect addressing modes incorrectly.

Note that straightforward instructions (like AND, DEC, INC) and simple addressing modes seldom cause any problems. Among the particularly annoying errors that are frequent in 6502 assembly language programming are using the Carry improperly after subtraction or comparison (the Carry is set if no borrow is required) and forgetting to clear the Decimal Mode flag.

Debugging Example 2: Sort into Decreasing Order

The program sorts an array of unsigned 8-bit binary numbers into decreasing order. The array begins in memory location 0041 and its length is in memory location 0040.

DEBUGGING A SORT PROGRAM

Initial Program (from flowchart in Figure 14-6):

```
            LDY    #0       ;CLEAR INTERCHANGE FLAG BEFORE PASS
            LDX    $40      ;GET LENGTH OF ARRAY
PASS        LDA    $41,X    ;IS NEXT PAIR OF ELEMENTS IN ORDER?
            CMP    $42,X
            BCC    COUNT    ;YES, NO INTERCHANGE NECESSARY
            STA    $42,X    ;NO, INTERCHANGE PAIR
COUNT       DEX             ;CHECK FOR COMPLETED PASS
            BNE    PASS
            DEY             ;WERE ALL ELEMENTS IN ORDER?
            BNE    PASS     ;NO, MAKE ANOTHER PASS
            BRK
```

The hand check shows that all the blocks in the flowchart have been implemented in the program and that all the registers have been initialized. The conditional branches must be examined carefully. The instruction BCC COUNT must force a branch if the value in A is greater than or equal to the next element in the array. Remember that we are sorting elements into decreasing order and we are moving backward through the array in the usual 6502 manner. The equality case must not result in an interchange, since such an interchange would create an endless loop, with the two equal elements always being swapped.

Try an example:

$$(0041) = 30$$
$$(0042) = 37$$

CMP $42,X results in the calculation of 30 - 37. The Carry is cleared since a borrow is required. This example should result in an interchange but does not.

BCS COUNT will provide the proper branch in this case. If the two numbers are equal, the comparison will set the Carry and BCS COUNT is again correct.

How about BNE PASS at the end of the program? If there are any elements out of order, the interchange flag will be one, so the branch is wrong. It should be BEQ PASS.

Now let's hand check the first iteration of the program. The initialization results in the following values:

$$X = LENGTH (2)$$
$$Y = 0$$

The effects of the loop instructions are:

```
            LDA    $41, X    ;A = (0043)
            CMP    $42, X    ;(0043)-(0044)
            BCS    COUNT
            STA    $42, X    ;(0044) = (0043)
COUNT       DEX              ;X = LENGTH -1 (1)
            BNE    PASS
```

The indexed addresses are clearly incorrect since they are both beyond the end of the array. We will change them by subtracting two from the addresses included in the indexed instructions. This offset is a common problem in 6502 assembly language programs, because arrays and tables have a zeroth element. Thus an array with five elements occupies memory addresses BASE through BASE+4, not BASE+1 through BASE+5. When using indexed addressing on the 6502 microprocessor, be careful that your addresses are not in error at one end of the array or the other.

14-19

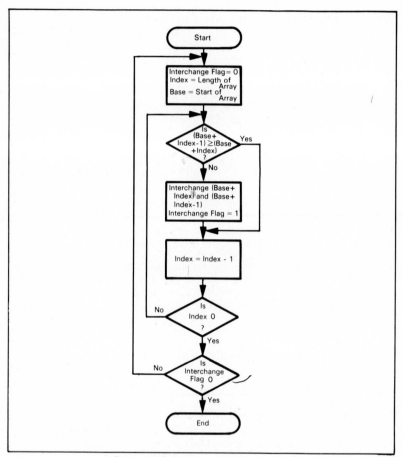

Figure 14-6. Flowchart of Sort Program

The initialization now results in the values:

$$X = LENGTH\ (2)$$
$$Y = 0$$

The effects of the loop instructions are:

```
        LDA    $3F,X      ;A = (0041)
        CMP    $40,X      ;(0041)-(0042)
        BCS    COUNT
        STA    $40, X     ;(0042) = (0041)
COUNT   DEX               ;X = LENGTH - 1 (1)
        BNE    PASS
```

Note that we have already checked the Conditional Branch instructions. Clearly the logic is incorrect. If the first two elements are out of order, the results after the first iteration should be:

$$(0041) = OLD\ (0042)$$
$$(0042) = OLD\ (0041)$$
$$X = LENGTH - 1$$

Instead, they are:

$$(0041) = UNCHANGED$$
$$(0042) = OLD\ (0041)$$
$$X = LENGTH - 1$$

The interchange requires a bit more care and the use of the Stack:

```
        PHA
        LDA    $40,X
        STA    $3F,X
        PLA
        STA    $40,X
```

An interchange always requires a temporary storage place in which one number can be saved while the other one is being transferred.

All these changes require a new copy of the program, i.e.,

```
        LDY    #0        ;CLEAR INTERCHANGE FLAG BEFORE PASS
        LDX    $40       ;GET LENGTH OF ARRAY
PASS    LDA    $3F,X     ;IS NEXT PAIR OF ELEMENTS IN ORDER?
        CMP    $40,X
        BCS    COUNT     ;YES, NO INTERCHANGE NECESSARY
        PHA             ;NO, INTERCHANGE ELEMENTS USING THE STACK
        LDA    $40,X
        STA    $3F,X
        PLA
        STA    $40,X
COUNT   DEX             ;CHECK FOR COMPLETED PASS
        BNE    PASS
        DEY             ;WERE ALL ELEMENTS IN ORDER?
        BEQ    PASS      ;NO, MAKE ANOTHER PASS
        BRK
```

How about the last iteration? Let's say that there are three elements:

$$(0040) = 03\ \ (number\ of\ elements)$$
$$(0041) = 02$$
$$(0042) = 04$$
$$(0043) = 06$$

each time through, the program decrements X by 1. So, during the third iteration, (X) = 1. The effects of the loop instructions are:

```
LDA    $3F,X      ;(A) = (0040)
CMP    $40,X      ;(0040) - (0041)
```

This is incorrect; the program has tried to move beyond the starting address of the data. The previous iteration should, in fact, have been the last one, since the number of pairs is one less than the number of elements. The first element in the array has no predecessor to which it can be compared. The correction is to reduce the number of iterations by one; this can be accomplished by placing DEX after LDX $40. We must also add 1 to all the addresses in the indexed instructions.

How about the trivial cases? What happens if the array contains no elements at all, or only one element? The answer is that the program does not work correctly and may change a whole block of data improperly and without any warning (try it!). The corrections to handle the trivial cases are simple but essential; the cost is only a few bytes of memory to avoid problems that could be very difficult to solve later.

The new program is:

```
        LDY    #0         ;CLEAR INTERCHANGE FLAG BEFORE PASS
        LDX    $40        ;GET LENGTH OF ARRAY
        CPX    #2         ;DOES ARRAY HAVE 2 OR MORE ELEMENTS?
        BCC    DONE       ;NO, NO ACTION NECESSARY
        DEX               ;NUMBER OF PAIRS = LENGTH - 1
PASS    LDA    $40,X      ;IS NEXT PAIR OF ELEMENTS IN ORDER?
        CMP    $41,X
        BCS    COUNT      ;YES, NO INTERCHANGE NECESSARY
        PHA               ;NO, INTERCHANGE ELEMENTS USING THE STACK
        LDA    $41,X
        STA    $40,X
        PLA
        STA    $41,X
COUNT   DEX               ;CHECK FOR COMPLETED PASS
        BNE    PASS
        DEY               ;WERE ALL ELEMENTS IN ORDER?
        BEQ    PASS       ;NO, MAKE ANOTHER PASS
DONE    BRK
```

Now it's time to check the program on the computer or on the simulator. A simple set of data is:

```
(0040) = 02    length of array
(0041) = 00    array to be sorted
(0042) = 01
```

This set consists of two elements in the wrong order. The program should require two passes. The first pass should reorder the elements, producing:

```
(0041) = 01    reordered array
(0042) = 00
    Y = 01    Interchange flag
```

The second pass should find the elements in the proper (descending) order and produce:

```
    Y = 00    Interchange flag
```

This program is rather long for single stepping, so we will use breakpoints instead. Each breakpoint will halt the computer and print the contents of all the registers. The breakpoints will come:

1) After DEX to check the initialization.
2) After CMP $41,X to check the comparison.
3) After STA $41,X to check the interchange.
4) After DEY to check the completion of a pass through the array

The contents of the registers after the first breakpoint were:

Register	Contents
X	01
Y	00
P (status)	25 (35 if you use BRK to create the breakpoint since the Break Command flag will be set)

These are all correct, so the program is performing the initialization correctly in this case.

The results at the second breakpoint were:

Register	Contents
A	00
X	01
Y	00
P (status)	A4 (B4 if you use BRK)

These results are also correct.

The results at the third breakpoint were:

Register	Contents
A	00
X	01
Y	00
P (status)	26 (36 if you use BRK)

Checking memory showed:

$$(0041) = 01$$
$$(0042) = 00$$

The results at the fourth breakpoint were:

Register	Contents
A	00
X	00
Y	FF
P (status)	A4 (B4 if you use BRK)

The Zero flag (bit 1 of the Status Register) is incorrect, indicating that no interchange occurred. Register Y does not contain the correct value — it should have been set to one after the interchange. In fact, a look at the program shows that no instruction ever changes Index Register Y to mark the interchange. The correction is to place the instruction LDY #1 after BCS COUNT.

Now the procedure is to load Index Register Y with the correct value (zero), set the Zero flag to 1, and continue. The second iteration of the second breakpoint gives:

Register	Contents
A	02
X	00
Y	00
P (status)	25 (35 if you use BRK)

Clearly the program has proceeded incorrectly without reinitializing the registers (particularly Index Register X). The Conditional Branch that depends on the interchange should transfer control back to a point that reinitializes X; note that we do not need to reinitialize Y (it will be zero anyway — why?) nor do we need to check the length of the array again.

The final version of the program is:

```
SORT    LDY    #0         ;CLEAR INTERCHANGE FLAG TO START
        LDX    $40        ;DOES ARRAY HAVE 2 OR MORE ELEMENTS?
        CPX    #2
        BCC    DONE       ;NO, NO ACTION NECESSARY
ITER    LDX    $40        ;YES, NUMBER OF PAIRS = LENGTH - 1
        DEX
PASS    LDA    $40,X      ;IS NEXT PAIR OF ELEMENTS IN ORDER?
        CMP    $41,X
        BCS    COUNT      ;YES, NO INTERCHANGE NECESSARY
        LDY    #1         ;NO, SET INTERCHANGE FLAG
        PHA               ;INTERCHANGE ELEMENTS USING THE STACK
        LDA    $41,X
        STA    $40,X
        PLA
        STA    $41,X
COUNT   DEX               ;CHECK FOR COMPLETED PASS
        BNE    PASS
        DEY               ;WERE ALL ELEMENTS IN ORDER?
        BEQ    ITER       ;NO, MAKE ANOTHER PASS
DONE    BRK
```

Clearly we cannot check all the possible input values for this program. Two other simple sets of data for debugging purposes are:

1) Two equal elements

$$
\begin{aligned}
(0040) &= 02 \\
(0041) &= 00 \\
(0042) &= 00
\end{aligned}
$$

2) Two elements already in decreasing order

$$
\begin{aligned}
(0040) &= 02 \\
(0041) &= 01 \\
(0042) &= 00
\end{aligned}
$$

INTRODUCTION TO TESTING

Program testing is closely related to program debugging. Surely some of the test cases will be the same as the test data used for debugging, such as:

USING TEST CASES FROM DEBUGGING

- Trivial cases such as no data or a single element
- Special cases that the program singles out for some reason
- Simple examples that exercise particular parts of the program

In the case of the decimal to seven-segment conversion program, these cases cover all the possible situations. The test data consists of:

- The numbers 0 through 9
- The boundary case 10
- The random case 6B

The program does not distinguish any other cases. **Here debugging and testing are virtually the same.**

In the sorting program, the problem is more difficult. The number of elements could range from 0 to 255, and each of the elements could lie anywhere in that range. The number of possible cases is therefore enormous. Furthermore, the program is moderately complex. How do we select test data that will give us a degree of confidence in that program? **Here testing requires some design decisions.** The testing problem is particularly difficult if the program depends on sequences of real-time data. How do we select the data, generate it, and present it to the microcomputer in a realistic manner?

Most of the tools mentioned earlier for debugging are helpful in testing also. Logic or microprocessor analyzers can help check the hardware; simulators can help check the software. Other tools can also be of assistance, e.g.,

TESTING AIDS

1) **I/O simulations** that can simulate a variety of devices from a single input and a single output device.

2) **In-circuit emulators** that allow you to attach the prototype to a development system or control panel and test it.

3) **ROM simulators** that have the flexibility of a RAM but the timing of the particular ROM or PROM that will be used in the final system.

4) **Real-time operating systems** that can provide inputs or interrupts at specific times (or perhaps randomly) and mark the occurrence of outputs. Real-time breakpoints and traces may also be included.

5) **Emulations** (often on microprogrammable computers) that may provide real-time execution speed and programmable I/O.[4]

6) **Interfaces** that allow another computer to control the I/O system and test the microcomputer program.

7) **Testing programs** that check each branch in a program for logical errors.

8) **Test generation programs** that can generate random data or other distributions.

Formal testing theorems exist, but they are usually applicable only to very short programs.

You must be careful that the test equipment does not invalidate the test by modifying the environment. Often, test equipment may buffer, latch, or condition input and output signals. The actual system may not do this, and may therefore behave quite differently.

Furthermore, extra software in the test environment may use some of the memory space or part of the interrupt system. It may also provide error recovery and other features that will not exist in the final system. A software test bed must be just as realistic as a hardware test bed, since software failure can be just as critical as hardware failure.

Emulations and simulations are, of course, never precise. They are usually adequate for checking logic, but can seldom help test the interface or the timing. On the other hand, real-time test equipment does not provide much of an overview of the program logic and may affect the interfacing and timing.

SELECTING TEST DATA

Very few real programs can be checked for all cases. The designer must choose a sample set that in some sense describes the entire range of possibilities.

Testing should, of course, be part of the total development procedure. Top-down design and structured programming provide for testing as part of the design. This is called structured testing.[5] Each module within a structured program should be checked separately. **Testing, as well as design, should be modular, structured, and top-down.**

```
STRUCTURED
TESTING
```

But that leaves the question of selecting test data for a module. The designer must first list all special cases that a program recognizes. These may include:

```
TESTING
SPECIAL
CASES
```

- Trivial cases
- Equality cases
- Special situations

The test data should include all of these.

You must next identify each class of data that statements within the program may distinguish. These may include:

```
FORMING
CLASSES
OF DATA
```

- Positive or negative numbers
- Numbers above or below a particular threshold
- Data that does or does not include a particular sequence or character
- Data that is or is not present at a particular time

If the modules are short, the total number of classes should still be small even though each division is multiplicative; i.e., three two-way divisions result in $2 \times 2 \times 2 = 8$ classes of data.

You must now separate the classes according to whether the program produces a different result for each entry in the class (as in a table) or produces the same result for each entry (such as a warning that a parameter is above a threshold). In the discrete case, one may include each element if the total number is small or sample if the number is large. The sample should include all boundary cases and at least one case selected randomly. Random number tables are available in books, and random number generators are part of most computer facilities.

```
SELECTING
DATA FROM
CLASSES
```

You must be careful of distinctions that may not be obvious. For example, an 8-bit microprocessor will regard an 8-bit unsigned number greater than 127 as negative. The programmer must consider this when using conditional branches that depend on the Sign flag. You must also watch for instructions that do not affect flags, overflow in signed arithmetic, and the distinctions between address-length (16-bit) quantities and data-length (8-bit) quantities.

Testing Example 1: Sort Program

The special cases here are obvious:

- No elements in the array
- One element, magnitude may be selected randomly

TESTING
A SORT
PROGRAM

The other special case to be considered is one in which elements are equal.

There may be some problem here with signs and data length. Note that the array itself must contain fewer than 256 elements. The use of the instruction LDY #1 rather than INY to set the Interchange flag means that there will be no problems if the number of elements or interchanges exceeds 128. We could check the effects of sign by picking half the regular test cases with numbers of elements between 128 and 255 and half between 2 and 127. All magnitudes should be chosen randomly so as to avoid unconscious bias as much as possible.

Testing Example 2: Self-Checking Numbers (see Chapter 8)

Here we will presume that a prior validity check has ensured that the number has the right length and consists of valid digits. Since the program makes no other distinctions, test data should be selected randomly. Here a random number table or random number generator will prove ideal; the range of the random numbers is 0 to 9.

TESTING AN
ARITHMETIC
PROGRAM

TESTING PRECAUTIONS

The designer can simplify the testing stage by designing programs sensibly. You should use the following rules:

RULES FOR TESTING

1) Try to eliminate trivial cases as early as possible without introducing unnecessary distinctions.

2) Minimize the number of special cases. Each special case means additional testing and debugging time.

3) Consider performing validity or error checks on the data prior to processing.

4) Be careful of inadvertent and unnecessary distinctions, particularly in handling signed numbers or using operations that refer to signed numbers.

5) Check boundary cases by hand. These are often a source of errors. Be sure that the problem definition specifies what is to happen in these cases.

6) Make the program as general as reasonably possible. Each distinction and separate routine increases the required testing.

7) Divide the program and design the modules so that the testing can proceed in steps in conjunction with the other stages of software development.[6]

CONCLUSIONS

Debugging and testing are the stepchildren of the software development process. Most projects leave far too little time for them and most textbooks neglect them. But designers and managers often find that these stages are the most expensive and time-consuming. Progress may be very difficult to measure or produce. Debugging and testing microprocessor software is particularly difficult because the powerful hardware and software tools that can be used on larger computers are seldom available for microcomputers.

The designer should plan debugging and testing carefully. We recommend the following procedure:

1) **Try to write programs that can easily be debugged and tested. Modular programming, structured programming, and top-down design are useful techniques.**

2) **Prepare a debugging and testing plan as part of the program design. Decide early what data you must generate and what equipment you will need.**

3) **Debug and test each module as part of the top-down design process.**

4) **Debug each module's logic systematically. Use checklists, breakpoints, and the single-step mode. If the program logic is complex, consider using the software simulator.**

5) **Check each module's timing systematically if this is a problem. An oscilloscope can solve many problems if you plan the test properly. If the timing is complex, consider using a logic or microprocessor analyzer.**

6) **Be sure that the test data is a representative sample. Watch for any classes of data that the program may distinguish. Include all special and trivial cases.**

7) **If the program handles each element differently or the number of cases is large, select the test data randomly.[7]**

8) **Record all test results as part of the documentation. If problems occur, you will not have to repeat test cases that have already been checked.**

REFERENCES

1. For more information about logic analyzers, see:

   N. Andreiev, "Special Report: Troubleshooting Instruments," EDN, October 5, 1978, pp. 89-99

   R. L. Down, "Understanding Logic Analyzers," Computer Design June 1977, pp. 188-191.

   R. Gasperini, "A Guide to Digital Troubleshooting Aids," Instruments and Control Systems, February 1978, pp. 39-42.

   R. Lorentzen, "Troubleshooting Microprocessors with a Logic Analyzer System," Computer Design, March 1979, pp. 160-164 (includes a 6502-based example).

   M. Marshall, "What to Look for in Logic Timing Analyzers," Electronics, March 29, 1979, p. 109-114.

   K. Pines, "What Do Logic Analyzers Do?", Digital Design, September 1977, pp. 55-72.

   I Spector, "Logic Analysis by Telephone," EDN, March 20, 1979, pp. 139-142.

2. W. J. Weller, Assembly Level Programming for Small Computers, Lexington Books, Lexington, MA, 1975, Chapter 23.

3. R. L. Baldridge, "Interrupts Add Power, Complexity to Microcomputer System Design," EDN, August 5, 1977, pp. 67-73.

4. H. R. Burris, "Time-Scaled Emulations of the 8080 Microprocessor," Proceedings of the 1977 National Computer Conference, pp. 937-946.

5. D. A. Walsh, "Structured Testing," Datamation, July 1977, pp. 111-118.

   P. F. Barbuto Jr. and J. Geller, "Tools for Top-Down Testing," Datamation, October 1978, pp. 178-182.

6. R. A. DeMillo et al., "Hints on Test Data Selection: Help for the Practicing Programmer," Computer, April 1978, pp. 34-41

   W. F. Dalton, "Design Microcomputer Software," Electronics, January 19, 1978, pp. 97-101.

7. T. G. Lewis, Distribution Sampling for Computer Simulation, Lexington Books, Lexington, MA, 1975.

   R. A. Mueller et al., "A Random Number Generator for Microprocessors," Simulation, April 1977, pp. 123-127.

Chapter 15
DOCUMENTATION AND REDESIGN

The working program is not the only requirement of software development. Adequate documentation is also an important part of a software product. Not only does documentation help the designer in the testing and debugging stages, it is also essential for later use and extension of the program. A poorly documented program will be difficult to maintain, use, or extend.

Occasionally, a program uses too much memory or executes too slowly. The designer must then improve it. This stage is called redesign, and requires that you concentrate on the parts of the program that can yield the most improvement.

SELF-DOCUMENTING PROGRAMS

Although no program is ever completely self-documenting, some of the rules that we mentioned earlier can help. These **include:**

> RULES FOR
> SELF-DOCUMENTING
> PROGRAMS

- Clear, simple structure with as few transfers of control (jumps) as possible
- Use of meaningful names and labels
- Use of names for I/O devices, parameters, numerical factors, etc.
- Emphasis on simplicity rather than on minor savings in memory usage, execution time, or typing

For example, the following program sends a string of characters to a teletypewriter:

```
        LDX     $40
W       LDA     $0FFF,X
        STA     $A000
        JSR     XXX
        DEX
        BNE     W
        BRK
```

Even without comments we can improve the program, as follows:

```
MESSG   =$1000
COUNT   =$40
TTYVIA  =$A000
        LDX     COUNT
OUTCH   LDA     MESSG-1,X
        STA     TTYVIA
        JSR     BITDLY
        DEX
        BNE     OUTCH
        BRK
```

Surely this program is easier to understand than the earlier version. Even without further documentation, you could probably guess at the function of the program and the meanings of most of the variables. **Other documentation techniques cannot substitute for self-documentation.**

Some further notes on choosing names:

CHOOSING USEFUL NAMES

1) **Use the obvious name** when it is available, like TTY or CRT for output devices, START or RESET for addresses, DELAY or SORT for subroutines, COUNT or LENGTH for data.

2) **Avoid acronyms** like S16BA for SORT 16-BIT ARRAY. These seldom mean anything to anybody.

3) **Use full words** or close to full words when possible, like DONE, PRINT, SEND, etc.

4) **Keep the names** as **distinct** as possible.

COMMENTS

The most obvious form of additional documentation is the comment. However, few programs (even those used as examples in books) have effective comments. You should consider the following guidelines for good comments.

1) **Don't repeat the meaning of the instruction code.** Rather, explain the purpose of the instruction in the program. Comments like

COMMENTING GUIDELINES

        DEX   ;X=X-1

   add nothing to documentation. Rather, use

        DEX   ;LINE NUMBER=LINE NUMBER-1

   Remember that you know what the operation codes mean and anyone else can look them up in the manual. **The important point is to explain what task the program is performing.**

2) **Make the comments as clear as possible.** Do not use abbreviations or acronyms unless they are well-known (like ASCII, VIA, or UART) or standard (like no for number, ms for millisecond, etc.). Avoid comments like

        DEX   ;LN=LN-1
                or
        DEX   ;DEC LN BY 1

   The extra typing simply is not all that expensive.

3) **Comment every important or obscure point.** Be particularly careful to mark operations that may not have obvious functions, such as

        AND #%00100000 ;TURN TAPE READER BIT OFF
   or
        LDA GCODL,X   ;CONVERT TO GRAY CODE USING TABLE

   Clearly, I/O operations often require extensive comments. If you're not exactly sure of what an instruction does, or if you have to think about it, add a clarifying comment. The comment will save you time later and will be helpful in documentation.

4) **Don't comment the obvious.** A comment on each line simply makes it difficult to find the important points. Standard sequences like

        DEX
        BNE   SEARCH

   need not be marked unless you're doing something special. One comment will often suffice for several lines, as in

        LSR   A   ;GET MOST SIGNIFICANT DIGIT
        LSR   A
        LSR   A
        LSR   A

        LDA $40   ;EXCHANGE MOST SIGNIFICANT, LEAST
        LDX $41   ; SIGNIFICANT BYTES
        STA $41
        STX $40

5) **Place comments on the lines to which they refer or at the start of a sequence.**

6) **Keep your comments up-to-date.** If you change the program, change the comments.

7) **Use standard forms and terms** in commenting. Don't worry about repetitiveness. Varied names for the same things are confusing, even if the variations are just COUNT and COUNTER, START and BEGIN, DISPLAY and LEDS, or PANEL and SWITCHES.

There's no real gain in not being consistent. The variations may seem obvious to you now, but may not be clear later; others will get confused from the very beginning.

8) **Make comments mingled with instructions brief.** Leave a complete explanation to header comments and other documentation. Otherwise, the program gets lost in the comments and you may have a hard time even finding it.

9) **Keep improving your comments.** If you come to one that you cannot read or understand, take the time to change it. If you find that the listing is getting crowded, add some blank lines. The comments won't improve themselves; in fact, they will just become worse as you leave the task behind and forget exactly what you did.

10) **Before every major section, subsection, or subroutine, insert a number of comments describing the functions of the code that follows.** Care should be taken to describe all inputs, outputs, and side effects, as well as the algorithm employed.

11) It is good practice **when modifying working programs** to **use comments to indicate the date, author, and type of modification made.**

Remember, comments are important. Good ones will save you time and effort. Put some work into comments and try to make them as effective as possible.

Commenting Example 1: Multiple-Precision Addition

The basic program is:

```
            LDX     $40
            CLC
ADDWD       LDA     $40,X
            ADC     $50,X
            STA     $40,X
            DEX
            BNE     ADDWD
            BRK
```

First, comment the important points. These are typically initializations, data fetches, and processing operations. Don't bother with standard sequences like updating pointers and counters. Remember that names are clearer than numbers, so use them freely.

The new version of the program is:

```
;
;MULTIPLE-PRECISION ADDITION
;
;
;THIS PROGRAM PERFORMS MULTI-BYTE BINARY ADDITION
;
;  INPUTS: LOCATION 0040 (HEX) = LENGTH OF NUMBERS (IN BYTES)
;          LOCATIONS 0041 THROUGH 0050 (HEX) = FIRST NUMBER STARTING
;          WITH MSB'S
;          LOCATIONS 0051 THROUGH 0060 (HEX) = SECOND NUMBER STARTING
;          WITH MSB'S
;  OUTPUTS: LOCATIONS 0041 THROUGH 0050 (HEX) = SUM STARTING WITH
;          MSB'S
;
LENGTH      =$40
NUMB1       =$41
NUMB2       =$51
            LDX     LENGTH      ;COUNT = LENGTH OF NUMBERS (IN BYTES)
            CLC
ADDWD       LDA     NUMB1-1,X   ;GET BYTE FROM STRING 1
            ADC     NUMB2-1,X   ;ADD BYTE FROM STRING 2
            STA     NUMB1-1,X   ;STORE RESULT IN STRING 1
            DEX
            BNE     ADDWD       ;CONTINUE UNTIL ALL BYTES ADDED
            BRK
```

Second, look for any instructions that might not have obvious functions and mark them. Here, the purpose of CLC is to clear the Carry the first time through.

Third, ask yourself whether the comments tell you what you would need to know if you wanted to use the program, e.g.:

1) Where is the program entered? Are there alternative entry points?

2) What parameters are necessary? How and in what form must they be supplied?

3) What operations does the program perform?

4) From where does it get the data?

5) Where does it store the results?

6) What special cases does it consider?

7) What does the program do about errors?

8) How does it exit?

Some of the questions may not be relevant to a particular program and some of the answers may be obvious. Make sure that you won't have to sit down and dissect the program to figure out what the answers are. Remember that too much explanation is just dead wood that you will have to clear out of the way. Is there anything that you would add to or subtract from this listing? If so, go ahead — you are the one who has to feel that the commenting is adequate and reasonable.

```
;
;MULTIPLE-PRECISION ADDITION
;
;
;THIS PROGRAM PERFORMS MULTI-BYTE BINARY ADDITION
;
;   INPUTS: LOCATION 0040 (HEX) = LENGTH OF NUMBERS (IN BYTES)
;           LOCATIONS 0041 THROUGH 0050 (HEX) = FIRST NUMBER STARTING
;           WITH MSB'S
;           LOCATIONS 0051 THROUGH 0060 (HEX) = SECOND NUMBER STARTING
;           WITH MSB'S
;   OUTPUTS: LOCATIONS 0041 THROUGH 0050 (HEX) = SUM STARTING WITH
;            MSB'S
;

LENGTH     =$40                 ;LENGTH OF NUMBERS (IN BYTES)
NUMB1      =$41                 ;MSB'S OF 1ST NUMBER AND RESULT
NUMB2      =$51                 ;MSB'S OF SECOND NUMBER
           LDX     LENGTH       ;COUNT = LENGTH OF NUMBERS (IN BYTES)
           CLC                  ;CLEAR CARRY TO START
ADDWD      LDA     NUMB1-1,X    ;GET BYTE FROM STRING 1
           ADC     NUMB2-1,X    ;ADD BYTE FROM STRING 2
           STA     NUMB1-1,X    ;STORE RESULT IN STRING 1
           DEX
           BNE     ADDWD        ;CONTINUE UNTIL ALL BYTES ADDED
           BRK
```

Commenting Example 2: Teletypewriter Output

The basic program is:

```
              LDA       $60
              ASL       A
              LDX       #11
      TBIT    STA       $A000
              JSR       BITDLY
              ROR       A
              SEC
              DEX
              BNE       TBIT
              BRK
```

Commenting the important points and adding names gives:

```
;
;TELETYPEWRITER OUTPUT PROGRAM
;
;THIS PROGRAM PRINTS THE CONTENTS OF MEMORY LOCATION 0060 (HEX) TO THE
;   TELETYPEWRITER
;
;   INPUTS: CHARACTER TO BE TRANSMITTED IN MEMORY LOCATION 0060
;   OUTPUTS: NONE
;
NBITS     =11                       ;NUMBER OF BITS PER CHARACTER
TDATA     =$60                      ;ADDRESS OF CHARACTER TO BE
                                    ;   TRANSMITTED
TTYVIA    =$A000                    ;TELETYPEWRITER OUTPUT DATA PORT
          LDA       TDATA           ;GET DATA
          ASL       A               ;SHIFT LEFT AND FORM START BIT
          LDX       #NBITS          ;COUNT = NUMBER OF BITS IN CHARACTER
TBIT      STA       TTYVIA          ;SEND NEXT BIT TO TELETYPEWRITER
          JSR       BITDLY          ;WAIT 1 BIT TIME
          ROR       A               ;GET NEXT BIT
          SEC                       ;SET CARRY TO FORM STOP BITS
          DEX
          BNE       TBIT            ;COUNT BITS
          BRK
```

Note how easily we could change this program so that it would transfer a whole string of data, starting at the address in page-zero locations DPTR and DPTR + 1 and ending with an "03" character (ASCII ETX). Furthermore, let us make the terminal a 30 character per second device with one stop bit (we will have to change subroutine BITDLY). Try making the changes before looking at the listing.

```
;
;STRING OUTPUT PROGRAM
;
;THIS PROGRAM TRANSMITS A STRING OF CHARACTERS TO A 30 CPS TERMINAL.
;   TRANSMISSION CEASES WHEN AN ASCII ETX (03 HEX) IS ENCOUNTERED
;
;   INPUTS: LOCATIONS 0060 AND 0061 (HEX) CONTAIN ADDRESS OF
;              STRING TO BE TRANSMITTED
;   OUTPUTS: NONE
;

DPTR      =$60                    ;POINTER TO OUTPUT DATA BUFFER
ENDCH     =$03                    ;ENDING CHARACTER = ASCII ETX
NBITS     =10                     ;NUMBER OF BITS PER CHARACTER
TRMVIA    =$A000                  ;TERMINAL OUTPUT DATA PORT
          LDY     #0              ;POINT TO START OF OUTPUT DATA BUFFER
TCHAR     LDA     (DPTR),Y        ;GET A CHARACTER FROM BUFFER
          CMP     #ENDCH          ;IS IT ENDING CHARACTER?
          BEQ     DONE            ;YES, DONE
          ASL     A               ;NO, SHIFT LEFT AND FORM START BIT
          LDX     #NBITS          ;COUNT = NUMBER OF BITS PER CHARACTER
TBIT      STA     TRMVIA          ;SEND NEXT BIT TO TERMINAL
          JSR     BITDLY          ;WAIT 1 BIT TIME
          ROR     A               ;GET NEXT BIT
          SEC                     ;SET CARRY TO FORM STOP BIT
          DEX
          BNE     TBIT            ;COUNT BITS
          INY                     ;PROCEED TO NEXT CHARACTER
          JMP     TCHAR
DONE      BRK
```

Good comments can make it easy for you to change a program to meet new requirements. For example, try changing the last program so that it:

• Starts each message with ASCII STX (02_{16}) followed by a three-digit identification code stored in memory locations IDCODE through IDCODE+2

• Adds no start or stop bits

• Waits 1 ms between bits

• Transmits 40 characters, starting with the one located at the address in DPTR and DPTR+1

• Ends each message with two consecutive ASCII ETXs (03_{16})

FLOWCHARTS AS DOCUMENTATION

We have already described the use of flowcharts as a design tool in Chapter 13. Flowcharts are also useful in documentation, particularly if:

HINTS FOR USING FLOWCHARTS

- They are not so detailed as to be unreadable
- Their decision points are clearly explained and marked
- They include all branches
- They correspond to the actual program listings

Flowcharts are helpful if they give you an overall picture of the program. They are not helpful if they are just as difficult to read as an ordinary listing.

STRUCTURED PROGRAMS AS DOCUMENTATION

A structured program can serve as documentation for an assembly language program if:

- You describe the purpose of each section in the comments
- You make it clear which statements are included in each conditional or loop structure by using indentation and ending markers
- You make the total structure as simple as possible
- You use a consistent, well-defined language

The structured program can help you to check the logic or improve it. Furthermore, since the structured program is machine-independent, it can also aid you in implementing the same task on another computer.

MEMORY MAPS

A memory map is simply a list of all the memory assignments in a program. The map allows you to determine the amount of memory needed, the locations of data or subroutines, and the parts of memory not allocated. The map is a handy reference for finding storage locations and entry points and for dividing memory between different routines or programmers. The map will also give you easy access to data and subroutines if you need them in later extensions or in maintenance. Sometimes a graphical map is more helpful than a listing.

A typical map would be:

TYPICAL
MEMORY
MAP

Program Memory		
Address	Routine	Purpose
E000-E1FF	INTRPT	Interrupt Service Routine for Keyboard
E200-E240	BRKPT	Service Routine for Break Instruction
E241-E250	DELAY	Delay Program
E251-E270	DSPLY	Display Control Program
E271-E3F9	MAIN	Main Program
E3FA-E3FF		Interrupt and Reset Vectors
Data Memory		
0000	NKEYS	Number of Keys
0001-0002	KPTR	Keyboard Buffer Pointer
0003-0041	KBFR	Keyboard Buffer
0042-0051	DBFR	Display Buffer
0051-006F	TEMP	Temporary Storage
0100-01FF	STACK	RAM Stack

Remember that the 6502 RAM Stack is always on page 1 of memory.

PARAMETER AND DEFINITION LISTS

Parameter and definition lists at the start of the program and each subroutine make understanding and changing the program far simpler. The following rules can help:

1) **Separate RAM locations, I/O units, parameters, definitions, and memory system constants.**

2) **Arrange lists alphabetically when possible,** with a description of each entry.

3) **Give each parameter that might change a name and include it in the lists.** Such parameters may include timing constants, inputs or codes corresponding to particular keys or functions, control or masking patterns, starting or ending characters, thresholds, etc.

4) **Make the memory system constants into a separate list.** These constants will include Reset and interrupt service addresses, the starting address of the program, RAM areas, Stack areas, etc.

5) **Give each port used by an I/O device a name,** even though devices may share ports in the current system. The separation will make expansion or reconfiguration much simpler.

A typical list of definitions will be:

```
;
;MEMORY SYSTEM CONSTANTS
;
INTRP      =$E200          ;INTERRUPT ENTRY POINT
RAMST      =$0             ;START OF DATA STORAGE AREA
RESET      =$E300          ;RESET ADDRESS
STPTR      =$01FF          ;TOP ADDRESS IN RAM STACK (ON PAGE 1)

;
; I/O UNITS
;
DSPLY      =$A000          ;OUTPUT VIA FOR DISPLAYS
KBDIN      =$A001          ;INPUT VIA FOR KEYBOARD
KBDOT      =$A000          ;OUTPUT VIA FOR KEYBOARD
TTYVIA     =$A800          ;TTY DATA PORT

;
;RAM LOCATIONS
;
           *=RAMST
NKEYS      *=*+1           ;NUMBER OF KEYS
KPTR       *=*+2           ;KEYBOARD BUFFER POINTER
KBFR       *=*+$40         ;KEYBOARD INPUT BUFFER
DBFR       *=*+$10         ;DISPLAY DATA BUFFER
TEMP       *=*+$14         ;TEMPORARY STORAGE

;
;PARAMETERS
;
BOUNCE     =2              ;DEBOUNCING TIME IN MS
GOKEY      =10             ;IDENTIFICATION OF 'GO' KEY
MSCNT      =$C7            ;COUNT FOR 1 MS DELAY
OPEN       =$0F            ;PATTERN FOR OPEN KEYS
TPULS      =1              ;PULSE LENGTH FOR DISPLAYS IN MS
```

```
;
;DEFINITIONS
;
ALLHI      =$FF                        ;ALL ONES PATTERN
STCON      =$80                        ;PATTERN FOR START CONVERSION PULSE
```

Of course, the RAM entries will usually not be in alphabetical order, since the designer must order these so as to minimize the number of address changes required in the program.

LIBRARY ROUTINES

Standard documentation of subroutines will allow you to build up a library of useful programs. The idea is to make these programs easily accessible. A standard format will allow you or anyone else to see at a glance what the program does. The best procedure is to make up a standard form and use it consistently. Save these programs in a well-organized manner (for example, according to processor, language, and type of program), and you will soon have a useful set. But **remember that, without organization and proper documentation, using the library may be more difficult than rewriting the program from scratch.** Debugging a system requires a precise understanding of all the effects of each subroutine.

Among the information that you will need in the standard form is:

STANDARD PROGRAM LIBRARY FORMS

- Purpose of the program
- Processor used
- Language used
- Parameters required and how they are passed to the subroutine
- Results produced and how they are passed to the main program
- Number of bytes of memory used
- Number of clock cycles required. This number may be an average or a typical figure, or it may vary widely. Actual execution time will, of course, depend on the processor clock rate and the memory cycle time.
- Registers affected
- Flags affected
- A typical example
- Error handling
- Special cases
- Documented program listing

If the program is complex, the standard library form should also include a general flowchart or a structured program. As we have mentioned before, a library program is most likely to be useful if it performs a single distinct function in a reasonably general manner.

LIBRARY EXAMPLES

Library Example 1: Sum of Data

Purpose: The program SUM8 computes the sum of a set of 8-bit unsigned binary numbers.

Language: 6502 Assembler.

Initial Conditions: Address one less than the starting address of the set of numbers in memory locations 0040 and 0041, length of set in Index Register Y.

Final Conditions: Sum in Accumulator.

Requirements:

```
          Memory  -  9 bytes.
            Time  -  7+12n clock cycles, where n is the length of the set of
                     numbers. May be longer if page boundaries are crossed.
       Registers  -  A,Y
            RAM   -  locations 0040 and 0041.
All flags affected.
```

Typical Case: (all data in hexadecimal)

```
   Start:
   (0040 and 0041)  =  004F
              Y  =  03
          (0050)  =  27
          (0051)  =  3E
          (0052)  =  26
   End:
              A  =  8B
```

Error Handling: Program ignores all carries. Carry bit reflects only the last operation. Initial contents of Index register Y must be 1 or more. Decimal Mode flag should be cleared.

Listing:

```
;
;SUM OF 8-BIT DATA
;
SUM8      LDA    #0          ;SUM =ZERO
ADD8      CLC                ;CLEAR CARRY EACH TIME
          ADC    ($40),Y     ;SUM = SUM + DATA ENTRY
          DEY
          BNE    ADD8
          RTS
```

Library Example 2: Decimal-to-Seven Segment Conversion

Purpose: The program SEVEN converts a decimal number to a seven-segment display code.

Language: 6502 Assembler.

Initial Conditions: Data in Index Register X.

Final conditions: Seven-segment code in Accumulator.

Requirements:

Memory	-	19 bytes, including the seven-segment code table (10 entries).
Time	-	16 clock cycles if the data is valid, 13 if it is not. May be longer if page boundaries are crossed.
Registers	-	A, X

All flags affected.

Input data in Index Register X is unchanged.

Typical Case: (data in hexadecimal)

Start:

X = 05

End:

A = 6D

Error Handling: Program returns zero in the Accumulator if the data is not a decimal digit.

Listing:

```
;
;DECIMAL TO SEVEN-SEGMENT CONVERSION
;
SEVEN    LDA    #0            ;GET ERROR CODE TO BLANK DISPLAY
         CPX    #10           ;IS DATA A DECIMAL DIGIT?
         BCS    DONE          ;NO, KEEP ERROR CODE
         LDA    SSEG,X        ;YES, GET SEVEN-SEGMENT CODE FROM
                              ;  TABLE
DONE     RTS
SSEG     . BYTE  $3F,$06,$5B,$4F,$66
         . BYTE  $6D,$7D,$07,$7F,$6F
```

Library Example 3: Decimal Sum

Purpose: The program DECSUM adds two multi-word decimal numbers.

Language: 6502 Assembler.

Initial Conditions: Address of MSBs of one number in memory locations 0040 and 0041, address of MSBs of other number in memory locations 0042 and 0043. Length of numbers (in bytes) in Index Register Y. Numbers arranged starting with most significant digits.

Final Conditions: Sum replaces number with starting address in memory locations 0040 and 0041.

Requirements:

Memory	-	14 bytes.
Time	-	11 + 22n clock cycles, where n is the number of bytes. May be longer if page boundaries are crossed.
Registers	-	A, Y
RAM	-	memory locations 0040 through 0043.
All flags affected	-	Carry shows if sum produced a carry. Decimal Mode flag is cleared.

Typical Case: (all data in hexadecimal)

```
Start:
(0040 and 0041) = 0060
(0042 and 0043) = 0050
         (Y) = 02

       (0060) = 55
       (0061) = 34

       (0050) = 15
       (0051) = 88
End:
       (0060) = 71
       (0061) = 22
       Carry = 0
```

Error Handling: Program does not check the validity of decimal inputs. The contents of Index Register Y must be 1 or more.

Listing:

```
;
;MULTI-DIGIT DECIMAL (BCD) ADDITION
;
DECSUM    SED                   ;MAKE ALL ARITHMETIC DECIMAL
          CLC                   ;CLEAR CARRY TO START
DECADD    DEY
          LDA      ($40),Y      ;GET 2 DECIMAL DIGITS FROM STRING 1
          ADC      ($42),Y      ;ADD PAIR OF DIGITS FROM STRING 2
          STA      ($40),Y      ;STORE RESULT IN STRING 1
          TYA
          BNE      DECADD
          CLD                   ;RETURN TO BINARY ARITHEMETIC MODE
          RTS
```

TOTAL DOCUMENTATION

Complete documentation of microprocessor software will include all or most of the elements that we have mentioned. So, the total documentation package may involve:

DOCUMENTATION PACKAGE

- **General flowcharts**
- **A written description of the program**
- **A list of all parameters and definitions**
- **A memory map**
- **A documented listing of the program**
- **A description of the test plan and test results**

The documentation may also include:

- **Programmers' flowcharts**
- **Data flowcharts**
- **Structured programs**

The documentation procedures outlined above are the minimal acceptable set of documents for non-production software. Production software demands even greater documentation efforts. The following documents should also be produced:

- Program Logic Manual
- User's Guide
- Maintenance Manual

The program logic manual expands on the written explanation produced with the software. It should be written for a technically competent individual who may not possess the detailed knowledge assumed in the written explanation in the software. The program logic manual should explain the system's design goals, the algorithms used, and what tradeoffs were necessary.

It should then explain in great detail what data structures were employed and how they are manipulated. It should provide a step-by-step guide to the operations of the program. Finally, it should contain any special tables or graphs that help explain the program. Code conversion charts, state diagrams, translation matrices, and flowcharts should be included.

The User's guide is probably the most important and most overlooked piece of documentation. No matter how well a system is designed, it is useless if no one can take advantage of its features. The User's guide should introduce the system to all users, sophisticated and unsophisticated. It should then provide detailed explanations of system features and their use. Frequent examples will help to clarify the points in the text. Step-by-step directions should be provided (and tested!). Programmers with detailed knowledge of a system often take shortcuts that the general reader cannot follow. Further discussion of the writing of User's guides is beyond the scope of this book. However, remember that you can never spend too much effort in preparing a User's guide, since it will be the most frequently referenced system document.

The maintenance manual is designed for the programmer who has to modify the system. It should outline step-by-step procedures for those reconfigurations designed into the system. In addition, it should describe any provisions built into the program for future expansion.

Documentation should not be taken lightly or postponed until the end of the software development. Proper documentation, combined with proper programming practices, is not only an important part of the final product but can also make development simpler, faster, and more productive. The designer should make consistent and thorough documentation part of every stage of software development.

REDESIGN

Sometimes the designer may have to squeeze the last microsecond of speed or the last byte of extra memory out of a program. As larger single-chip memories have become available, the memory problem has become less serious. The time problem, of course, is serious only if the application is time-critical; in many applications the microprocessor spends most of its time waiting for external devices, and program speed is not a major factor.

Squeezing the last bit of performance out of a program is seldom as important as some writers would have you believe. In the first place, the practice is expensive for the following reasons:

COST OF
REDESIGN

1) It requires extra programmer time, which is often the single largest cost in software development.
2) It sacrifices structure and simplicity with a resulting increase in debugging and testing time.
3) The programs require extra documentation.
4) The resulting programs will be difficult to extend, maintain, or re-use.

In the second place, the lower per-unit cost and higher performance may not really be important. Will the lower cost and higher performance really sell more units? Or would you do better with more user-oriented features? **The only applications that would seem to justify the extra effort and time are very high-volume, low-cost and low-performance applications where the cost of an extra memory chip will far outweigh the cost of the extra software development.** For other applications, you will find that you are playing an expensive game for no reason.

However, if you must redesign a program, the following hints will help. First, determine how much more performance or how much less memory usage is necessary. If the required improvement is 25% or less, you may be

MAJOR OR
MINOR
REORGANIZATION

able to achieve it by reorganizing the program. If it is more than 25%, you have made a basic design error; you will need to consider drastic changes in hardware or software. We will deal first with reorganization and later with drastic changes.

Note particularly that saving memory can be critical if it allows a program to fit into the limited amount of ROM and RAM available in a simple one-chip or two-chip microcomputer. The hardware cost for small systems can thus be substantially reduced, if their requirements can be limited to the memory size and I/O limitations of that particular one-chip or two-chip system.

REORGANIZING TO USE LESS MEMORY

The following procedures will reduce memory usage for 6502 assembly language programs:

1) **Replace repetitious in-line code with subroutines.** Be sure, however, that the Call and Return instructions do not offset most of the gain. Note that this replacement usually results in slower programs because of the time spent in transferring control back and forth.

2) **Place the most frequently used data on page zero and access it with one-byte addresses.** You may even want to place a few I/O addresses there.

3) **Use the Stack when possible.** The Stack Pointer is automatically updated after each use so that no explicit updating instructions are necessary. Remember, however, that the 6502 Stack can never be longer than one page.

4) **Eliminate Jump instructions.** Try to reorganize the program instead.

5) **Take advantage of addresses that you can manipulate as 8-bit quantities.** These include page zero and addresses that are multiples of 100_{16}. For example, you might try to place all ROM tables in one 100_{16}-byte section of memory, and all RAM variables into another 100_{16}-byte section.

6) **Organize data and tables so that you can address them without worrying about address calculation carries or without any actual indexing.** This will again allow you to manipulate 16-bit addresses as 8-bit quantities.

7) **Use the Bit Test or Shift instructions to operate on bit positions at either end of a word.**

8) **Use leftover results from previous sections of the program.**

9) **Take advantage of such instructions as ASL, DEC, INC, LSR, ROL, and ROR, which operate directly on memory locations without using registers.**

10) **Use INC or DEC to set or reset flag bits.**

11) **Use relative jumps rather than jumps with direct addressing.**

12) **Use BRK, RTS, and RTI to perform jumps and reach subroutines, if they are not already being used.** These instructions can act as one-byte CALL instructions if the required data and addresses are already in the Stack.

13) **Watch for special short forms of instructions** such as the Accumulator shifts (ASL A, LSR A, ROL A, and ROR A) and BIT.

14) **Use algorithms rather than tables** to calculate arithmetic or logical expressions and to perform code conversions. Note that this replacement may result in slower programs.

15) **Reduce the size of mathematical tables by interpolating** between entries. Here again, we are saving memory at the cost of execution time.

16) **Take advantage of the CPX and CPY instructions to perform comparisons without involving the Accumulator.**

Although some of the methods that reduce memory usage also save time, you can generally save an appreciable amount of time only by concentrating on frequently executed loops. Even completely eliminating an instruction that is executed only once can save at most a few microseconds. But a savings in a loop that is executed frequently will be multiplied many times over.

So, **if you must reduce execution time, proceed as follows:**

1) **Determine how frequently each program loop is executed.** You can do this by hand or by using the software simulator or another testing method.

2) **Examine the loops in the order determined by their frequency of execution,** starting with the most frequent. Continue through the list until you achieve the required reduction.

3) **First, see if there are any operations that can be moved outside the loop,** i.e., repetitive calculations, data that can be stored in a register or on the Stack, data or addresses that can be stored on page zero, special cases or errors that can be handled elsewhere, etc. Note that this will require extra initialization and memory but will save time.

4) **Try to eliminate Jump statements.** These are very time-consuming.

5) **Replace subroutines with in-line code.** This will save at least a Call and a Return instruction.

6) **Use page zero for temporary data storage.**

7) **Use any of the hints mentioned in saving memory that also decrease execution time.** These include the use of 8-bit addresses, BRK, RTI, special short forms of instructions, etc.

8) **Do not even look at instructions that are executed only once.** Any changes that you make in such instructions only invite errors for no appreciable gain.

9) **Avoid indexed and indirect addressing whenever possible** because they take extra time.

10) **Use tables rather than algorithms;** make the tables handle as much of the tasks as possible even if many entries must be repeated.

MAJOR REORGANIZATIONS

If you need more than a 25% increase in speed or decrease in memory usage, do not try reorganizing the code. Your chances of getting that much of an improvement are small unless you call in an outside expert. You are generally better off making a major change.

The most obvious change is a better algorithm. Particularly if you are doing sorts, searches, or mathematical calculations, you may be able to find a faster or shorter method in the literature.

```
BETTER
ALGORITHMS
```

Libraries of algorithms are available in some journals and from professional groups. See, for example, the references at the end of this chapter.

More hardware can replace some of the software. Counters, shift registers, arithmetic units, hardware multipliers, and other fast add-ons can save both time and memory. Calculators, UARTs, keyboards, encoders, and other slower add-ons may save memory even though they operate slowly. Compatible parallel and serial interfaces, and other devices specially designed for use with the 6502 or 6800, may save time by taking some of the burden off the CPU.

Other changes may help as well:

```
OTHER
MAJOR
CHANGES
```

1) **A CPU with a longer word will be faster** if the data is long enough. Such a CPU will use less total memory. 16-bit processors, for example, use memory more efficiently than 8-bit processors, since more of their instructions are one word long.

2) **Versions of the CPU may exist that operate at higher clock rates.** But remember that you will need faster memory and I/O ports, and you will have to adjust any delay loops.

3) **Two CPUs may be able to do the job in parallel or separately** if you can divide the job and solve the communications problem.

4) **A specially microprogrammed processor may be able to execute the same program much faster.** The cost, however, will be much higher even if you use an off-the-shelf emulation.

5) **You can make tradeoffs between time and memory.** Lookup tables and function ROMs will be faster than algorithms, but will occupy more memory.

This kind of problem, in which a large improvement is necessary, usually results from lack of adequate planning in the definition and design stages. In the problem definition stage you should determine which processor and methods will be

```
DECIDING
ON A MAJOR
CHANGE
```

adequate to handle the problem. If you misjudge, the cost later will be high. A cheap solution may result in an unwarranted expenditure of expensive development time. Do not try to just get by; the best solution is usually to do the proper design and chalk a failure up to experience. If you have followed such methods as flowcharting, modular programming, structured programming, top-down design, and proper documentation, you will be able to salvage a lot of your effort even if you have to make a major change.

REFERENCES

1. Collected Algorithms from ACM. ACM, Inc., P. O. Box 12105, Church Street Station, New York 10249.

2. T. C. Chen, "Automatic Computation of Exponentials, Logarithms, Ratios, and Square Roots," IBM Journal of Research and Development, Volume 18, pp. 380-388, July, 1972.

3. H. Schmid, Decimal Computation, Wiley-Interscience, New York, 1974.

4. D. E. Knuth, The Art of Computer Programming, Volume 1: Fundamental Algorithms, Addison-Wesley, Reading, Mass., 1967.

5. D. E. Knuth, The Art of Computer Programming, Volume 2: Seminumerical Algorithms, Addison-Wesley, Reading, Mass., 1969.

6. D. E. Knuth, The Art of Computer Programming, Volume 3: Sorting and Searching, Addison-Wesley, Reading, Mass., 1973.

7. B. Carnahan et al., Applied Numerical Methods, Wiley, New York, 1969.

8. A. M. Despain, "Fourier Transform Computers Using CORDIC Iterations," IEEE Transactions on Computers, October 1974, pp. 993-1001.

9. Y. L. Luke, Algorithms for the Computation of Mathematical Functions, Academic Press, New York, 1977.

10. K. Hwang, Computer Arithmetic, Wiley, New York, 1978.

11. New methods for performing arithmetic operations on computers are often discussed in the triennial Symposium on Computer Arithmetic. The Proceedings (starting with 1969) are available from the IEEE Computer Society, 5855 Naples Plaza, Long Beach, CA 90803.

12. A. D. Edgar, and S. C. Lee, "FOCUS Microcomputer Number System," Communications of the ACM, March 1979, pp. 166-177.

Chapter 16
SAMPLE PROJECTS

PROJECT #1: A Digital Stopwatch

Purpose: This project is a digital stopwatch. The operator enters two digits (minutes and tenths of minutes) from a calculator-like keyboard and then presses the GO key. The system counts down the remaining time on two seven-segment LED displays (see Chapter 11 for a description of unencoded keyboards and LED displays).

```
STOPWATCH
INPUT
PROCEDURE
```

Hardware: The project uses one input port and one output port (one 6522 Versatile Interface Adapter or VIA), two seven-segment displays, a 12-key keyboard, a 7404 inverter, and either a 7400 NAND gate or a 7408 AND gate, depending on the polarity of the seven-segment displays. The displays may require drivers, inverters, and resistors, depending on their polarity and configuration.

The hardware is organized as shown in Figure 16-1. Output lines 0, 1, and 2 are used to scan the keyboard. Input lines 0, 1, 2, and 3 are used to determine whether any keys have been pressed. Output lines 0, 1, 2, and 3 are used to send BCD digits to the seven-segment decoder/drivers. Output line 4 is used to activate the LED displays (if line 4 is '1', the displays are lit). Output line 5 is used to select the left or right display; output line 5 is '1' if the left display is being used, '0' if the right display is being used. Thus, the common line on the left display should be active if line 4 is '1' and line 5 is '1', while the common line on the right display should be active if line 4 is '1' and line 5 is '0'. Output line 6 controls the right hand decimal point on the left display. It may be driven with an inverter or simply left on.

Keyboard Connections: The keyboard is a simple calculator keyboard available for 50¢ from a local source. It consists of 12 unencoded key-switches arranged in four rows of three columns each. Since the wiring of the keyboard does not coincide with the observed rows and columns, the program uses a table to identify the keys. Tables 16-1 and 16-2 contain the input and output connections for the keyboard. The decimal point key is present for operator convenience and for future expansion; the current program does not actually use the key.

In an actual application, the keyboard would require pullup resistors to ensure that the inputs would actually be read as logic '1's when the keys were not being pressed. It would also require current-limiting resistors or open-collector drivers on the output port to avoid damaging the VIA drivers in the case where two outputs were driving against each other. This could occur if two keys in the same row were pressed at the same time, thus connecting two different column outputs.

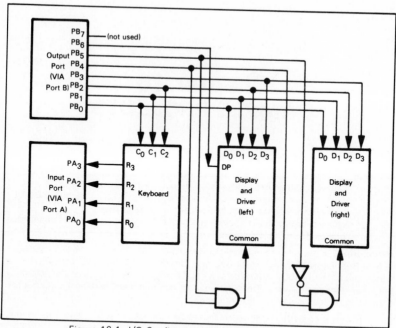

Figure 16-1. I/O Configuration for a Digital Stopwatch

Table 16-1. Input Connections for Stopwatch Keyboard

Input Bit	Keys Connected
0	'3', '5', '8'
1	'2', '6', '9'
2	'0', '1', '7'
3	'4', '.', 'GO'

Table 16-2. Output Connections for Stopwatch Keyboard

Output Bit	Keys Connected
0	'0', '2', '3', '4'
1	'1', '8', '9', 'GO'
2	'5', '6', '7', '.'

General Program Flowchart:

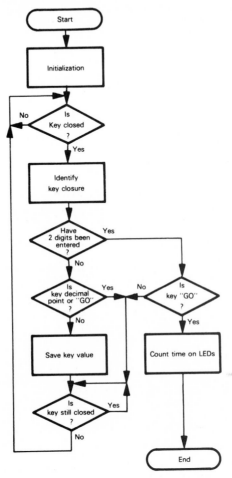

Display Connections: The displays are standard seven-segment displays with their own integral decoders. Clearly, undecoded seven-segment displays would be cheaper but would require some additional software (the seven-segment conversion routine shown in Chapter 7). Data is entered into the display as a single binary coded decimal digit; the digits are represented as shown in Figure 11-22. The decimal point is a single LED that is turned on when the decimal point input is a logic '1'. You can find more information about displays in References 12 and 13 at the end of this chapter.

Program Description:

The program is modular and uses several subroutines. The emphasis is on clarity and generality rather than efficiency; obviously, the program does not utilize the full capabilities of the 6502 processor. Each section of the listing will now be described in detail.

1) **Introductory Comments**

   The introductory comments fully describe the program; these comments are a reference so that other users can easily apply, extend, and understand the program. Standard formats, indentations, and spacings increase the readability of the program.

2) **Variable Definitions**

   All variable definitions are placed at the start of the program so that they can easily be checked and changed. Each variable is placed in a list alphabetically with other variables of the same type; comments describe the meaning of each variable. The categories are:

   a) Memory system constants that may vary from system to system depending on the memory space allocated to different programs or types of memories

   b) Temporary storage (RAM) used for variables

   c) I/O (VIA) addresses

   d) Definitions

   The memory system constants are placed in the definitions so that the user may relocate the program, temporary storage, and memory stack without making any other changes. The memory constants can be changed to accommodate other programs or to coincide with a particular system's allocation of ROM and RAM addresses.

   Temporary storage is allocated by advancing the location counter as shown in Chapter 3. An = (Equate) pseudo-operation names the temporary storage locations. An ORG (origin) pseudo-operation places the temporary storage locations in a particular part of memory. No values are placed in these locations so that the program could eventually be placed in ROM or PROM and the system could be operated from power-on reset without reloading.

   Each memory address occupied by a VIA is named so that the addresses can easily be changed to handle varied configurations. The naming also serves to clearly distinguish control registers from data registers.

   The definitions clarify the meaning of certain constants and allow parameters to be changed easily. Each definition is given in the form (binary, hex, octal, ASCII, or decimal) in which its meaning is the clearest. Parameters (such as debounce time) are placed here so that they can be varied with system needs.

3) **Initialization**

   Memory locations FFFC and FFFD (the 6502 RESET locations) contain the starting address of the main program. The main program can thus be placed anywhere in memory and reached via a "RESET" signal.

   The initialization consists of three steps:

   a) Place a starting value in the Stack Pointer. The Stack is used only to store subroutine return addresses. Note that the Stack Pointer is only 8 bits long since the 6502 Stack is always on page one of memory.

   b) Configure the VIA.

   c) Start the number of digit keys pressed at zero.

4) **Look for Key Closure**
   Flowchart:

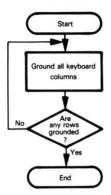

Key closures are identified by grounding all the keyboard columns and then checking for grounded rows (i.e., column-to-row switch closures). Note that the program does not assume that the unused input bits are all high; instead, the bits attached to the keyboard are isolated with a logical AND instruction.

5) **Debounce Key**

The program debounces the key closure in software by waiting for two milliseconds. This is usually long enough for a clean contact to be made. Subroutine DELAY counts with Index Register X for one millisecond. The number of milliseconds is in Index Register Y. DELAY would have to be adjusted if a slower clock or slower memories were being used. You could make the change simply by redefining the constant MSCNT.

6) **Identify Key Closure**

   Flowchart:

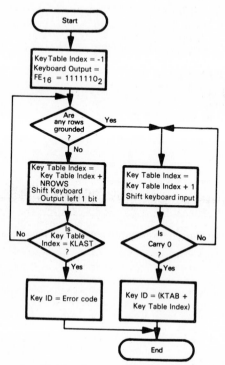

The particular key closed is identified by grounding single columns and observing whether a closure is found. Once a closure is found (so the key column is determined), the key row can be determined by shifting the input until a grounded bit is found.

The output patterns required to ground single keyboard columns are obtained by shifting the original pattern left one bit after each column is examined. The highest numbered key in the keyboard is used as a marker to indicate that all the columns have been grounded without a closure being found. When this value is reached, the error code FF is placed in the Accumulator to indicate to the main program that the closure could not be identified (i.e., the key closure ended or a hardware error occurred).

The key identifications are in table KTAB in memory. The keys in the first column (attached to the least significant output bit) are followed by those in the second column, etc.

KEY TABLE

Within a column, the key in the row attached to the least significant input bit is first, etc. Thus, each time a column is scanned without finding a closure, the number of keys in a column (NROWS) must be added to the key table index in order to move to the next column. The key table index is also incremented before each bit in the row inputs is examined; this process stops when a zero input is found. Note that the key table index is initialized to -1, since it is always incremented once in the search for the proper row.

If we cannot identify the key closure, we simply ignore it and look for another closure.

7) **Act on Key Identification**

If the program has enough digits (two in this simple case), it looks only for the GO key and ignores all other keys. If it finds a digit key, it saves the value in the key array, increments the number of digit keys pressed, and increments the key array pointer.

If the entry is not complete, the program must wait for the key closure to end so that the system will not read the same closure again. The user must wait between key closures (i.e., release one key before pressing another one). Note that the program will identify double key closures as one key or the other, depending on which closure the identification routine finds first. An improved version of this program would display digits as they were entered and would allow the user to omit a leading or trailing zero, (i.e., key in ".", "7", "GO" to get a count of seven-tenths of a minute).

8) **Set Up Display Output**

The digits are placed in memory locations with bit 4 set so that the output is sent to the displays. Bits 5 and 6 are set for the most significant digit to direct the output to the left display and to light the decimal point LED.

9) **Pulse the LED Displays**

Each display is turned on for two milliseconds. This process is repeated 1500 times in order to get a total delay of 0.1 minutes, or 6 seconds. The pulses are frequent enough so that the LED displays appear to be lit continuously.

10) **Decrement Display Count**

Flowchart:

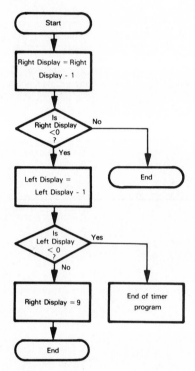

The value of the less significant digit is reduced by one. If this affects bit 4 (LEDON — used to turn the displays on), the digit has become negative. A borrow must then be obtained from the more significant digit. If the borrow from the more significant digit affects bit 4, the count has gone past zero and the countdown is finished. Otherwise, the program sets the value of the less significant digit to 9 and continues.

Note that comments describe both sections of the program and individual statements. The comments explain what the program is doing, not what specific instruction codes do. Spacing and indentation have been used to improve readability.

```
;PROGRAM NAME: STOPWATCH
;DATE OF PROGRAM:4/28/79
;PROGRAMMER: LANCE A. LEVENTHAL
;PROGRAM REQUIREMENTS: DD(221) BYTES
;RAM REQUIREMENTS: 5 BYTES
;I/O REQUIREMENTS: 1 INPUT PORT, 1 OUTPUT PORT (1 6522 VIA)
;
;
;THIS PROGRAM IS A DIGITAL STOPWATCH THAT ACCEPTS INPUTS FROM A
;   CALCULATOR-LIKE KEYBOARD AND THEN PROVIDES A COUNTDOWN
;   ON TWO 7-SEGMENT LED DISPLAYS IN MINUTES AND TENTHS
;   OF MINUTES
;
;KEYBOARD
;
;A 12-KEY KEYBOARD IS ASSUMED
;THREE COLUMN CONNECTIONS ARE OUTPUTS FROM THE PROCESSOR
;   SO THAT A COLUMN OF KEYS CAN BE GROUNDED
;FOUR ROW CONNECTIONS ARE INPUTS TO THE PROCESSOR SO THAT
;   COMPLETED CIRCUITS CAN BE IDENTIFIED
;THE KEYBOARD IS DEBOUNCED BY WAITING FOR TWO MILLISECONDS
;   AFTER A KEY CLOSURE IS RECOGNIZED
;A NEW KEY CLOSURE IS IDENTIFIED BY WAITING FOR THE OLD ONE
;   TO END SINCE NO STROBE IS USED
;THE KEYBOARD COLUMNS ARE CONNECTED TO BITS 0
;   TO 2 OF THE VIA B PORT
;THE KEYBOARD ROWS ARE CONNECTED TO BITS 0
;   TO 3 OF THE VIA A PORT
;
;DISPLAYS
;
;TWO 7-SEGMENT LED DISPLAYS ARE USED WITH SEPARATE DECODERS
;   (7447 OR 7448 DEPENDING ON THE TYPE OF DISPLAY)
;THE DECODER DATA INPUTS ARE CONNECTED TO BITS 0 TO 3
;   OF THE VIA B PORT
;BIT 4 OF THE VIA B PORT IS USED TO ACTIVATE THE LED
;   DISPLAYS (BIT 4 IS 1 TO SEND DATA TO LEDS)
;BIT 5 OF THE VIA B PORT IS USED TO SELECT WHICH
;   LED IS BEING USED (BIT 5 IS 1 IF THE LEADING DISPLAY
;   IS BEING USED, 0 IF THE TRAILING DISPLAY IS BEING USED)
;BIT 6 OF THE VIA B PORT IS USED TO LIGHT THE DECIMAL
;   POINT LED ON THE LEADING DISPLAY (BIT 6 IS 1 IF
;   THE DISPLAY IS TO BE LIT)
;
;METHOD
;
;STEP 1 - INITIALIZATION
;   THE MEMORY STACK POINTER (USED FOR SUBROUTINE RETURN
;   ADDRESSES) IS INITIALIZED. THE NUMBER OF DIGIT KEYS PRESSED IS SET
;   TO ZERO
;
;STEP 2  - LOOK FOR KEY CLOSURE
;   ALL KEYBOARD COLUMNS ARE GROUNDED AND THE KEYBOARD ROWS
;   ARE EXAMINED UNTIL A CLOSED CIRCUIT IS FOUND
;
```

```
;STEP 3 - DEBOUNCE KEY CLOSURE
;   A WAIT OF 2 MS IS INTRODUCED TO ELIMINATE KEY BOUNCE
;STEP 4 - IDENTIFY KEY CLOSURES
;   THE KEY CLOSURE IS IDENTIFIED BY GROUNDING SINGLE KEYBOARD
;   COLUMNS AND DETERMINING THE ROW AND COLUMN OF THE KEY
;   CLOSURE. A TABLE IS USED TO ENCODE THE KEYS ACCORDING TO THEIR
;   ROW AND COLUMN NUMBER
;   IN THE KEY TABLE, THE DIGITS ARE IDENTIFIED BY THEIR VALUES,
;   THE DECIMAL POINT KEY IS NO. 10, THE "GO" KEY IS NO. 11
;STEP 5 - SAVE KEY CLOSURE
;   DIGIT KEY CLOSURES ARE SAVED IN THE DIGIT KEY ARRAY UNTIL
;   TWO DIGITS HAVE BEEN IDENTIFIED. DECIMAL POINTS, FURTHER DIGITS,
;   AND CLOSURES OF THE "GO" KEY BEFORE TWO DIGITS HAVE BEEN
;   IDENTIFIED ARE IGNORED
;   AFTER TWO DIGITS HAVE BEEN FOUND, THE "GO" KEY IS USED TO
;   START THE COUNTDOWN PROCESS
;STEP 6 - COUNT DOWN TIMER INTERVAL ON LEDS
;   A COUNTDOWN IS PERFORMED ON THE LEDS WITH THE LEADING DIGIT
;   REPRESENTING THE REMAINING NUMBER OF MINUTES AND THE TRAILING
;   DIGIT REPRESENTING THE REMAINING NUMBER OF TENTHS OF MINUTES
;
;
;
;STOPWATCH VARIABLE DEFINITIONS
;
;MEMORY SYSTEM CONSTANTS
;
BEGIN    =$0400                    ;STARTING ADDRESS FOR PROGRAM
STKBGN   =$FF                      ;STARTING STACK ADDRESS ON PAGE 1
TEMP     =0                        ;STARTING ADDRESS FOR RAM STORAGE
;
;RAM TEMPORARY STORAGE
;
         *=TEMP
DCTR     *=*+2                     ;16-BIT COUNTER FOR TIMING LOOP
KEYNO    *=*+2                     ;DIGIT KEY ARRAY — HOLDS IDENTIFICA-
                                   ;   TIONS OF DIGIT KEYS THAT HAVE BEEN
                                   ;   PRESSED
NKEYS    *=*+1                     ;NUMBER OF DIGIT KEYS PRESSED
;
;I/O UNITS AND VIA ADDRESSES
;
VIAORB   =$A000                    ;OUTPUT PORT FOR KEYBOARD AND DISPLAY
VIAORA   =$A001                    ;INPUT PORT FOR KEYBOARD
VIADDRB  =$A002                    ;DATA DIRECTION REGISTER FOR PORT B
VIADDRA  =$A003                    ;DATA DIRECTION REGISTER FOR PORT A
VIAPCR   =$A00C                    ;VIA PERIPHERAL CONTROL REGISTER
;
;DEFINITIONS
;
DECPT    =%01000000                ;CODE TO LIGHT DECIMAL POINT LED
ECODE    =$FF                      ;ERROR CODE IF ID ROUTINE DOES NOT FIND
                                   ;   KEY
GOKEY    =11                       ;IDENTIFICATION NUMBER FOR "GO" KEY
KLAST    =11                       ;HIGHEST NUMBERED KEY
```

```
LEDON    =%00010000              ;CODE TO SEND OUTPUT TO LEDS
LEDSL    =%00100000              ;CODE TO SELECT LEADING DISPLAY
MSCNT    =$C7                    ;COUNT NEEDED TO GIVE 1 MS DELAY TIME
MXKEY    =2                      ;MAXIMUM NUMBER OF DIGIT KEY
                                 ;   CLOSURES USED
NROWS    =4                      ;NUMBER OF ROWS IN KEYBOARD
OPEN     =%00001111              ;INPUT FROM KEYBOARD IF NO KEY CLOSED
TPULS    =2                      ;NUMBER OF MS BETWEEN DIGIT DISPLAYS
TWAIT    =2                      ;NUMBER OF MS TO DEBOUNCE KEYS
;
;
;
;
         *=$FFFC
;
;RESET ADDRESS TO REACH STOPWATCH PROGRAM
;
         .WORD    BEGIN          ;VECTOR TO START OF STOPWATCH
                                 ;   PROGRAM
;
;INITIALIZATION OF STOPWATCH PROGRAM
;
         *=BEGIN
         LDA      #0
         STA      VIADDRA        ;MAKE PORT A LINES INPUTS
         STA      VIAPCR         ;MAKE ALL CONTROL LINES INPUTS
         LDA      #$FF
         STA      VIADDRB        ;MAKE PORT B LINES OUTPUTS
         LDX      #STKBGN        ;INITIALIZE STACK POINTER
         TXS
;
;INITIALIZE DIGIT KEY COUNTER
;
INITL    LDA      #0             ;NUMBER OF DIGIT KEYS = ZERO
         STA      NKEYS
;
;SCAN KEYBOARD LOOKING FOR KEY CLOSURE
;
SRCHK    JSR      SCANC          ;WAIT FOR KEY CLOSURE
;
;WAIT FOR KEY TO BE DEBOUNCED
;
         LDY      #TWAIT         ;GET DEBOUNCE TIME IN MS
         JSR      DELAY          ;WAIT FOR KEY TO STOP BOUNCING
;
;IDENTIFY WHICH KEY WAS PRESSED
;
         JSR      IDKEY          ;IDENTIFY KEY CLOSURE
         CMP      #ECODE         ;WAS KEY CLOSURE IDENTIFIED?
         BEQ      SRCHK          ;NO, WAIT FOR NEXT CLOSURE
```

```
;
;START TIMING IF "GO" KEY PRESSED AND ENOUGH DIGITS ENTERED
;
            LDX     NKEYS          ;HAS MAXIMUM NUMBER OF DIGIT KEYS
                                   ;   BEEN ENTERED?
            CPX     #MXKEY
            BNE     ENTDG          ;NO, GO ENTER DIGIT KEY
            CMP     #GOKEY         ;YES, IS KEY "GO"?
            BEQ     STTIM          ;YES, START TIMING
            BNE     WAITK          ;NO, IGNORE KEY
;
;ENTER DIGIT KEY INTO ARRAY, IGNORE DECIMAL POINT OR "GO" KEY
;
ENTDG       CMP     #10            ;IS KEY A DIGIT?
            BCS     WAITK          ;NO, IGNORE IT
            INC     NKEYS          ;YES, INCREMENT NUMBER OF DIGIT KEYS
                                   ;   ENTERED
            STA     KEYNO,X        ;SAVE DIGIT KEY IN ARRAY
;
;WAIT FOR CURRENT KEY CLOSURE TO END
;
WAITK       JSR     SCANO          ;WAIT FOR ALL KEYS TO BE RELEASED
            BEQ     SRCHK          ;LOOK FOR NEXT CLOSURE (SCANO ALWAYS
                                   ;   SETS Z)
;
;PROCESS DIGITS FOR DISPLAY
;
STTIM       LDA     KEYNO          ;GET LEADING DIGITS
            ORA     #DECPT         ;TURN ON DECIMAL POINT FOR LEADING
                                   ;   DIGIT
            ORA     #LEDON         ;SET OUTPUT TO LEDS
            ORA     #LEDSL         ;SELECT LEADING DISPLAY
            STA     KEYNO
            LDA     KEYNO+1        ;GET TRAILING DIGIT
            ORA     #LEDON         ;SET OUTPUT TO LEDS
            STA     KEYNO+1
;
;PULSE THE LED DISPLAYS
;
LEDLP       LDA     #6             ;SET COUNTERS FOR 1500 PULSES
            STA     DCTR+1
TLOOP       LDA     #250
            STA     DCTR
DSPLY       LDA     KEYNO          ;SEND LEADING DIGIT TO LED 1
            STA     VIAORB
            LDY     #TPULS         ;DELAY BETWEEN DIGITS
            JSR     DELAY
            LDA     KEYNO+1        ;SEND TRAILING DIGIT TO LED 2
            STA     VIAORB
            LDY     #TPULS         ;DELAY BETWEEN DIGITS
            JSR     DELAY
            DEC     DCTR
            BNE     DSPLY
            DEC     DCTR+1
            BNE     TLOOP
```

```
;
;DECREMENT COUNT ON LED DISPLAYS
;
          LDA      #LEDON        ;GET BIT PATTERN TO LOOK FOR CARRIES
          DEC      KEYNO+1       ;COUNT DOWN TRAILING DIGIT
          BIT      KEYNO+1       ;IS TRAILING DIGIT PAST ZERO?
          BNE      LEDLP         ;NO, DISPLAY NEW TIME
          DEC      KEYNO         ;YES, COUNT DOWN LEADING DIGIT
          BIT      KEYNO         ;IS LEADING DIGIT PAST ZERO?
          BEQ      INITL         ;YES, WAIT FOR NEXT TIMING TASK
          LDA      #9            ;NO, MAKE TRAILING DIGIT 9
          ORA      #LEDON        ;SET OUTPUT TO LEDS
          STA      KEYNO+1
          BNE      LEDLP         ;RETURN TO PULSING DISPLAYS

;
;SUBROUTINE SCANC SCANS THE KEYBOARD WAITING FOR A KEY CLOSURE
;  ALL KEYBOARD INPUTS ARE GROUNDED
;
SCANC     LDA      #0            ;GROUND ALL KEYBOARD COLUMNS
          STA      VIAORB
KEYCLS    LDA      VIAORA        ;GET KEYBOARD ROW DATA
          AND      #OPEN         ;IGNORE UNUSED INPUTS
          CMP      #OPEN         ;ARE ANY INPUTS GROUNDED?
          BEQ      KEYCLS        ;NO, WAIT
          RTS

;
;SUBROUTINE DELAY WAITS FOR THE NUMBER OF MS SPECIFIED
;  IN INDEX REGISTER Y BY COUNTING WITH INDEX REGISTER X
;
DELAY     LDX      #MSCNT        ;COUNT FOR 1 MS DELAY
WTLP      DEX                    ;WAIT 1 MS
          BNE      WTLP
          DEY                    ;COUNT MS
          BNE      DELAY
          RTS

;
;SUBROUTINE IDKEY DETERMINES THE ROW AND COLUMN NUMBER OF
;  THE KEY CLOSURE AND IDENTIFIES THE KEY FROM A TABLE
;
IDKEY     LDA      #%11111110    ;GET PATTERN TO GROUND COLUMN ZERO
          STA      VIAORB        ;GROUND COLUMN ZERO
          LDX      #$FF          ;KEY TABLE INDEX = -1
FCOL      LDA      VIAORA        ;FETCH KEYBOARD ROW DATA
          AND      #OPEN         ;IGNORE UNUSED INPUTS
          CMP      #OPEN         ;ARE ANY INPUTS GROUNDED?
          BNE      FROW          ;YES, DETERMINE WHICH ONE
          ROL      VIAORB        ;NO, GROUND NEXT COLUMN
          TXA                    ;MOVE KEY TABLE INDEX TO NEXT COLUMN
          ADC      #NROWS-1
          TAX
          CMP      #KLAST        ;HAVE ALL COLUMNS BEEN EXAMINED?
          BNE      FCOL          ;NO, EXAMINE NEXT COLUMN
          LDA      #ECODE        ;YES, RETURN WITH ERROR CODE IN A
          RTS
```

```
;
;
;DETERMINE ROW NUMBER OF CLOSURE
;
FROW    INX                      ;INCREMENT KEY TABLE INDEX
        LSR     A                ;SHIFT INPUTS LOOKING FOR GROUNDED
                                 ;  ROW
        BCS     FROW
;
;IDENTIFY KEY FROM TABLE
;
        LDA     KTAB,X           ;GET KEY NUMBER FROM TABLE
        RTS
;
;KEYBOARD TABLE
;
;COLUMNS ARE PRIMARY INDEX, ROWS SECONDARY INDEX.
;THE KEYS IN THE COLUMN ATTACHED TO OUTPUT BIT 0 ARE FOLLOWED
;  BY THOSE IN THE COLUMN ATTACHED TO OUTPUT BIT 1 ETC. WITHIN
;  A COLUMN, THE KEY ATTACHED TO INPUT BIT 0 IS FIRST, FOLLOWED
;  BY THE ONE ATTACHED TO INPUT BIT 1, ETC.
;
;THE DIGIT KEYS ARE 0 TO 9, THE DECIMAL POINT IS 10, AND "GO" IS 11
;
KTAB    .BYTE                    3,2,0,4,8,9,1,11,5,6,7,10
;
;SUBROUTINE SCANO WAITS FOR ALL KEYS TO BE RELEASED SO THAT THE
;  NEXT CLOSURE CAN BE FOUND
;
SCANO   LDA     #0               ;GROUND ALL KEYBOARD COLUMNS
        STA     VIAORB
KEYOPN  LDA     VIAORA           ;GET KEYBOARD ROW INPUTS
        AND     #OPEN            ;IGNORE UNUSED INPUTS
        CMP     #OPEN            ;ARE ANY KEYS BEING PRESSED?
        BNE     KEYOPN           ;YES, WAIT UNTIL ALL RELEASED
        RTS
        .END
```

PROJECT #2: A Digital Thermometer

Purpose: This project is a digital thermometer which shows the temperature in degrees Celsius on two seven-segment displays.

Hardware: The project uses one input port and one output port, two seven-segment displays, a 74LS04 inverter, a 74LS00 NAND gate or a 74LS08 AND gate depending on the polarity of the displays, an Analog Devices AD7570J 8-bit monolithic A/D converter, an LM311 comparator, and various peripheral drivers, resistors, and capacitors as required by the displays and the converter. (See Chapter 11 and Reference 1 at the end of this chapter for discussions of A/D converters.)

Figure 16-2 shows the organization of the hardware. Control line CB2 from the VIA is used to send a Start Conversion signal to the A/D converter. Input lines 0 through 7 are attached directly to the eight digital data lines from the converter. Output lines 0 through 3 are used to send BCD digits to the seven-segment decoder/drivers. Output line 4 activates the displays and output line 5 selects the left or right display (line 5 is '1' for the left display). Control line CA1 is used to determine when the conversion is complete ($\overline{BUSY}$ becomes one).

The analog part of the hardware is shown in Figure 16-3. The thermistor simply provides a resistance that depends on temperature. Figure 16-4 is a plot of the resistance and Figure 16-5 shows the range of current values over which the resistance is

> **THERMOMETER ANALOG HARDWARE**

constant. The conversion to degrees Celsius in the program is performed with a calibration table. The two potentiometers can be adjusted to scale the data properly. A clock for the A/D converter is generated from an RC network, as shown in Figure 16-3. The values are $R7=33\,k\Omega$ and $C1=1000$ pF, so that the clock frequency is about 75 kHz. At this frequency, the maximum conversion time for eight bits is about 50 microseconds. When $\overline{BUSY}$ goes high, it sets bit 1 of the VIA Interrupt Flag register. The 8-bit version of the converter requires the following special connections. The eight data lines are DB2 through DB9 (DB1 is always high during conversion and DB0 low). The Short Cycle 8-bit input (pin 26-$\overline{SC8}$) is tied low so that only an 8-bit conversion is performed. In the present case, High Byte Enable (pin 20-HBEN) and Low Byte Enable (pin 21-LBEN) were both tied high so that the data outputs were always enabled.

The A/D converter uses the successive approximation method to perform a conversion. The ADC's data register is connected to the inputs of an internal D/A converter whose output (available at OUT1 and OUT2) is compared to the analog input. When a conversion is initiated, the ADC logic sets the data register to all zeroes with the exception of the most significant bit (MSB), which is set to one. If the analog input is less than the resulting internally generated analog value, then the MSB is reset to zero; otherwise it remains a one. The next most significant bit is then set to one and the process repeated until all eight bits have been "tested" in this way. After the eighth cycle, the value in the register is the value which most closely corresponds to the analog input.

This method is fast, but it requires that the input be stable during the conversion process. Rapidly changing or noisy inputs would require additional signal conditioning. The references at the end of this chapter describe more accurate methods for handling analog I/O.

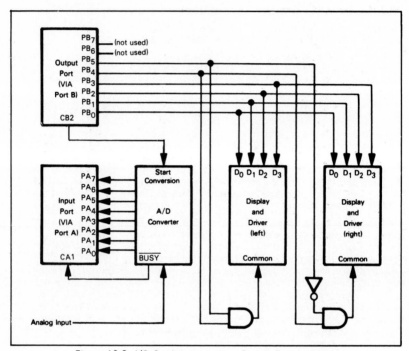

Figure 16-2. I/O Configuration for a Digital Thermometer

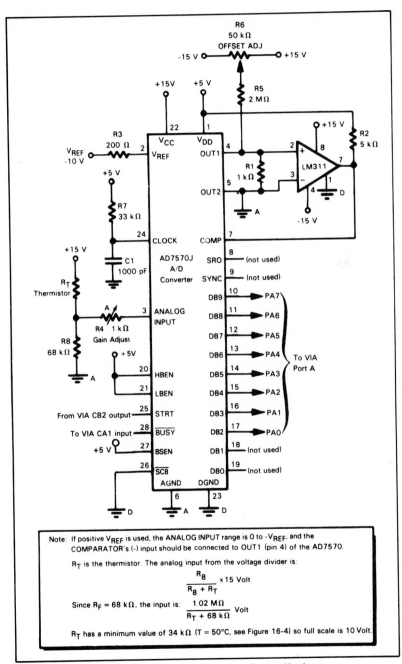

Figure 16-3. Digital Thermometer Analog Hardware

Note: If positive V_{REF} is used, the ANALOG INPUT range is 0 to $-V_{REF}$, and the COMPARATOR's (-) input should be connected to OUT1 (pin 4) of the AD7570.

R_T is the thermistor. The analog input from the voltage divider is:

$$\frac{R_8}{R_8 + R_T} \times 15 \text{ Volt}$$

Since $R_F = 68 \text{ k}\Omega$, the input is: $\dfrac{1.02 \text{ M}\Omega}{R_T + 68 \text{ k}\Omega}$ Volt

R_T has a minimum value of 34 kΩ (T = 50°C, see Figure 16-4) so full scale is 10 Volt.

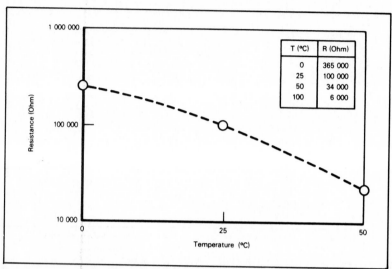

T (°C)	R (Ohm)
0	365 000
25	100 000
50	34 000
100	6 000

Figure 16-4. Thermistor Characteristics
(Fenwal GA51J1 Bead)

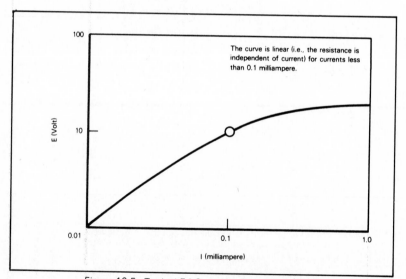

The curve is linear (i.e., the resistance is
independent of current) for currents less
than 0.1 milliampere.

Figure 16-5. Typical E-I Curve for Thermistor (25°C)

General Program Flowchart:

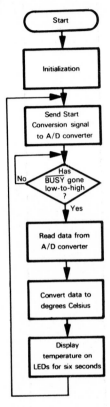

Program Description:

1) **Initialization**

   Memory locations FFFC and FFFD (the 6502 Reset locations) contain the starting address of the program. The initialization configures the VIA and places a value in the Stack Pointer. The Stack is used only to store subroutine return addresses. Remember that Chapter 11 contains numerous examples of how to configure VIAs.

2) **Send Start Conversion Signal to A'D Converter**

   The CPU pulses the Start Conversion line by first placing a one and then a zero on output line CB2. Each input from the converter requires a starting pulse.

3) **Wait for Conversion to be Completed.**

   A '0' to '1' transition on the BUSY line sets bit 1 of the VIA Interrupt Flag Register. Actually, the converter only requires a maximum of 50 microseconds for an 8-bit conversion, so a short delay would also be adequate. Note that reading the converter data clears bit 1 of the VIA Interrupt Flag Register so that the next operation can proceed correctly.

4) **Read Data from A'D Converter**

   Reading the data involves a single input operation. We should note that the Analog Devices AD7570J has an enable input and tristate outputs, so that it could be tied directly to the Microprocessor Data Bus. The 7570 converter is, of course, underutilized in this particular application, particularly since we are interfacing it to the 6502 processor through a VIA. A simpler 8-bit converter such as the National 5357 described in Chapter 11 would do the job at lower cost.

5) **Convert Data to Degrees Celsius**

   Flowchart:

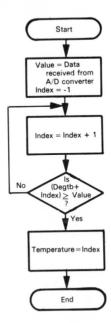

The conversion uses a table that contains the largest input value corresponding to a given temperature. The program searches the table, looking for a value greater than or equal to the value received from the converter. The first

USING A CALIBRATION TABLE

such value it finds corresponds to the required temperature; that is, if the tenth entry is the first value larger than or equal to the data, the temperature is ten degrees. This search method is inefficient but adequate for the present application.

The conversion subroutine returns a binary value which is then converted to BCD by repeatedly subtracting ten and counting operations until the remainder becomes negative. The final ten is then added back to produce the least significant digit.

The table could be obtained by calibration or by a mathematical approximation. The calibration method is simple, since the thermometer must be calibrated anyway. The table occupies one memory location for each temperature value to be displayed.[1] Reference 2 describes a method that uses far less memory. To calibrate the thermometer, you must first adjust the potentiometers to produce the proper overall range and then determine the converter output values corresponding to specific temperatures.

6) **Prepare Data for Display**

Flowchart:

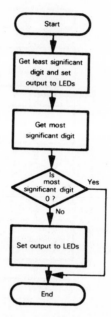

For the least significant digit, we simply set the bit that turns on the displays. The result is saved in page zero address LSTEMP.

BLANKING A LEADING ZERO

The only difference for the most significant digit is that a leading zero is blanked (i.e., the displays show "blank 7" rather than "07" for 7°C). This simply involves not setting the bit that turns on the displays if the digit is zero. The result is saved in page zero address MSTEMP.

7) **Display Temperature for Six Seconds**
   Flowchart:

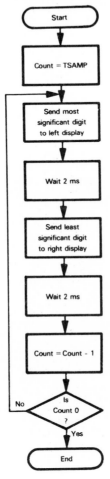

Each display is pulsed often enough so that it appears to be lit continuously. If TPULS were made longer (say 50 ms), the displays would appear to flash on and off.

The program uses a 16-bit counter in two page-zero memory locations to count the time between temperature samples.

```
;
;PROGRAM NAME:  THERMOMETER
;DATE OF PROGRAM:  5/1/79
;PROGRAMMER:  LANCE A. LEVENTHAL
;PROGRAM MEMORY REQUIREMENTS:  173 BYTES
;RAM REQUIREMENTS:  5 BYTES
;I/O REQUIREMENTS:  1 INPUT PORT, 1 OUTPUT PORT (1 6522 VIA)
;
;THIS PROGRAM IS A DIGITAL THERMOMETER THAT ACCEPTS INPUTS FROM
;   AN A/D CONVERTER ATTACHED TO A THERMISTOR, CONVERTS THE INPUT
;   TO DEGREES CELSIUS, AND DISPLAYS THE RESULTS ON TWO
;   SEVEN-SEGMENT LED DISPLAYS
;
;A/D CONVERTER
;
;THE A/D CONVERTER IS AN ANALOG DEVICES 7570J MONOLITHIC CONVERTER
;   WHICH PRODUCES AN 8-BIT OUTPUT
;THE CONVERSION PROCESS IS STARTED BY A PULSE ON THE START
;   CONVERSION LINE (CONTROL LINE 2 ON VIA PORT B)
;THE CONVERSION IS COMPLETED IN 50 MICROSECONDS AND THE
;   DIGITAL DATA IS LATCHED
;
;DISPLAYS
;
;TWO SEVEN-SEGMENT LED DISPLAYS ARE USED WITH SEPARATE DECODERS
;   (7447 OR 7448 DEPENDING ON THE TYPE OF DISPLAY)
;THE DECODER DATA INPUTS ARE CONNECTED TO BITS 0 TO 3 OF
;   VIA PORT B
;BIT 4 OF VIA PORT B IS USED TO ACTIVATE THE LED DISPLAYS
;   (BIT 4 IS 1 TO SEND DATA TO LEDS)
;BIT 5 OF VIA PORT B IS USED TO SELECT WHICH LED IS BEING
;   USED (BIT 5 IS 1 IF THE LEADING DISPLAY IS BEING USED,
;   0 IF THE TRAILING DISPLAY IS BEING USED)
;
;METHOD
;
;STEP 1 - INITIALIZATION
;   THE MEMORY STACK (USED FOR SUBROUTINE RETURN ADDRESSES) IS
;   INITIALIZED
;STEP 2 - PULSE START CONVERSION LINE
;   THE A/D CONVERTER'S START CONVERSION LINE (CONTROL LINE 2 OF VIA
;   PORT B) IS PULSED
;STEP 3 - WAIT FOR A/D OUTPUT TO SETTLE
;   THE BUSY LINE FROM THE CONVERTER IS ATTACHED TO CONTROL
;   LINE 1 ON PORT A OF THE VIA. WHEN BUSY GOES HIGH TO SIGNAL
;   CONVERSION COMPLETED, IT SETS BIT 1 OF THE VIA INTERRUPT
;   FLAG REGISTER
;STEP 4 - READ A/D VALUE, CONVERT TO DEGREES CELSIUS
;   A TABLE IS USED FOR CONVERSION. IT CONTAINS THE MAXIMUM
;   INPUT VALUE FOR EACH TEMPERATURE READING
;STEP 5 - DISPLAY TEMPERATURE ON LEDS
;   THE TEMPERATURE IS DISPLAYED ON THE LEDS FOR SIX SECONDS
;   BEFORE ANOTHER CONVERSION IS PERFORMED
;
;
```

```
;
;THERMOMETER VARIABLE DEFINITIONS
;
;
;MEMORY SYSTEM CONSTANTS
;
BEGIN    =$0400                    ;STARTING ADDRESS FOR PROGRAM
STKBGN   =$FF                      ;STARTING STACK ADDRESS ON PAGE 1
TEMP     =0                        ;STARTING ADDRESS FOR RAM STORAGE

      I/O UNITS AND VIA ADDRESSES

VIAORB   =$A000                    ;OUTPUT PORT DISPLAYS
VIAORA   =$A001                    ;INPUT PORT FOR CONVERTER
VIADDRB  =$A002                    ;DATA DIRECTION REGISTER FOR PORT B
VIADDRA  =$A003                    ;DATA DIRECTION REGISTER FOR PORT A
VIAPCR   =$A00C                    ;VIA PERIPHERAL CONTROL REGISTER
VIAIFR   =$A00D                    ;VIA INTERRUPT FLAG REGISTER

      RAM TEMPORARY STORAGE

          *=TEMP
DCTRC     *=*+2                    ;DISPLAY PULSE COUNTER
INPUT     *=*+1                    ;TEMPORARY STORAGE FOR CONVERTER
                                   ;   INPUT
LSTEMP    *=*+1                    ;LEAST SIGNIFICANT DIGIT OF
                                   ;   TEMPERATURE
MSTEMP    *=*+1                    ;MOST SIGNIFICANT DIGIT OF
                                   ;   TEMPERATURE


      DEFINITIONS

BUSYF    =%00000010               ;PATTERN FOR EXAMINING BUSY
                                   ;   STATUS
LEDON    =%00010000               ;CODE TO SEND OUTPUT TO LEDS
LEDSL    =%00100000               ;CODE TO SELECT LEADING DISPLAY
MSCNT    =$C7                      ;COUNT NEEDED TO GIVE 1 MS DELAY
TSAMPH   =6                        ;TSAMPH X TSAMPL IS THE NUMBER OF
                                   ;TIMES THE DISPLAYS ARE PULSED IN A
TSAMPL   =250                      ;   TEMPERATURE SAMPLING PERIOD.
                                   ;   THE LENGTH OF A SAMPLING PERIOD
                                   ;   IS THUS 2*TPULS*TSAMPH*TSAMPL
                                   ;   MILLISECONDS  THE FACTOR OF 2*TPULS
                                   ;   IS INTRODUCED BY THE FACT THAT
                                   ;   EACH OF 2 DISPLAYS IS PULSED FOR
                                   ;   TPULS MS
TPULS    =2                        ;DISPLAY PULSE LENGTH IN MS


          *=$FFFC

      RESET ADDRESS TO REACH THERMOMETER PROGRAM

          WORD      BEGIN
```

```
;
;INITIALIZATION OF THERMOMETER PROGRAM
;
            *=BEGIN
            LDX       #STKBGN     ;INITIALIZE STACK POINTER
            TXS
            LDA       #0          ;MAKE PORT A LINES INPUTS
            STA       VIADDRA
            LDA       #$FF        ;MAKE PORT B LINES OUTPUTS
            STA       VIADDRB
            LDA       #%11000001  ;START CONVERSION LOW, BUSY
                                  ;   ACTIVE LOW-TO-HIGH
            STA       VIAPCR      ;CONFIGURE VIA PERIPHERAL CONTROL
            LDA       #BUSYF      ;CLEAR BUSY FLAG INITIALLY
            STA       VIAIFR
;
;PULSE START CONVERSION LINE
;
START   LDA       #%11100001  ;SEND START CONVERSION HIGH
            STA       VIAPCR
            LDA       #%11000001  ;SEND START CONVERSION LOW
            STA       VIAPCR
;
;WAIT FOR BUSY TO GO HIGH AND READ DATA
;
            LDA       #BUSYF
WTBSY   BIT       VIAIFR      ;HAS CONVERSION BEEN COMPLETED?
            BEQ       WTBSY       ;NO, WAIT
            LDA       VIAORA      ;YES, READ DATA FROM CONVERTER
;
;CONVERT DATA TO TEMPERATURE IN DECIMAL
;
            JSR       CONVR       ;CONVERT DATA TO TEMPERATURE
                                  ;   IN BINARY
            JSR       BINBCD      ;CONVERT BINARY TO BCD
;
;CONFIGURE DIGITS FOR DISPLAY
;
            ORA       #LEDON      ;SET OUTPUT TO LEDS (LSD IN A)
            STA       LSTEMP      ;SAVE LEAST SIGNIFICANT DIGIT
            TXA                   ;GET MOST SIGNIFICANT DIGIT
            BEQ       SVMSD       ;LEAVE DISPLAY OFF IF MSD IS ZERO
            ORA       #LEDON      ;SET OUTPUT TO LEDS
            ORA       #LEDSL      ;SELECT LEADING DISPLAY
SVMSD   STA       MSTEMP      ;SAVE MOST SIGNIFICANT DIGIT
;
;PULSE THE LED DISPLAYS
;
PULSE   LDA       #TSAMPH     ;16-BIT COUNTER FOR DISPLAY PULSES
            STA       DCTR+1
TLOOP   LDA       #TSAMPL
            STA       DCTR
```

```
DSPLY   LDA     MSTEMP      ;OUTPUT TO LEADING DISPLAY
        STA     VIAORB
        LDY     #TPULS      ;DELAY DISPLAY PULSE LENGTH
        JSR     DELAY
        LDA     LSTEMP      ;OUTPUT TO TRAILING DISPLAY
        STA     VIAORB
        LDY     #TPULS      ;DELAY DISPLAY PULSE LENGTH
        JSR     DELAY
        DEC     DCTR
        BNE     DSPLY
        DEC     DCTR+1      ;HAS COUNT REACHED ZERO?
        BNE     TLOOP       ;NO, KEEP PULSING DISPLAYS
        BEQ     START       ;YES, GO SAMPLE TEMPERATURE AGAIN
;
;SUBROUTINE DELAY WAITS FOR THE NUMBER OF MS SPECIFIED IN
;   INDEX REGISTER Y BY COUNTING WITH INDEX REGISTER X
;
DELAY   LDX     #MSCNT      ;COUNT FOR 1 MS DELAY
WTLP    DEX                 ;WAIT 1 MS
        BNE     WTLP
        DEY
        BNE     DELAY       ;COUNT MS
        RTS
;
;SUBROUTINE CONVR CONVERTS INPUT FROM A/D CONVERTER TO
;   DEGREES CELSIUS BY USING A TABLE. INPUT DATA IS IN
;   THE ACCUMULATOR AND THE RESULT IS A BINARY NUMBER IN
;   THE ACCUMULATOR
;
;REGISTERS USED: A,X
;MEMORY LOCATION USED: INPUT
;
CONVR   STA     INPUT       ;SAVE INPUT READING
        LDX     #$FF        ;START TABLE INDEX AT -1
CHVAL   INX                 ;INCREMENT TABLE INDEX
        LDA     DEGTB,X     ;GET ENTRY FROM TABLE
        CMP     INPUT       ;IS A/D INPUT BELOW ENTRY?
        BCC     CHVAL       ;NO, KEEP LOOKING
        TXA                 ;YES, RETURN WITH T IN ACCUMULATOR
        RTS
;
;TABLE DEGTB WAS FOUND BY CALIBRATION.
;DEGTB CONTAINS THE LARGEST INPUT VALUE WHICH CORRESPONDS
;   TO A PARTICULAR TEMPERATURE READING (I.E., THE FIRST ENTRY
;   IS DECIMAL 58 SO AN INPUT VALUE OF 58 IS THE LARGEST
;   VALUE GIVING A ZERO TEMPERATURE READING  — VALUES
;   BELOW ZERO ARE NOT ALLOWED
;
DEGTB   .BYTE               58,61,63,66,69,71,74,77,80,84
        .BYTE               87,90,93,97,101,104,108
        .BYTE               112,116,120,124,128,132,136
        .BYTE               141,145,149,154,158,163,167
        .BYTE               172,177,181,186,191,195,200
        .BYTE               204,209,214,218,223,227,232
        .BYTE               236,241,245,249,253,255
```

```
;
;SUBROUTINE BINBCD CONVERTS A BINARY NUMBER LESS THAN 100 INTO
;  TWO BCD DIGITS. THE INPUT DATA IS IN THE ACCUMULATOR AND THE
;  RESULT IS IN INDEX REGISTER X (MOST SIGNIFICANT DIGIT) AND THE
;  ACCUMULATOR (LEAST SIGNIFICANT DIGIT)
;
;REGISTERS USED: A,X
;
BINBCD  LDX     #$FF            ;TENS COUNT = -1
        SEC                     ;SET CARRY INITIALLY
SUBTEN  INX                     ;INCREMENT TENS COUNT
        SBC     #10             ;CAN TEN STILL BE SUBTRACTED?
        BCS     SUBTEN          ;YES, CONTINUE
        ADC     #10             ;NO, ADD BACK LAST TEN
        RTS
        .END
```

REFERENCES

1. E. R. Hnatek, A User's Handbook of D/A and A/D Converters, Wiley, New York, 1976

2. T. A. Seim, "Numerical Interpolation for Microprocessor-Based Systems," Computer Design, February 1978, pp. 111-116.

3. D. H. Sheingold, ed., Analog-Digital Conversion Notes, Analog Devices, Inc., P. O. Box 796, Norwood, MA. 02062, 1977

4. D. P. Burton, and A. L. Dexter, Microprocessor Systems Handbook, Analog Devices, Inc., P. O. Box 796, Norwood, MA 02062, 1977

5. J. B. Peatman, Microcomputer-based Design, McGraw-Hill, New York, 1977

6. F. Molinari, et al., "Shopping for the Right Analog I/O Board," Electronic Design, October 11, 1978, pp. 238-243.

7. Auslander, D. M. et al., "Direct Digital Process Control: Practice and Algorithms for Microprocessor Applications," Proceedings of the IEEE, February 1978, pp. 199-208

8. R. J. Bibbero, Microprocessors in Instruments and Control, Wiley, New York, 1977

9. A. Mrozowski, "Analog Output Chips Shrink A-D Conversion Software," Electronics, June 23, 1977, pp. 130-133

10. P. R. Rony et al., "Microcomputer Interfacing: Sample and Hold Devices," Computer Design, December 1977, pp. 106-108

11. P. H. Garrett, Analog Systems for Microprocessors and Minicomputers, Reston Publishing Co., Reston, VA., 1978

12. The Optoelectronics Data Book, Texas Instruments, Inc., P. O. Box 5012, Dallas, TX., 1978

13. The Optoelectronic Designer's Catalog, Hewlett-Packard, Inc., 1820 Embarcadero Road, Palo Alto, CA 94303, 1978.

Index

Index (Continued)

Index (Continued)

About the Author

Lance A. Leventhal is a partner in Emulative Systems Company, a San Diego-based consulting firm specializing in microprocessors and microprogramming. He serves as Technical Editor of the Society for Computer Simulation and as a Contributing Editor for Digital Design. He is a national lecturer on microprocessors for the IEEE, the author of five books and over forty articles on microprocessors, and a regular contributor to such publications as Simulation, Digital Design, and Kilobaud.

Dr. Leventhal's previous experience includes affiliations with Linkabit Corporation, Intelcom Rad Tech, Naval Electronics Laboratory Center and Harry Diamond Laboratories. He received a B.A. degree from Washington University in St. Louis, Missouri, and M.S. and Ph.D. degrees from the University of California at San Diego. He is a member of SCS, ACM, and IEEE.

Other Osborne/McGraw-Hill Publications